Mary Borden

YOU, THE JURY

A NOVEL

LONGMANS, GREEN AND CO.

NEW YORK   LONDON   TORONTO

1952

LONGMANS, GREEN AND CO., INC
55 FIFTH AVENUE, NEW YORK 3

LONGMANS, GREEN AND CO., Ltd
6 & 7 CLIFFORD STREET, LONDON W I

LONGMANS, GREEN AND CO.
215 VICTORIA STREET, TORONTO I

YOU, THE JURY

W

Library of Congress Catalog Card Number 52-5646

Printed in the United States of America

You, the Jury

Part One

Chapter One

I

WE grew up together. I didn't get on with him too
well once the first excitement wore off (it was
wonderful making a friend of our very own), but my brother
Francis adored him, they were like David and Jonathan, so I
had to go on being friends if I wasn't to be left out of everything. And I wanted him to think well of me, he was a glorious
boy, but he wasn't the sort of person you could be comfortably
fond of, he was too independent and expected too much. Eventually you either gave in to him and loved him blindly, or came
to hate him; it was the same with almost everyone who knew
him.

His father was our village doctor. I don't know just when
it was that he took over the practice and brought his family to
live in the old doctor's house on the green; but we must have
been quite small. There were four Merriedew children when
we got to know them. Martin was the eldest; Kate came next,
then Edward. Michael, the youngest, was, I think, born in
Crabbe village; he was only two when we first went to see them.
Their house was white with green shutters. It had a little white
gate and a flagged path led to the front door, then round to the
garden at the back. There was a peaked porch over the door
and a large clear window to either side of it: a sturdy, pleasant,
welcoming house. It was close by our north lodge and we
liked it very much, but we didn't meet Martin until Dr. Merriedew had been looking after Francis for nearly a year, because
we seldom went down to the village.

There was something wrong with Francis' legs when he was

3

born, and none of the specialists whom my mother kept getting down from London seem to have been able to put them right, perhaps because, in her fury to get him well she never stuck to any of them long enough. She was an impatient woman, one of those people who assume that health, wealth and happiness are theirs by right, and any misfortune most unfair. She felt it an outrage that her son shouldn't be a fine healthy specimen, and didn't hesitate to say so in our presence. "The best blood in England," she'd say to the bigwigs from Harley Street. "And look at him!"

He wasn't, I daresay, much to look at, just a skinny little boy with silky red hair, a small white face and legs that didn't work properly, but he had a heavenly smile; and he was such a trusting friendly chap, and longed so for her to be proud of him that I thought it beastly of her to make him feel that his legs were his fault.

The last greybeard from London had put him in irons, and he had been dragging round in them patiently for months when she suddenly sent for Dr. Merriedew and handed Francis over to him. It was the best thing she could have done, but God knows why she did it. Jasper Merriedew was a plain country doctor of no great reputation, but he gave Francis confidence. A big man with steady eyes. He took the beastly things off, and in the end, with exercises and massage, Francis learnt to walk very well. Even so, it was many months before he could get about like other boys, and it was a mile from our front door to the park gates, so if we wanted to go to the village we either went in the pony cart or Nannie would push Francis in his wheel chair while I raced ahead on my pony or bicycle. But Francis hated being seen in the village in his pushcart and I didn't like going without him, so we stayed at home most days with Nannie and our two Scotties and Phyllis, the nursery maid, to look after us.

Our parents didn't come down much except for weekends,

4

but we didn't mind. There was plenty to do without going outside the park.

II

In my father's time there were two villages, Crabbe Major and Crabbe Minor, with three miles between. Crabbe Major had a grammar school, a hospital, two movies, and a railway station. Crabbe Minor had none of these and, according to my mother, didn't want them; but I suspect that it had cost our family a pretty penny to preserve its Old World charm and it did look a duck of a place on a summer evening, with the whitewashed cottages round the green glimmering under the trees like fat mushrooms. Most of the cottagers were our tenants, so the village had its face washed each spring and my mother used to bully and bribe the people into planting the flowers she liked beside their front doors; not to attract tourists — O dear no! — to please herself. She wanted the place to look nice because, according to her view, it belonged to her.

Snug houses behind towering elms, geese lording it on the green, a lovely old church, and the Triumphant Chariot everything that a decent public house should be: the ideal picturebook village, in fact, with just a bit more than the normal content of greed, humbug, and furtive vice lurking behind its snug windows. My father suspected none of this. His approach to the place was more subtle than my mother's. It had come to him as a legacy, together with a great deal else that he had not earned or asked for, and he took his responsibility to it very seriously; but he would never have ventured to interfere in its private affairs and thought, poor sweet, that the people were friendly because they touched their caps to him. He was a conscientious if pernickety landlord, spent hundreds of pounds getting water laid on from the main and electric light put into the cottages, and fussed himself into a fever over drains and the conditions prevailing in the back lanes, where such people as

5

the Larnigans and Popskis continued, in spite of his efforts, to live in contented squalor. He couldn't turn them out because the fringe of the village didn't belong to him. It was bad land, and my father in a moment of aberration had let it go to a speculator called Stubbs in Crabbe Major, who had put up half a dozen gimcrack hovels and cut up the rest into building lots.

Dr. Merriedew was my father's great supporter in matters of hygiene and public decency. They waged war together against cesspools, and sat side by side on the magistrates' bench in Crabbe Major. But they were defeated by Mr. Stubbs. At the mention of Mr. Stubbs my father's chin would quiver with anger and his long thin face go red.

Francis and I didn't know him very well. He had little to do with us or our early upbringing, leaving all domestic matters to my mother, and seldom came up to our quarters unless Francis was ill in bed with one of his goes of bronchitis. Then he wouldn't know what to say and would only stay for a minute. I daresay he was afraid of Nannie. He was a timid man and very much under my mother's thumb. Francis and I came to feel rather sorry for him, but he may have liked being bullied by his wife. How could one tell?

Her name was Charlotte, and I called her that after I married. She was a big handsome jolly-looking woman with a high colour and round prominent eyes. His looks were insignificant. He was shorter than she and very slight, with a narrow head and the long mournful Patche nose. There was nothing impressive about him, but I believe that my mother was devoted to him in her rough domineering way; she seldom let him out of her sight, and to the best of my belief had no lovers.

I think now that he cared for Francis and me quite a lot and would have liked to show his affection had he known how, but we were not aware of this as children. His manner with us was shy and awkward. Sometimes he would come on us during one of his solitary walks in the park, and he would then appear surprised, as if he had forgotten our existence and took us, at first, for a couple of strange children from the village. He would stop for a moment when this happened, mutter something about the weather, fidget with his drooping moustache, giving us quick, diffident, surprised looks as if he couldn't quite believe we belonged to him, then call to his couple of Corgis and walk on. He always wore cinnamon-coloured plus fours on these walks and a checked cap rather too large for his head. His legs were thin sticks, his chest narrow. He would walk quickly, stiffly away from us; he looked very small under the great trees.

And he was all in all a slight man, not weighty nor much considered in the great world in spite of my mother's efforts. As the seventh Earl and the biggest landowner in those parts he was called upon to play a leading role in the county, and he took these duties too very seriously; but he always avoided taking the chair at formal functions if he could, and suffered agonies when he couldn't. He was happiest among the neighbouring farmers, but had a morbid dislike of privilege, and I fancy would not have entered his Saddlebacks and his Jerseys at the county show had he not felt he owed it to his bailiff and herdsmen. We had a fine herd of Jerseys at the home farm. He would take us down there with him sometimes, and I recall that look of surprise in his eye mixed with an air mournful and quizzical as he contemplated the magnificence of these dumb creatures. It was as if he wondered how it was that they belonged to him, and knew that his great house, his acres, the dumpy village that stood for England, the England that was warm and deep-rooted and intimate, was as fleeting as thistledown and would soon be gone.

III

Crabbe Minster isn't one of the biggest country houses in England, it is only one of the most beautiful; but it is big enough to make a good home for mental deficients when Francis pops off. Thirty bedrooms, half a dozen reception rooms, picture gallery, library, ballroom, that sort of thing. Henry Tudor gave us the place when he turned out the monks, and with it the fat fields that made it the richest abbey in the West Country. Not for love, for services rendered. The Simon Patche of the day fought for him in France. You can see him looking down his long nose in the tapestry of the Field of the Cloth of Gold, in the ballroom. He has the same nose as my father and Francis, and the same pale-red hair. Afterwards he helped Henry get rid of a wife or two. We seem to have been a godless lot, even those of us who became dignitaries of the new established church. They were the greediest of the lot, and if the records are true the most worldly. Decidedly not my favourite forebears. But some of the others would seem to merit respect. We don't count now as a family, but we did once; and taking it by and large I should say that we did quite a lot for England. Soldiers, sailors, traders: if India and the Empire helped make us rich, what of it? We didn't give the Empire away, we helped to build it; and if my ancestors didn't believe in God with all their hearts, they at least believed in England.

But we were not interested in our family history as children and had no conscious sense of the Minster's great beauty. We were fond of the place because we had never lived anywhere else, but my mother was too careless and my father too detached and too diffident to tell us about its history. He drifted about the spacious rooms as vaguely and quietly as a dry leaf. It didn't occur to us to think of him as a man of great possessions and considerable culture. Though we knew that he spent a good many hours on rainy days in the library climbing up and down ladders, he never put a book in my hands and I believe that the only room in the house that he felt to be his own was a poky hole behind the gun room where he kept his stamp collection, and my mother was constantly pulling him out of it to go with her to some social or political function. He was a

8

Liberal but not a keen politician and he exasperated her with what she called his crazy notions. She said to me once: "Your father's only idea in politics is to reform himself out of the House of Lords."

There was nothing subtle or diffident about my mother. She was busy, slapdash, outspoken, and a great worldling. Unlike my father, she had a well-developed sense of property and was proud of Crabbe, but having such a high opinion of herself she treated it as if were quite an ordinary house, showing her motley guests round if they insisted, but impatient all the while for her bridge, her game of billiards or her dinner.

So we took our home and its treasures for granted. We must have been aware in our dim childish fashion of the harmony of the great aged jumbled whole with its central block of hoary stone, its wings of rosy brick, its innumerable slender mullioned windows, framed in carvings cunning as lace and I daresay we took into our young savage lungs some breath of beauty from the softly gleaming vistas of the panelled drawing rooms with their shimmer of crystal and glint of gold, the warm tones of worn velvet and old brocade, the delicate arrested dance of chair legs mirrored in polished floors. We knew the name of some painters; Giovanni Bellini's "Madonna" hung over the chimneypiece in the Italian drawing room and Francis liked the "Lady in Green Brocade" by Bronzino on the opposite wall, he said she had a nice face, but the cabinets full of snuffboxes and old Sèvres, the jades, the ivories, the Chinese porcelain meant nothing to us, and the long portrait gallery on the first floor above the Monks' Walk had no charms even for Francis, who liked doing sunsets in water colours or queer little drawings that he called portraits of God. We would dare each other sometimes to go into the Monks' Walk after sundown, it was a gloomy place with rows of statues that one could pretend were ghosts, but the series of empty bedrooms with the blinds down from Monday to Friday didn't trouble us. We had our

9

own quarters in the South Wing, our own door giving onto the terrace with steps to the sunk rose garden, and never went down the great staircase to the front hall unless we were summoned. That seldom happened even at weekends. My mother wasn't proud enough of her peaky son and plain daughter to care to show us to her friends, she preferred to come up to see us unless she was alone, when she would have us down to lunch and, although we understood her reasons for keeping us out of sight except when there were aunts or uncles about, we were thankful. We didn't feel in the least lonely or neglected. But we had as companions of our own age only each other, so it was very exciting to meet Martin Merriedew.

IV

That was thirty-six years ago. We made friends with him in the summer of 1914. He was seven years old and the most beautiful human being I have ever seen. I may not have known it then, but I know it now, for I can see him as he was quite distinctly, the light in his glowing face, the vital hair springing back from his fair young forehead, the shining eyes. He had a radiance when he was happy that made one laugh with delight. His hips were narrow like a Spanish dancer's, and he held his head high on a strong neck. He was proud and free and totally unself-conscious; he seemed to have wings to his feet; and he would come running and fling his arms round Francis and hug him for sheer joyous affection. He didn't know what it was to hide his feelings. When he loved he showed his love. Then quickly his mood would change, his sunny face would become so sombre, so strangely concentrated that one wanted to get away from him, but one couldn't easily; the fascination was too great. There was the longing for relief, and the other longing to understand, to see what he was going to do next, and of course the longing to please him, to do what he wanted one to do.

Sometimes, abruptly in the middle of a game, he would say:

"I must go now; I must be by myself, goodbye." And we never thought of asking him to stay with us when he spoke like that; it was final. Francis and I were both, I think, rather afraid of him almost from the beginning, but we reacted to this differently. Being scared made me cantankerous but with Francis it seemed to be a part of the rapture of devotion. For him there was a kind of ecstasy in watching Martin's face go dark. I know; I've seen it; it used to exasperate me, but I could do nothing. I was no match for Martin. He paid no attention when I tried to interfere; he didn't quarrel; he simply ignored me.

A strange boy. A strange frightening man. He would draw people to him, get them under his spell, impose his will on theirs, then if they showed the least sign of rebellion would drop them, cut them clean out of his life. His own family, his mother, his brothers, his sister, even those who wanted to help him and stand by him when he was in trouble; but I didn't think he would do it to Francis, for he loved Francis. For nineteen years Martin's friendship was the one absorbing interest and the most powerful influence in my brother's life. Then suddenly Martin put an end to it. He threw Francis over and refused to have anything more to do with him. Why? Because Francis couldn't do what he asked. Francis gave him everything that was his to give, his heart, his mind, first call on his very life, and he would have given as well great wads of money if Martin had consented to take it. But that apparently wasn't enough. Martin must have, not first call on his life, but his whole life; total devotion, total submission. And because Francis wasn't free to do the one last thing Martin demanded, Martin broke his heart and ruined him.

Oh, Francis wasn't the only one. The strange, ill-fated man dismissed everyone who didn't see eye to eye with him on everything and give him everything. No man or woman who had a mind of their own or a life of their own to lead, or a lover, a sweetheart, a mother, a husband, a child with a claim, was tolerated. And the result was, naturally enough, that with a few rare exceptions only the most insignificant creatures stuck to him. Nobodies or, worse, half-wits, cranks of all sorts, unfortunate women like Teresa Larnigan, who had nothing to lose and to whom the austerity he offered was heaven compared with what they had known before. Or humbugs who made up to him and proposed to use him for their own ends, like Gideon Fish, millionaire socialist M.P. for the central division of Greymouth. A strange pair of intimates for Martin Merriedew. I don't know which of the two was the more curious, Teresa the guttersnipe and nymphomaniac, or Gideon Fish, the middle-class revolutionary and would-be dictator. But I think Gideon Fish is the greater enigma. All one has to do in Teresa's case is accept the facts. One isn't obliged to explain them. They are astonishing but quite simple; and they cast no light on the mystery of Martin Merriedew. She fell in love with him. She loved him consumingly. She loved him enough in fact to become a new person, and he accepted her love, that is all there is to it. But in Gideon's story there is no clarity, there is not even the simplicity of pure hatred.

I have questioned Teresa and some of the men who formed Martin's group and worked with him before and during the war. They all abhor Gideon's conduct now, but they disagree about his motives. Some say he despised Martin from the beginning, that he was a man of inordinate vanity, consumed by ambition, gifted with brains, money, influence, a public position and great powers of persuasion. He had everything in fact except charm, the one thing necessary for the success he wanted. He even had good looks of a hard spectacular sort, but he couldn't make people love him. He knew what he wanted; he wanted power, he wanted to be a great popular leader and to bring about a revolution. He hated the world, and the squalor, the disease, the meanness, the stupidity of life. He wanted to change it, he wanted to save the people, but he could not, he was helpless because they didn't love him. So he fastened on Martin, who inspired love. He would make Martin into a public idol, and be the revolutionary power behind him. Then, when Martin refused to become a public leader, he turned on him.

But Teresa says no. She says that Gideon Fish may have chosen for evil reasons to join forces with Martin, but that he fell under his sway as they all did, and that a dreadful struggle went on in his soul between himself and Martin's self. And when I asked her why Martin trusted him, she said: "I don't think he did, but he loved him." And what is one to make of that? Martin Merriedew had an uncanny gift for reading one's thoughts. I know; I've experienced it. Then why didn't he know that Gideon's thoughts were black, and were growing more and more deadly? Why did he put up with him for years, and why did Fish continue to cling to Martin through repeated rebuffs and disappointments? I don't believe that Martin loved him. I don't believe that they loved each other. It is impossible. But it was as if they could not bear to give up hope of each other. That for me was the story that emerged from the evidence brought out in court, the story of a fatal bond, binding two men together who were each mistaken in the other's identity.

Francis doesn't agree. Francis will not admit that Martin made mistakes. He says that Martin understood Gideon Fish perfectly, and knew from the beginning that he was a deadly enemy, but nevertheless loved him. Francis says that ordinary people like ourselves love those who give us pleasure, but that Martin loved most of all the ones who hurt him. But that I can no more believe than the other. Martin Merriedew to my mind made innumerable mistakes; his whole life was a mistake; but he wasn't morbid, and he wasn't a fool, and he wasn't a criminal.

I know, in other words, what he was not. But what was he? A failure, yes. And in his failure he brought disgrace and disaster

13

to his family, his friends, and himself. But is that all? His name is loathed now in the village where he grew up, and the world has forgotten him; he made the headlines for a bare week. So he would seem to have accomplished nothing. And yet — I wonder. There is no one left but Teresa and her obscure little group to remember him. And me? Yes, and Francis. But Francis, who swears to this day that he was the most glorious man he has ever known, is a wreck; and I am miserable. I am impelled to write down what I know of him by the pain of extreme uncertainty. I had escaped him; I had hated him and then forgotten him, until I saw him standing in the dock, being tried for his life. Now I cannot forget him.

v

I passed the Merriedews' house the other day when I went down to see Francis. It has a new front. The village is being engulfed in a satellite town, and the Doctor's house is a teashop with flats above. Katharine is dead and buried beside her husband in the churchyard by our north lodge; Edward, Kate and Michael have gone away; all the family is scattered; and of ours only Francis and I are left.

My father died in 1930, and my mother took herself off in disgust to her villa in the South of France when the last war ended and the Socialists came in. She is dividing her time, I understand, between her jasmine farm and the casinos of Monte Carlo and Cannes. I don't know what she has to live on. She wrote some months ago that she was making money out of the farm. I don't believe it; I should think she is running up debts that Francis someday will be called on to pay, but I don't know. We seldom hear from her. I only know that she isn't a woman to let a little thing like currency restrictions stand in her way. She says no one in his senses would attempt to live nowadays in a place like Crabbe.

The Patche family has a long past but no future. Of the

younger branches too many were killed, there is no one to inherit Crabbe who could afford to keep the place up, and it looks as if Francis would have no children. So I daresay most people would agree in thinking Francis a fool to go on living there, if you can call it living, with the gardens and principal reception rooms open to the public four days a week, and all but the bedrooms in the South Wing closed. Francis and Daphne have installed themselves in our old nurseries, and come and go by the side door we always used.

Many of the treasures are gone and Francis had to sell a great deal of land to pay death duties, the town planners are eating up the fields outside the park walls, and you can hear the steam drills from the terrace on a still day. Even the park has a dreary look. The best of the oaks were cut down during the war and went to the bottom of the sea in the hulks of good ships. The deer are gone of course, and the peacocks that used to preen themselves on the lawn. Not that we cared about those silly birds. But there are bins dotted about for the use of picnicking tourists and signs saying "Keep off the grass"; the boathouse by the lake is tumbling down, and the great house rises up out of this desolation like a ship sailing gently, proud and serene, to destruction.

"No one in his senses." But Francis isn't sane on the subject of Crabbe. He spends his days limping up and down the great ghostly rooms, setting traps for mice, looking for moth and dry rot, swatting flies.

I found him in the Spanish drawing room mending one of the crimson hangings. He had taken off his leg for comfort and it was lying beside him in a sea of red velvet, so he didn't get up. He wasn't very pleased to see me, and he only interrupted his work for a minute when I kissed him, then went on painstakingly plying his needle.

I am sore and angry about Francis. No one could have been more unlucky. He was thirty-two when Neville Chamberlain told us we were at war with Germany and his legs were almost as good as most men's. He had his pilot's certificate and had done a lot of civilian flying, so he was certain they would take him on in the R.A.F. But they told him he was too old to fly, and put him in a cellar in London on the operational side. He stayed in it for three years. It wasn't until '42 that they sent him up as an observer, and he had done only ten hours in the air when they crashed in a fog in Norfolk. He deserved a decent death if anyone did, but they put him together again, and he is alive and alone with Daphne at Crabbe.

I sympathize up to a point with his feeling for Crabbe, but I desperately hate seeing him all twisted and warped. It is only a house, after all. I could wish now that he could go back to the days of his innocence when he drew pencil portraits of God and looked with sublime indifference at the Bellini "Madonna." She is still there, waiting serenely for the day when she will go to the National Gallery, but I say if the Socialists want Crabbe so much, let them have it now; or if what they really want is simply to drive the likes of us out of the country, let's help them to get on with it by clearing out. There are places one can still go to with one's money: Ireland, for instance, or Rhodesia. If Francis sold the library and the tapestries and the few good things still left, he could invest the money in a farm in Rhodesia and be a free man. But nothing will induce him to leave England, or Crabbe, though he knows that the moment he's dead the Government carpenters will move in.

I wanted to talk to Francis about Martin. There were things I wanted to know, but it was difficult with Daphne about. A boring young woman, very devoted no doubt to Francis and Crabbe, she seems to approve of his ruining himself to keep the place up and to be quite satisfied to spend her life helping him do it. I fancy he married her with that idea and on the definite understanding that they would stay on, even if it meant giving up everything else. She doesn't appear to want anything else.

16

She is a trained librarian by profession but was in the W.A.A.F.s during the war, that's how Francis met her, and she has taken on Crabbe as a professional might do, some highly qualified civil servant employed by the Government to guard and cherish a unique national treasure. Her housekeeping is a marvel of organization. With a skeleton staff and three dailies from the village, she manages to keep the whole great empty place aired and clean. The dailies come in on a Monday morning and attack the great staircase, on Tuesdays they move to the South Wing, on Wednesdays work back through the picture gallery. By Friday night they've done a complete round and deliver the house up to the trampings of weekend sightseers.

She isn't a bad soul really, nor ill-looking if you like them outsize. She is half a head taller than Francis, with broad shoulders, lean sinewy arms, and good strong legs. I've seen her carry Francis upstairs on her back. He had slipped on a polished floor and fainted. Poor Daphne! On top of this magnificent manly physique is a small round childish face. She waits on Francis hand and foot. It's very bad for him. He is often peevish and sometimes quite rude to her; then she goes scarlet and her eyes fill with tears.

She does what is expected of her in the district, very efficiently. Even the Socialist Borough Council still for some reason likes to have ladies of title open things; but Francis has dropped out of almost everything and they see very few people. She has catalogued the library quite beautifully. Otherwise her fun is to take tourists round. She knows the family history much better than we do, and is as glib as a professional guide.

"You will notice the ceilings and panelling. Much of the last Abbot's ornamental work remains. He employed cunning craftsmen, adepts at mingling native Gothic with Italian Renaissance. The great staircase is by Inigo Jones. The stonework is very rich, and as fine as any in England."

Poor Daphne, poor Francis. He was in love with Kate Merriedew, and she with him. And he could have married her in spite of Martin. She took Francis' side. She said he was right and Martin wrong, that he couldn't do what Martin asked. But now Francis holds it against Kate that she did side with him against her brother, and declares that they were both guilty of disloyalty to the one human being who had a right to ask everything.

There it is again. That is the effect Martin had on nice, normal people. He put before them an impossible ideal, roused them to unnatural and incredible efforts, then when they failed him left them with a feeling of guilt.

I was always tougher than Francis. I got away, thank God, and married Charles. And if Charles hadn't happened to be Martin's judge I would probably be as indifferent now to his fate as the rest of the unconcerned world. It was just bad luck that I married the man who was going to decide Martin's fate. And I don't feel guilty, and I don't blame Charles, but Martin gives me bad dreams.

Chapter Two

I

I WAS nine years, two months, and one week old, the day we met Martin. It was Saturday the 4th of July, 1914. He would be seven, he said, on the 25th of September, just ten days before Francis. We swapped this information in the raspberry patch, and I remember how pleased Francis was to discover that he and Martin were the same age with birthdays only ten days apart. I told the boys that the 4th of July was the anniversary of the American Declaration of Independence, for I had read about this in my history book and wanted to impress Martin; but I didn't feel that the murder of an archduke in Serbia or the rumours of war that had upset our housekeeper, Mrs. Trumper, would interest them.

My mother had arrived from town at noon the day before, and had sent almost immediately for our new governess, Miss Worthington, who had then come in a breathless fluster to fetch us. "It's all so very dreadful — the news, you know, so very serious. You must do nothing to add to her worries." But my mother had seemed much as usual. She was lunching off a sandwich and a glass of milk in her sitting room, put us through the normal tiresome questions about lessons, then dismissed us with the remark: "Mind you behave properly to that poor creature. She's all the education you're likely to get for some time." And we didn't expect to see her again until she said goodbye on the Monday, as the house by dinnertime had filled up with what seemed, even to us, a very odd collection of people.

Their presence, however, would not, we felt fairly certain,

interfere with our plans. After watching their several arrivals from the high window above the front door, we had decided that we were safe. Not an aunt, uncle, or recognizable relation in the lot; not a single old lady who would want to pat our heads. Sportsmen in tweed caps driving their own cars with their wives beside them, their chauffeurs and maids behind, a bevy of girls in our old Daimler, who had evidently come by train to Crabbe Major, and a roadster full of young men in goggles who were probably from the Cavalry Depot at Greymouth. All these were down obviously for the races. Naturally we knew about the races. Everyone in and outside the house, except Matilda Worthington, had contributed to Mr. Bowles's sweepstake. He had as much as ten pounds locked up in his safe with the silver. Even Nannie and Phyllis each had half a crown on the 3:30, and they were usually lucky, thanks to Jim, the stud groom, who was friends with someone in the know.

The racing lot arrived in good time for tea, but it was seven and Francis had already had his bath when Phyllis reported that his Lordship had just turned up in a taxi (he had missed his train) with two Cabinet Ministers and a second taxi following with three pale men in black coats and a young woman in a mackintosh, all loaded down with tin boxes and typewriters.

"Secretaries, Mrs. Trumper says, and is she in a fuss?" Phyllis giggled, bringing in the porridge next morning for breakfast.

"What about?" we asked.

"Never you mind," said Nannie. "It's no concern of yours."

We agreed. We preferred having Crabbe to ourselves but we didn't actively resent these weekend invasions. With luck we wouldn't be sent for even on Sunday at teatime, and could get on with our lives undisturbed. We were very private in our own quarters, and very complete. The box hedge enclosing the rose garden beyond our own door gave excellent cover. We could get round to the stables and the kitchen garden without being seen. We had our friend Jim in the stables, and Nannie always let us have six lumps of sugar on Saturday mornings for my mother's four hunters and our ponies. Francis was afraid to go into the loose boxes, but he would wait patiently while I did. And Phil in the kitchen garden was going to let us pick enough peas for our lunch, and old Bill had promised to take us fishing in the afternoon on the lake, so we must see about worms. We had felt obliged to invite Miss Worthington to join the fishing expedition, but she had declined, much to our satisfaction and Nannie's.

Nannie treated Miss Worthington with frigid courtesy and whipped us away from her the minute lessons were over, so we knew she was jealous and were rather pleased than otherwise; but we thought it unreasonable, for Miss Worthington was very plain whereas Nannie was a fine figure of a woman. Though she wasn't old, not really old, about thirty, we thought, she had lovely soft white hair, and was big and strong, with a comfortable lap. She had bright blue eyes, a profile like a Roman emperor, and stood no nonsense, from us or anyone. No one, not even our parents, could interfere in Nannie's domain and Miss Worthington didn't dream of doing so.

Miss Worthington was long in tooth and limb, with limp mouse-coloured hair, and a bad circulation that made her nose and hands red. She was of course well educated and accomplished. She read Homer in the original Greek for her own pleasure, and banged away on the schoolroom piano with brilliant fervour. I hated my piano lessons, but Francis loved his and had taken her down several times to the music room when the house was empty so that she could play to him on the Steinway. She had, I felt, a romantic turn of mind and had been disappointed in love, but hadn't given up hope, for she always chose the sloppiest poems in our *Child's Book of English Verse* for us to learn by heart, and would listen with her long red hands clasped on her chest and a wistful smile wavering round her mouth while we recited them. Though Francis was sorry for her, we were afraid that she was rather silly, but I said that it didn't matter; we needn't be fond of her, nor she of us. She had a friend called Elizabeth to whom she wrote nearly every day. Nannie and our dogs were fond of us, that was enough affection.

The one tiresome thing about the weekend parties was that Mrs. Trumper would get in a fuss if there were too many visiting maids and valets, and would find time to come up to grumble to Nannie. The trouble they gave with their early cups of tea and their late pints of beer! And some that pert, and the carryings-on and the language! She couldn't do, that she couldn't, with language.

She would come billowing into the nursery, all bosom and black satin, bringing echoes of turmoil, of greed, of passion, that were faintly troubling even though we didn't understand her allusions. On the other hand, there were pickings. Phyllis would produce lovely ices, and little cakes with sugared cherries on top.

On this particular Saturday morning Mrs. Trumper was in a great to-do. Her Ladyship had changed round all the rooms yesterday at the last minute. Five more than expected. His Lordship had telephoned at three o'clock. Two members of the Government and three secretaries. The Prime Minister had asked his Lordship to help him with the Government, and he didn't want to. Mrs. Trumper was pompous. "But her Ladyship says he can't get out of it this time because of the National Emergency. Every man in the country, his Lordship included, must put his shoulder to the wheel, and it's no good his saying he's needed in the County. The County can do very well without him but the Prime Minister can't."

Mrs. Trumper had had to move Lady Jane and the Major out of the Tudor suite and into the Mandarin. She had wanted to put the secretaries at the far end of the North Wing, but her Ladyship said his Majesty's Ministers must have their secretaries near them, so the Cavalry had had to be moved from their nice rooms that looked out on the stables. Mrs. Trumper didn't wish to criticize, but her Ladyship didn't always pay the attention she should to what was proper. The Honourable Alathea and pretty Miss Fairweather shouldn't be put next to Colonel Curtis and that gay spark Captain Brown. Mrs. Trumper had ventured to point this out and her Ladyship had said, "Nonsense, they'll be gone to the war in another month," as if that had anything to do with it! Then the first kitchen maid had gone down with a sore throat and she had had to send for Dr. Merriedew, who'd be coming any minute. Mrs. Trumper conveyed the impression that life was hard, but that she was eminently fitted to cope with it, even if the first kitchen maid did lie abed croaking.

II

Francis and I had just finished breakfast; Miss Worthington had gone to her room to write letters, and Nannie was doing my pigtails. I'd done them once but not to please her, so they were all undone again. It had rained in the night, but now the sun was shining. The grownups were still asleep or seemed to be. The terrace was empty, the park spread serene, deer were moving down by the lake but they didn't disturb the sunny stillness; and I was wild to be out.

Nannie kept saying: "For pity's sake, Barbara, stand still! I never did see such a fidget." Then I saw Martin. He had appeared down below on the terrace. He was holding his father's hand and was staring with a serious expression at the prophets by our door. I waved to him but he took no notice, so I broke away from Nannie and rushed downstairs, the dogs after me, shouting to Francis: "There's a boy outside with the Doctor, come quick!"

Francis followed as quickly as he could. He couldn't do three steps at a time like me, but he could slide down the banisters on his stomach and he joined me in a minute. Dr. Merriedew introduced us. "This is my eldest son, Martin," he said. "As it's Saturday, and he isn't in school, I brought him along to have a look at the prophets."

We were delighted to see Martin but we didn't want to waste his time and our own staring at a couple of stone prophets. They stood each in a niche to either side of our door. It had once been the door to the Abbot's quarters and they were very old. One was Hosea, the other Amos. Hosea was lifting his hand but Amos was clasping a book. Hosea's nose was worn away and Amos had lost a part of his right foot. We were quite fond of them, but what were ancient prophets in stone when the sun was shining and the fruit pen bursting, not to mention our ponies and my mother's hunters, who were expecting their sugar? We dragged Martin off to the stables, then to the raspberry patch, while his father climbed to the kitchen maid's bedroom behind Mrs. Trumper's ample petulant petticoats.

Francis began at once to tell Martin all about his legs and how the Doctor had made them better. "First he took the irons off, then he showed me how to do exercises and taught Nannie massage. Now I can run downstairs almost as fast as Babs. Not run exactly, I hop mostly and slide, but I hardly ever have to get into my pushcart now when we go for walks." Martin didn't appear impressed. He seemed to think it quite natural that his father should teach a boy to walk, but he looked at Francis while he rattled on as if he liked him very much.

I think I am right in saying that we didn't realize in those days how incredibly beautiful he was. Children take miracles for granted. To us at the time he was simply a manly little boy with a fair frank open face, and just possibly that wonderful thing, a new friend; but I know that I noticed his way of looking at Francis. It was grave, it was searching, it was clear and bright; but it was more than that. I can only describe it as deep; and it gave me, suddenly, a jealous pang. He seemed to be getting to know Francis all at once, and to be loving him the way I loved him. It made me squirm, but Francis wasn't in the least uncomfortable. His pale little pointed face was lighted up as if by the other boy's shining eyes, and he smiled back into that young, strangely compelling face with complete confidence.

I stood off and compared them. They wore the same sort of clothes, open shirt, grey knickers, and sandals; but Martin was taller than Francis, his shoulders were broader and he held his head very erect on his strong round neck. Francis' neck was so slender that his head often seemed too heavy for it, and he would let it droop to one side. Francis' pale-red hair was thin and silky, his eyes often had a languid sleepy look though not now; but Martin's fair hair was so thick and strong that it seemed to rush back from his forehead as if blown by the wind. Vital hair. Never had I seen anyone so alive. I cannot have noticed that day the contrasts in the strong lovely face, but looking back to that sunny bit of garden I see his high serious forehead, his level, rather thick eyebrows, and I feel the impact of that fierce, fearless, innocent gaze. Then he smiled at Francis, a smile of utter sweetness. He had made up his mind, he loved my brother, and I too came under the spell. It was stupid to be jealous. We had found a new friend and I didn't mean to be left out.

But he was not, as I recall, very oncoming. It was we who made all the advances. He showed no curiosity about our affairs. He didn't laugh or chatter, he was quiet, but he set us chattering, he made us want to laugh and shout. And we wanted to know all about him. We pelted him with questions and waited eagerly for his answers. Sometimes he kept us waiting. He would draw his brows together and look at us thoughtfully before he answered a question. At moments there was a touch of scorn on his firm lips that made us feel we were rather silly and much too inquisitive. Then he would smile again, his slow smile, and we would begin again. I think we realized that he was very reserved, but we were too excited to match his reluctance with a tactful shyness.

Yes, he admitted, he went to the village school. He did reading, writing, arithmetic, and geography. Yes, he had two brothers and a sister, Kate was six, Edward was five, Michael only two years old. No, they had no ponies, no pets of any kind. Kate wanted a kitten, but his mother said it would grow into a cat and frighten away the birds.

Gradually he became more communicative. He always fed the birds, he told us, in winter. The robins would hop onto his shoulder if he held a piece of bacon rind in his mouth and peck at it. No, they never tried to catch them. Who would want to put birds in a cage? The look of scorn was unmistakable and made us feel very small. But they had found a thrush one day with a broken wing in the potato patch and had kept it in an old hen coop in the garden until the wing was mended. His father had put the wing in a splint, and they had fed the bird on bread crumbs and worms until the wing was quite better. Then it had flown right over the apple tree at the bottom of the garden and disappeared.

Yes, of course, they had a garden. Not as big as this, but they grew nearly everything you could think of, peas, beans, potatoes, roses, his mother could grow anything. You could tell from watching her fingers. He helped sometimes, but she had Gus to dig the potatoes. Gus couldn't talk very well but he was good at digging. He was big, almost as big as a man; but he had never learned to read and you had to know him intimately to understand what he was saying. Martin wanted his father to teach Gus to talk, but his father said he hadn't the time and that Gus was quite happy digging potatoes and chopping wood without talking. That was true. But Gus hadn't always been happy. When he first came to work in the garden he had been frightened when anyone spoke to him, and his face had been all swollen down one side and a dark-purple colour as if he had fallen down a coal hole or something.

We were very interested in Gus, but we wanted most of all to know about Martin himself. What did he do when he came home from school? He helped his mother get tea, then he put Michael to bed. "Is that all?" No, there was an old apple tree at the bottom of the garden, and he was building himself a house high up in the branches so that he could sit among the leaves. His father had given him some wooden planks and a hammer and nails. It was almost finished.

Could we come and see? Yes, he said gravely, he would show us the house, but it was only big enough to hold two at a time. When could we come? Today? This afternoon? No, not today. Today was Saturday and they were going on a picnic. All the family? Yes, all the family unless his father was called out on a case. Even Michael? Of course. They couldn't leave Michael alone at home.

Francis and I longed to be asked to the picnic, but he didn't suggest our coming so we couldn't say anything, though we did hint. We said we had never been on a real picnic, but that if he and his family would come we were sure Nannie would let us take tea down by the lake. There was a boathouse, we said, and two rowboats and a canoe. We weren't allowed to go in the canoe, it capsized very easily, but I could go out alone in the rowboat because I could swim. Could he swim? Yes, he could swim. We were going fishing that afternoon. If they would all come to tea we could go swimming before tea and fish afterwards. We always collected our own worms for bait. There were lots of worms in the garden. Would he help us? If he liked he could take some home, if they were going to fish on their picnic. We knew where to find big fat ones. I would get a tin to put them in.

But just then the Doctor came to fetch him and we had to let him go.

27

"You'll come again soon, won't you?" Francis said.

"Perhaps." He thought a moment, not frowning, but with his brows puckered; then added, as if relieved at finding the solution to a serious problem: "But it would be better if you came to our house."

"Why?" I flared up. "Don't you like it here?"

He hesitated again, looking for help to his father, but Dr. Merriedew wasn't inclined to help him; he stood like us, waiting for the boy's answer. So at last Martin said: "It's a very big house and like something in a book, but I don't think it's real, do you?"

The question was addressed to Francis, and Francis answered after only a second's hesitation: "It's real for us, because, you see, it's all we've got. But I expect your house is more friendly."

Dr. Merriedew smiled. "Come and see," he said. "Now then, Martin, we must be getting home."

We went with them as far as the drive and stood watching them walk away, hoping that Martin would turn and wave to us, but he didn't. He seemed to be talking a lot, he kept looking up at his father; perhaps he was talking about us and saying that he liked us. We did hope he liked us, even if our house wasn't real. Then we rushed up to tell Nannie all about him.

Nannie didn't snub us when we burst in on her to insist that we must have the whole Merriedew family to tea next day. She only said, "Not with the house full of people," and when Francis insisted, remarked that she didn't suppose the Doctor and his wife would think much of being asked to a schoolroom tea or a picnic down by the lake.

"But they always do everything together, Nannie. All the family; Martin said so. They are all going on a picnic today, and tomorrow's Sunday — they could come on a Sunday — but Monday's no good. Martin and Edward both go to school, and if we can't have them this Sunday we'll have to wait a whole week, and then it will probably be just the same. All Saturdays and Sundays are full of people, you know they are."

But that made her quite cross. She couldn't think what had got into us. Didn't we understand that our parents were very worried about what was happening in the world?

"Pooh!" I said. "They're all going racing. You know they are."

"Not your father, Barbara. And don't you say pooh when you speak of your parents. It's very ill-mannered. You don't suppose your father has got half the Cabinet down here and all those secretaries just to take them racing."

"Not half the Cabinet, only two."

"Now listen to me, child — else you can go to your room for the rest of the day. You are being very silly and selfish. What's more you've been rude, and that I won't have. There — take this newspaper and read it. You are quite old enough to try to understand what's going on."

"But, Nannie, we've found a new friend."

"You read the middle page of that paper, then we'll see about your new friend."

It was the *Daily Mail* and it was all about the danger of war breaking out in the Balkans, and about Austria mobilizing. There was a picture of the German Kaiser reviewing some troops somewhere in Germany, and then something Mr. Asquith had said in the House of Commons. I knew about Mr. Asquith, he was Prime Minister and a friend of my father's; but I knew nothing about the Balkans and cared less.

Francis waited patiently standing by Nannie's chair while I read. The news made not the slightest impression on me, but I realized that I must be good, otherwise we would never see Martin again. So I said I was sorry when I gave back the paper, and wouldn't she please — oh, please! — help us? We did so want to ask Martin to tea.

She relented. She didn't see why we shouldn't have Martin and his brother Edward someday quite soon. There was plenty of time on a weekday; they came home from school at half past three; but she had best have a word first with my mother. In fact, she said, it would be best for her Ladyship to do the asking. Her Ladyship knew the Doctor's wife quite well, and could easily send down a note or ring up on the telephone.

Francis and I were surprised to hear that our mother already knew Martin's mother. We felt cheated. Perhaps she knew Martin too. Perhaps she had known him ever since the Doctor had come to Crabbe village.

How was it, we demanded, that we had never seen him when we went down in the governess cart to post letters? We knew lots of people in the village, though not of our own age, we admitted. Miss Sally and Miss Molly Tripp at the post office were quite old, so was Mr. Bullit, the cobbler who mended our shoes, he must be a hundred. And we didn't go often. But Martin must surely go sometimes to the post office to buy sweets just as we did. It was most unfair and very mysterious.

Nannie's explanation only added to our anxiety. "Maybe the Merriedews like to keep themselves to themselves," she said.

"Do you mean you don't think they would want to come?"

"I didn't say so; and I'm sure I don't see why they shouldn't."

"We could have hot buttered scones and honey for tea," I suggested.

"And cherry cake." Francis always liked cherry cake better than anything else.

"Or if we took our tea down to the lake, we could go swimming. The Merriedew children like picnics; and Martin knows how to swim, he said so."

"Be off with you." Nannie was quite put out again, we could see, by our pestering. "I've promised, haven't I, to talk to your mother?"

She kept her promise, and my mother did send down a note

30

on the Sunday night; but our tea party wasn't easily arranged. The answer brought back was in the nature, it seemed, of thanks and a polite refusal. Edward and Kate were too young to go out to tea, and Martin was needed at home after school to look after the baby. My mother, so Mrs. Trumper told us, was quite annoyed. "She went straight to the phone on Monday morning, did her Ladyship — it was the last thing she did before leaving for town — and rang up the Doctor. 'Aren't my brats good enough for yours?' she said — her very words. Then she listened a bit, said, 'Rubbish!' and slammed down the receiver."

III

My mother was a great worldling and a blatant snob, but she didn't know it. She chose her friends as and where she pleased; she was to take up Gideon Fish later on, and because she collected a number of oddities she considered herself very democratic.

The Merriedews were not among them. The Doctor and his wife were a worthy couple, but not to her mind in the least odd, and she didn't collect them. The village was not asked to meals, only to teas for the local Liberal Association, the Red Cross or the Women's Institute; and then only those women were invited who actively supported these worthy institutions. On such occasions we were called on to pass round sandwiches and cakes, so we had come to know what Nannie called the respectable people of the place quite well. Miss Molly and Miss Sally Tripp we considered old friends. They were so much alike that we were not quite sure which was which; but it was Miss Molly usually who stayed inside the cage at the post office to deal with stamps, and Miss Sally who sold us sweets over the counter. They both wore eyeglasses and grey woollen blouses each with a cameo brooch at the throat, and their hair was very neat inside nets. They called Francis "the young Lord" and always asked after the Countess' health. They loved a good

31

gossip with Nannie and would say: "Dearie me, just fancy! What a very interesting life you do live, Miss Crouch, with so many famous people coming and going — quite an education, I'm sure."

Then there was Mrs. Holt, the seamstress. She was a mild little mousy creature but a great worker for the Red Cross. The number of flannel bags she made for hot-water bottles, Nannie said, ran into thousands. Nannie often went to Mrs. Holt to try on or fetch something, and had introduced us to Mrs. Holt's daughter Bessie, whom she described as a very well-brought-up child, and there'd be no harm in it if I wanted to make friends with her. But I didn't like Bessie. Her eyes were too close together, she had a loose wet mouth and a great untidy mass of straight straw-coloured hair straggling down her back. She would giggle at everything I said, then catch her breath as if she had frightened herself.

Nannie didn't consider Mrs. Blundle of the Chariot respectable; but you couldn't keep her out, she must have her nose in everything, so she came to all the "do's" at the Minster, and seemed to be on easy terms with my mother. She was a big bouncing woman with red cheeks and snapping brown eyes. Mr. Blundle was big too, but we didn't know him. We would see him sometimes in the yard at the Chariot, and we admired very much the way he heaved beer barrels about; but he never came to the Minster, and Nannie never let us linger outside the Chariot; she was temperance.

The Vicar was different. The living being in my father's gift, he was treated almost as a part of the household and came to lunch usually on Sundays. If he had a wife, she came too, but I don't recall there being one, and I fancy this was because my mother preferred unmarried divines. The first whom I remember suited her perfectly. His name was Mr. Septimus Brown, and he might have walked out of a novel by Anthony Trollope. He had a red face and a jolly laugh, rode to hounds two days a week and played a good enough game of bridge to make up a four if he was wanted. My mother used to take him out to the stables after lunch on Sunday. But he had come a cropper in the hunting field shortly before we met Martin and had broken his neck, so now we had Mr. Nightingale.

Mr. Nightingale, though a widower, was a great trial to my mother, but my father got on with him very well. He was a vague harmless little man with a taste for antiquities, and my mother stopped asking him to lunch quite soon because he spilt his food and his waistcoat had spots down the front. He and my father would potter about together in the church crypt, deciphering inscriptions on old tombs, and spend hours in the library hauling heavy volumes down from the high shelves. The vicarage faced the village green, but there was a door in the garden wall that gave into the park, and we would see him trotting toward us on a Saturday morning. Mr. Nightingale found it awkward to climb a ladder because of his round belly, so my father would do the climbing while the Vicar held the ladder, peering up through his eyeglasses and saying, "Dear, dear! Do be careful, my lord." Then, when my father was safely down again, they would each have a glass of sherry.

Mr. Nightingale came of course to the Red Cross teas; and Mr. Spink the schoolmaster would come sometimes. They were the only men, as I remember, the rest were women; but the Doctor's wife wasn't among them. She seemed to take no part in such village activities. Nannie said her Ladyship had done her best but given her up as a bad job. Secretly, as I learned later, my mother was jealous of Katharine, but thought her a fool. It was outrageous that such a vague childish woman should have four splendid children, and among them a son like Martin, when she had only Francis and me.

I had seen Mrs. Merriedew in the village, but didn't know that she was Martin's mother until at last we were invited to the Doctor's for tea. She was tall, ample and tranquil, with

33

the round face of an innocent child. Her small shapely head, long full throat, and deep bosom gave her an old-fashioned air, or perhaps it was merely her clothes. She always wore full long dresses of some dark woollen material, and her dense curly hair was usually rather untidy. Martin, when he was tall enough to reach up, would tuck a stray curl behind her ear, then they would laugh into each other's eyes. She had dreamy eyes, a small round chin, and a mysterious little smile would come and go at the corners of her sweetly curved lips. Her hands were large and rough from housework. She had a low vibrating voice and often hummed to herself as she cooked or washed up. I came to admire her very much. Dressed in brocade with pearls in her soft hair she would have fitted perfectly into a Renaissance frame, but her beauty was not noticeable when one met her bicycling down the village street, her heavy skirts flapping round her large useful feet, or came on her bending her long back among her cabbages.

I think what exasperated my mother about Katharine was her helplessness and her serenity. There was something mysterious about her, and my mother hated mystery. She would drop in on Katharine of a morning and tick her off for doing her own housework when she needn't, and for doing it badly; for planting too many cabbages and not enough Brussels sprouts; for rocking the baby's cradle — one should never rock a baby — and for keeping the cradle in the kitchen. Katharine would listen, her graceful head tilted a little to one side, then go her own dreamy way, rocking young Michael with her foot and humming to him while she peeled the potatoes.

My mother was often in the village poking her nose into matters that didn't concern her. My father kept his shy distance. He would have felt it awkward to go knocking on the doors of people who couldn't very well refuse him admittance. And what, after all, would he say to them? He had so little to say to anyone, even the Doctor. He wasn't afraid of the

Doctor, and he would stand up to a troublesome ruffian in court; but he couldn't stand up to Blossom, his head gardener, and he always sloped off to his den when the Bishop came to tea. My mother was afraid of no one. She treated Blossom in an offhand way that greatly impressed Francis and me, and didn't give a fig for the good opinion of bishops. She went to church most Sundays, and didn't find the sermon a bore because she didn't listen. "I've thought out your speech for Tuesday, Simon," she'd say to my father. "I did it during the sermon."

She had never thought it necessary to send us to church. What was the point? Nannie was there to see that we said our prayers. Francis was too young anyhow. If I wanted to go, Nannie could take me, but I didn't. If we had only known that Martin, Kitty and Edward all went to church every Sunday with their parents! But we only found out later what a chance we had missed. Then of course Francis insisted on doing the same. My mother was surprised but uninterested. "Oh, very well then — have it your own way."

My mother was irreligious but she took her politics seriously. Like my father, she came of a great Whig family, and she bullied him into taking part now and then in the debates in the Lords. But not even my mother's prodding could make an orator of my father, or a leader of men, so she consoled herself with dreams of a distinguished public career for her son. Her idea of preparing the way for him was to ask promising young Liberal M.P.'s to stay, and give vast political parties twice a year in her house in town. It is natural to say "her" house, because everything that was my father's always seemed much more hers than his. But she had never given much time or attention to either of us. She would map out our lives, then leave those in charge to get on with it. What were nurses and tutors for, if not to take one's children off one's hands, especially sickly children?

I was as strong as a horse, but that was no consolation to her. I was what Francis should have been, and vice versa. He had the long eyelashes, fine transparent skin, and small hands and feet that should have been mine. My hands and feet were enormous. I didn't grow up to them until I was well on in my teens. I was black as a gypsy and fractious. I could ride anything in the stables, was practically tone deaf, and couldn't be taught to dance. Francis was a dreamer, a bookworm, and a bit of an artist. He loved music and poetry, and learned to paint nicely in water colours. He had natural beautiful manners. Such graces would have been welcomed in me, had I had them. I had none, not even the makings of a beauty. I had brains of a sort instead, a passionate longing to please, and an abrupt manner that put people off. My mother didn't like either of us much, but I irritated her most.

She wanted us both to cut figures in the great world and saw little hope of it, but refused to renounce her ambitions for Francis. Winchester, Oxford, a year or so abroad; then a seat in the House of Commons and a Government job before my father died (he mustn't die too soon, that would spoil everything) was the programme for Francis.

Chapter Three

WE felt immediately at home in Martin's house when we were at last invited to tea. Four whole weeks had passed since we made friends with him and, according to Mrs. Trumper like as not, if my mother hadn't stopped on her way through the village to give the Doctor's wife a piece of her mind, we might never have seen him to speak to again.

We knew that couldn't be true, but the mere suggestion made us quite sick with dismay. We had been badgering Nannie daily to do something. We had been down to the village repeatedly in the pony cart, and had made Jim drive very slowly past the Merriedews' gate; we had haunted the post office, but our only glimpse of him was in the schoolyard, playing prisoners' base with the other children; he didn't see us, and Nannie wouldn't let us go boldly up to the Doctor's front door and ask for him; she said it wasn't proper to push one's way into other people's houses when those people didn't want to come and see us; we had done all we could do; fate was against it.

We didn't agree. We were certain that we would meet Martin someday, quite soon, if we only kept on. The trouble was, we said, that we always seemed to have to go home to tea just when we were most likely to run into him on his way back from school. Nannie, we knew, was put out because she felt we had been slighted, but we didn't feel that way. We refused to believe that Martin didn't like us a little. There must be reasons.

"And what's so special about Martin Merriedew?" she asked.

We didn't know. "If you want other children to play with, why don't you get your mother to ask your cousins to stay?" But we detested the cousins she meant. They made fun of Francis, and galloped our ponies all over the lawn.

She was obliged to agree about the cousins; so was Mrs. Trumper; she called them pests. Mrs. Trumper was very cross during those days. My mother was planning to turn Crabbe into a hospital and Mrs. Trumper was in a state. She wouldn't be wanted, she presumed, if that happened. And if she were she didn't know as she could put up with hospital nurses and orderlies swarming all over the place and her stillroom made into a chemist's shop. With all due respect to Nannie, Mrs. Trumper couldn't abide hospital nurses, and to think of stripping the drawing rooms and putting up hospital beds on the beautiful polished floors made her go quite queer. "Sixty beds, her Ladyship says, she's been counting up; twenty in the ballroom, ten each in the three drawing rooms, and five of the best bedrooms upstairs for ten officers."

Mrs. Trumper kept coming up to the nursery to complain of what a nuisance the war was going to be. She was shocked by the Kaiser's behaviour. Just to think of it, grandson to Queen Victoria, nephew to our late King Edward and asked him on his yacht only last summer then did this, upsetting everybody!

Two of the outside men had already gone to join up, and John the second footman had given notice and was persuading Robert to do the same. Mr. Bowles would soon be alone in the pantry. Lord Kitchener wouldn't want him, he said, he was too old and he knew where his duty lay, it lay with the house; but he was very perturbed, oh, very perturbed. When he asked her Ladyship who was going to do the silver, her Ladyship said that was quite simple, it would go to the bank.

"And I do feel with Mr. Bowles," Mrs. Trumper said, "that if things is to be done they should be done properly. It's not as if her Ladyship was moving out. She and his Lordship will come and go, she says. They're to keep their own suite for themselves, and the North Wing for anyone they want to bring down. 'But there'll be no weekend parties, Mrs. Trumper,' she said, as if that was any comfort! When it was a question of weekend parties, one had some satisfaction, one knew what to expect and was prepared; and it was gentry, the best in the land. But ever since they got at his Lordship for the Government it's been come and go, one night up and one night down, and half the Borough Council to lunch on a Friday, and the Boy Scouts to tea on a Sunday; and now her Ladyship is going to have her meals with the hospital matron and eat off kitchen plates."

All this was depressing. When, oh, when would there be a quiet moment? That was what my mother said when we attacked her about again asking Mrs. Merriedew to bring the children to tea. "How tiresome you are! Oh, very well, I will, when I have a quiet moment." The war seemed to be raising new barriers every day between ourselves and Martin. Mrs. Trumper found time, however, in her welter of troubles to take an irate interest in the Merriedew situation. For my mother, it seemed, did say a word to the Doctor and again Mrs. Merriedew had refused for her children as well as herself.

"No one to send with them indeed, and the boy Martin needed at home to look after the baby! She could get one of the neighbours to keep an eye on the child, couldn't she, or wheel him up in the pram herself? What was to prevent her?" Mrs. Trumper didn't hold with people who made things difficult for those who meant to be pleasant. The Doctor's wife was a nice lady, no doubt, but she had no call to give herself airs. "False pride, that's what it is," Mrs. Trumper said. "She doubtless feels herself above the schoolroom yet not quite up to the drawing room, if you get my meaning?"

Francis and I didn't. We merely felt uneasily that Nannie

39

was siding with Mrs. Trumper against the Merriedews; and when at last the invitation came, we were bewildered to discover that she and Mrs. Merriedew were on the most friendly terms.

II

The front door was open when we arrived; it appears in my memory to have always stood open, just as the house seems to have been filled with a gayer light and a fresher, more exhilarating air than most houses. There was a card tucked above the doorbell with the words, in a round childish script, "Out of order," so we walked in. The hall seemed rather full of bicycles, prams, a doll's carriage, and overcoats of various sizes suspended from pegs; but it continued past the staircase to the back, where a second door was open on the garden, and through this we saw Mrs. Merriedew with the children. She had on a long dress of a soft blue colour, it was her best, we discovered, Martin had asked her to put it on for the party; she was pulling a lettuce for our tea, and when Martin shouted "They've come!" she straightened up, holding out the fresh earthy curly lettuce in welcome, and said, "Oh dear — how nice, but I'm afraid I'm late!"

It was the sort of thing, we were to learn, that was always happening. Time was ignored in that house; it seemed to have no reality. The Doctor had none of his own; his belonged to everyone else; he could never be counted on for meals, and often missed tea or lunch altogether. And Katharine would forget all about the time. She lived in a private world where there was no such thing. For the children there was the sun; they rose with it in summer. As no blinds were ever drawn over the open windows of bedrooms, it was easy enough to wake up; and even Kitty, who was only five, was able to dress herself, with Martin to do up her buttons at the back and remind her to brush her teeth. Katharine left a great deal to Martin. He

40

would see to it in autumn and winter that he and Edward got off to school in good time; but first the three of them, if their mother wasn't down, would get their own breakfast of bread and milk. Then Martin would take his mother a cup of tea and wake her.

Not that Katharine was lazy. It was simply that she and the Doctor kept different hours from most people. If he were out late, she would wait up for him, though he told her not to. Perhaps she would forget to go to bed until he came home; or if he were summoned in the middle of the night or the early hours, she would go down and make him a cup of cocoa while he dressed, then go back to sleep again and lie dreaming with the sun bright on her face, a smile on her lips, and her cup of tea cold beside her, until Mrs. Thimble began rattling her brooms and dustpans.

Then she would get up and say "Oh dear! I'm afraid, Mrs. Thimble, that I overslept." But there was no harm in it. She knew she could count on Martin. Martin would have tended to young Michael, putting him on his pot and giving him his milk before he took himself off. Indeed the fact that no one in the family ever looked at the clock — there was one in the kitchen, but it wasn't to be depended on — seemed to answer very well on the whole, save for Kitty. Kitty would get hungry. She was a mere wisp, with big wistful brown eyes, but she was always eating between meals and complaining that lunch was late.

These habits naturally set the Merriedews somewhat apart in the community. We understood quite soon why Mrs. Merriedew had found it so difficult to accept our invitation. She had long ago got out of the way of going to tea parties. If you have no sense of time you cannot be expected to go out to tea at four-thirty, and you are not asked again if you turn up at six. No one in the family minded this in the least. They meant to be friendly. Anyone who came to see them was sure of a warm if vague welcome; but they were happiest at home by themselves.

Where the time idiosyncrasy did create difficulties for Katharine was in regard to help with the housework; no servant would stay on; no woman could be persuaded to live in the house. The only creature Katharine could find to put up with her ways was old Mother Thimble, whose day was regulated by opening time at the Chariot, and who consented to come for two hours in the morning to make beds and scrub. Katharine did the rest with Martin as houseboy and half-witted Gus to chop wood, carry coals, and work in the garden. And the children seemed to thrive, perhaps because, though she was, judged by Mrs. Trumper's standards, a very inadequate housewife, she was an excellent cook.

Mrs. Trumper's standards didn't apply in that house. How could they? Why should they? Katharine Merriedew lived for love, of her husband, her children, her home. She had a gift for happiness, and no social sense whatever. Nothing could have been more idiotic than to accuse her of false pride. She hadn't made difficulties about sending Martin to see us; there were difficulties. She needed Martin at home, and she didn't see the point of making the necessary effort to ask us to her house until she found that Martin did very much want to see Francis again. She had been interested in Francis because he was a delicate little boy and her husband's patient, but she wasn't in the least interested in his mother or in the great house where he lived, and she saw no reason, as Martin had taken a fancy to the poor child, why Francis and I shouldn't come to her when it was so much easier than the other way round.

So she asked us to please Martin, and then when it was at last arranged she did make an effort. The children wanted this to be an occasion, so she would make it one. Martin asked her to put on her best dress, so she put it on. Edward and Kitty said they must have a big tea and a special spice cake which they very much liked themselves, so Katharine made the cake and set out the table with her nicest teacups and arranged a lovely flower piece in the centre. The only thing she couldn't do to please the children was have it all ready on time, but that didn't matter.

What mattered to Katharine was happiness, comfort was a poor second. She concentrated on what in her view were essentials. To polish floors or pursue the dust left by Mrs. Thimble in corners was to her mind no more essential than to dress in the fashion or leave cards on her country neighbours. The children were forever running in and out of the garden leaving marks on the bare floors. Mrs. Thimble would grumble, but Katharine said, "They can't help it," and refused to nag. The slipcovers in the living room were shabby, they remained and grew shabbier with the years. No one could have said it was a comfortable house, but Francis and I liked it awfully.

There was a living room on the left of the hall, a combined dining room-schoolroom on the right. Both were quite big and rather gaunt and empty, with high ceilings, bare white walls and little furniture, and both were chilly in winter. No one seemed to mind, except Kitty. The boys took their chilblains for granted, and Katharine seemed unaware of the cold. There was a stove in the dining room and Martin would light it before breakfast, but his mother like as not would let it go out while he was at school, so he would light it again when he came home.

The living room had a few good pieces of old mahogany, and a small Bechstein piano. We used to gather round it while Katharine played, and sing carols and folk songs. There was a couch in front of the fireplace with sagging springs, and the faded hangings at the windows needed renewing as badly as the loose covers; yet the room had grace, and we thought it delightful.

Francis had been puzzled and worried by Martin's remark about our house not being real. "What do you suppose he meant, Babs?"

"Nothing; he was just talking nonsense; and it was a very rude thing to say anyhow."

But Francis wouldn't have that. "I'm quite sure he didn't mean to be rude."

"Well, it was, even if he didn't mean it to be."

Francis didn't want Nannie to think ill of Martin, so he didn't tell her; but one day he asked her: "Would you say our house wasn't a real house, Nannie?"

"Good gracious, child, whatever put that into your head? Some of it is three hundred years old. It's got more history to the square inch, Mr. Bowles says, than any house in the country. There's whole books about it in the library, all about the great Abbot and the monks, and Queen Elizabeth coming to stay, and Cromwell wanting to burn the place down, and the Countess sending him packing with a flea in his ear, the Earl of the day being off to the wars."

Nannie had got her history rather muddled, we discovered when we went down to the library with Miss Worthington and found a great heavy book with *History of Crabbe Minster* in what she told us was Gothic lettering stamped in gold on the shabby brown leather. It called Crabbe an architectural document of rich interest, and was full of pictures of the house inside and out. All sorts of bits had been photographed and were, it seemed, greatly admired. The main façade was, we read, an architectural gem, a perfect example of Italian Renaissance imposed on English Gothic. Inigo Jones had let his imagination run riot, it seemed, in the rich stonework of the great sweeping staircase, and the stables were of equal interest. There were pages of what the book called "detail." The gargoyles holding our own gutters in place above the nursery grimaced at us, and our old friends Amos and Hosea looked out

44

in their vague and benign way from a glossy page. It was most reassuring, but when we compared it to Martin's house we felt that we understood what he had meant. Our house was famous and public, Martin's was private. No one would ever want to photograph Martin's front door with its little peaked porch; even if it did stand open most days, his house didn't belong to the world, it belonged only to his family, that was what made it so nice.

And indeed everything in the Doctor's house had been so much used that even the tables and chairs had taken on the look of the family. They couldn't have belonged to anyone else. The Doctor's armchair had adapted itself for so long to his sturdy shape that it looked like him, a kind, sturdy, tired but comforting chair. And Katharine's, opposite, had a high rounded back and was cushioned in old, worn, crimson velvet. Her desk, a really good piece, stood open in the corner by the window, its pigeonholes crammed with papers; and though she didn't use it the Doctor did. I have never seen her sit down to it to write a letter, make out a list, or do accounts. The Doctor did such things. He paid all bills, answered all letters, he even went through the laundry list on a Thursday; and I have seen him measuring Martin for a new pair of shorts while Katharine drifted about arranging flowers. There were always tall vases with flower sprays or branches of fruit blossom or tawny and glossy leaves standing against the white walls; and Katharine's presence in the room often seemed to be as tranquil and fragrant. She would sit at peace in her crimson chair with a child in her arms and her workbasket beside her on the floor spilling over with boys' socks, Kitty's knickers, the Doctor's linen, as if she had nothing in the world to do.

I thought her fascinating. It didn't occur to me to criticize her. If she left more household tasks to Martin than were generally expected of a small boy, who was to blame her if the Doctor didn't? Francis and I soon got used to the way things were done. We would help Martin lay the table for tea or supper, then we would all wash up afterwards. No one in her family wanted Katharine to be practical and efficient, they loved her; her husband and her eldest son looked after her as if she were the child.

Sometimes when she was cooking she would forget what she was doing and stand dreaming at the kitchen window while the pots on the stove boiled over. Then when Martin or Kitty rushed to the rescue she would laugh, they would all laugh together; and the meal, whatever it was, when it did appear was delicious.

III

We had tea that first day in the dining room at a table by the open window. It was used for anything and everything between meals, the children's homework, Katharine's dressmaking (her sewing machine was behind the Doctor's chair on a shelf beside a pile of his medical journals), but the scarred surface was hidden for tea by a fresh white cloth, and the colours of the gay flower piece in the centre glowed in the sunlight. A gay, untidy, rollicking room. The low shelves along the wall were crammed with books; battered toys were heaped in corners, there was a pen for Michael. His mother put him into it when we sat down and he bounced about inside it making pleased noises while we ate. We ate in silence, watching one another.

Katharine poured out, with Nannie beside her. Francis came next, then Martin. I was opposite, with the Doctor's empty place between us, Kate beside me, then Edward next his mother.

I can see the table and the faces round it quite clearly. Nannie is handsome in her nurse's bonnet, Francis very pale. Kitty is what Nannie called a pretty puss, with a mass of soft curls like her mother's. I like Edward the least. He has a tight little face and scowls at Kitty when she sneaks an extra piece of spice cake and stuffs it quickly into her mouth. But Martin is delighted with his party. He faces me, his back to the window, and his fair head shines against the sunny vista outside; he beams at everyone, but especially at his mother. You can see that he thinks his mother very beautiful.

It was a lovely tea. There was a new brown loaf with a crackling crust, the fresh lettuce from the garden, a pot of honey, another of strawberry jam, and the big round spice cake, which Edward and Kitty liked so much, warm and sticky from the oven. Francis was too excited to eat, but I made up for him, and I daresay was quite as greedy as Kitty.

Then Dr. Merriedew rushed in and everything became animated. He kissed his wife, he greeted Francis and me as if we were quite grown up; he said he was sorry to be late for the party; he was hungry, he was in a hurry, he had only five minutes. "Yes, tea — and strong, please, Katharine, none of your wishy-washy brew."

Martin had jumped up to pull out his chair. The Doctor sat down and began rapidly eating lettuce. "Brown bread, Father?"

"Yes, please, and cut it thick. And honey — lots of honey."

There was a new baby, he said, at the Larnigans'. That made seven, and not a thing to eat in the house, so he had told Teresa, the eldest girl, to come round, they could always find something. Some eggs perhaps — were there any eggs? "And a brown loaf like this one, and what's left of that spice cake when Kate has finished. Martin, you see to it," he said. "The child will be along presently. And now I'm off," he said. "Expect me when you see me. There's a meeting at the hospital in Crabbe Major. The War Office have asked us to double the number of beds, don't know how, but it will be done — it must be. Afterwards I must go out to Oxshott. Old Mrs. Heatherington is very bad. There's a consultation. The two bigwigs from Harley Street have failed. They can't get away, so I must — though there's nothing we can do. Goodbye, everybody — don't move."

But Martin jumped up, and Katharine stopped the Doctor as he made for the door.

"Any news, Jasper?"

"Bad, I'm afraid."

"And you?"

"I don't know. The idea is that I should stay on here and do medical at the various hospitals. They want to put me in uniform. As I say, I don't know. We'll see."

Martin followed his father. Presently we heard the car starting up. Katharine's face was troubled as she collected Michael. We were all depressed for a moment and, I think, a little frightened, but only for a moment. Katharine said: "Run along. Nannie and I will clear up." So we went out into the garden and forgot the war.

It was a long deep garden, not very wide nor very tidy, but full to bursting with flowers and vegetables. The apple tree was halfway down on the right with a bit of rough grass under it and the potato patch beyond. Gus was digging potatoes and Martin, joining us, introduced him "This is Gus," he said. "Gus, this is Barbara and this is Francis."

Gus was big and clumsy. He had a big round red face, a shock of straw-coloured hair, and he bobbed his head at us half a dozen times, grinning delightedly and making strange gulping noises.

"He is saying," Martin told us, "that he is glad to meet you. Come, I'll show you my house."

To reach Martin's perch you had to shin up the trunk of the tree first, then hoist yourself by your arms, clinging to a thick branch. It wasn't really very high, not more than fifteen feet from the ground. Martin was up like a monkey, and I could have done it in a second; but Martin didn't ask me to come, he asked Francis, and Francis at first thought he couldn't. He wanted to, but he was afraid because of his legs. He had never climbed a tree before, and I could tell from his face that he was desperately divided between his longing to try and his fear that his legs wouldn't behave properly. So was I. I was sick with fright, but I passionately wanted him to prove that he could do it.

Martin had no qualms. He had told Francis he would show him his tree house and he meant him to come. He slid down, and we all stood together looking up.

"You can do it easily," Martin said, "if you want to. Don't you want to?"

"Oh, yes, very much."

"Then come; don't be afraid, just follow me. I promise you it will be all right."

Suddenly I couldn't bear it. "Don't, Francis. Don't. Martin, don't let him. He might fall."

Martin looked at me with the touch of scorn he usually showed for girls. "He won't fall," he said.

"Are you certain?"

"Quite certain."

So Francis shinned up the tree after Martin, swung in space by his strong skinny arms while I held my breath, and was hauled into safety just as Nannie and Katharine with Michael in her arms came out of the house.

They saw Kitty and Edward and me standing staring up into the apple tree and Nannie hurried toward us, calling: "Where's Francis?"

"Up in the tree," Kitty piped, dancing up and down waving her doll. "They're both up in the tree in Martin's house!"

Nannie was in a quandary. She stood under the tree staring up, very red in the face, and the two boys grinned down at her from their leafy height. I knew what she was thinking. She saw no reason why Francis should risk his neck to prove that he was as good as the Doctor's brat and I was dreadfully afraid that she was going to tell him to come down this minute, but when

49

I tried to take her hand and whisper to her, she flung mine away. She was frightened and angry. On the other hand, he was up there, he had to get down again and she couldn't go after him, so she contained herself and only said, "Well, I never!"

Katharine was quite unperturbed. "Don't worry, Bertha," she said. "He'll be quite all right with Martin. Kitty, show Barbara the young chicks."

But just then Teresa Larnigan appeared outside the gate at the bottom of the garden and Katharine put Michael down on the grass and went to meet her. I followed, leaving Nannie on guard under the tree. What a fuss about nothing! Why should I be palmed off on Kitty and her young chicks? Kitty was only six and played with dolls. I loathed dolls. I could climb trees every bit as well as Martin. It was mean of him not to say I could come up next.

The strange sight of Teresa restored my good humour. She was about nine at the time, a few months older than me, but very small for her age and so thin and pale that she looked in the distance more like a wraith than a flesh-and-blood child; but she was wheeling two large solid infants in a pram made out of a packing case. It was a rude affair and the children were too big to fit into it comfortably. They looked to me very ugly and fat, and one of them was asleep with his heavy head hanging over the side of the box. They were all three very dirty.

Teresa seemed to have nothing on but a grimy cotton dress that had slipped off one shoulder and a pair of men's shoes. She had twisted her fair hair into an untidy knot on top of her head, and the silky silvery strands falling about her small white face and delicate neck gave her a rakish look. Her nose was rather flat and her mouth wide, with full heavy lips. I thought it ugly; but her eyes were enormous and intensely blue. They were fringed with almost black lashes, in startling contrast to her silvery hair, and their expression was wise as an old woman's. They gleamed with malice. She was disreputable and fascinating. There was a smudge on her cheek, and she stood with one dirty hand on a jaunty hip and stared at us frowning, her mouth sulky.

"The Doc told me to come," she said.

Katharine opened the gate. "Yes, I know; come in, my child."

"Thanks, I'll wait here; I can't leave the kids."

"Bring them in."

"Not me! We'll wait." Her manner was impudent. She gave me a sidelong look. "I haven't got on me party dress."

"Just as you wish."

Katharine moved away; I stayed where I was; Teresa and I stared at each other in silence. It was a vicious little face, the face of a child already depraved, but defiant. I didn't understand it. I didn't feel sorry for her, I was fascinated. It was like looking at a face covered with cobwebs.

I don't know if her father had already abused her. She was, I think, thirteen when she had her baby; but I daresay Pat Larnigan had already had her in the shed behind the house where he was accustomed to use his wife in the presence of his children. I wouldn't have understood what this meant had I been told. Years were to pass before I learnt that incest was not a rare occurrence in our model village.

It was she who broke the silence. "What's your name?"

"Barbara, Barbara Patche."

"Mine's Teresa — Teresa Larnigan. That's Reginald." She gave the pram a jerk. "Him with his head hangin' out. The other's Patrick, same as Dad. There's lots more at home — a new one since this morning." She seemed to brood; but suddenly she grinned. "Lor, what fun and games! The Doc put us all in the shed, locked us in, he did, good old Doc — but I got out the window and had a good look, and there was Ma kickin' and screamin' on the bed, and Miss Withers, she's the district nurse, runnin' round with basins. You shut up, Patrick!

And remember what I was tellin' you — if you climb out o' your pram I'll leave you behind and you'll get no supper."

And with that Patrick got a good smack on the side of his ugly head, and the spell was broken.

An exciting afternoon with much begun that we didn't foresee. The pact of friendship between Martin and Francis was sealed while I stood staring at Teresa, and the course of her strange life was already set presumably. But she didn't see Martin that afternoon. He and Francis only came down from their perch after she'd gone away pushing her pram with one skinny arm and swinging Katharine's basket of food on the other. She wasn't interested in Martin in those days. Why should she have been? He was only a kid to her mind, half the size of her big brother, and she was already as old as Eve, but she stuck out her tongue at me, as she turned and shuffled off down the lane.

I wasn't to see her again for fifteen years. Crabbe village was a small place, but with a guardian like Miss Bertha Crouch standing between us and the world, the Larnigans' riotous hovel might as well have been in the middle of Africa, for all I was allowed to see of it or them.

The guns were pounding on the Austrian frontier when we got into the pony cart. War had begun and was spreading north from Central Europe as we whirled gaily home through the iron gates with stone lions rampant, past the lodge and up the drive, behind a fat pony with a glistening coat.

IV

I don't know how many times we sat down to tea or supper at Katharine's table during the war. Martin never much liked coming to us, but we seem to have run in and out of his house as if it were our own. Time, to which the Merriedew family paid so little attention, flows through my own memory like a sunny river gay with the laughter of young, confident voices.

Katharine's home is peaceful and filled with light even during the war years.

The small faces change. Edward's turns solemn, Kitty's petulant, Michael's is fierce with worship of his eldest brother. The Doctor grows grim with fatigue, his strong shoulders sag, his heavy step falters. Katharine changes least of all. Martin most. There is something eternal about Katharine, but Martin shoots up, at ten he is nearly as tall as his mother, and he seems much older than Francis, indeed at times older than any of us not excepting his mother.

He is still very beautiful, though the village doesn't notice it, and strong and straight as an arrow, still lights up the room when he comes in, with the glow of his radiant vitality but his face is more sensitive, it has new expressions. He is both boy and man now and flashes from one to the other.

How intimate they all are, Francis and I had never dreamed that parents and children could be such friends, and how Martin loves them: but his father is the one he looks up to and obeys. He listens to his father, I notice, but to no one else. He treats his mother as if she were the child, she never attempts to correct him and he takes for granted that his brothers and sisters will do just what he says. His air of authority irritates me. I was ready in those days to find fault with him. Not only from jealousy. He fascinated and infuriated me even then. There were moments when the friendly goodwill in his shining eyes filled me with such happiness that I longed to hug him as he hugged little Michael or his mother, but I was afraid to touch him, and just when I was feeling most loving he would turn away as if he were bored with me. Often he would hardly seem to know that I was there.

Sometimes he would disappear for a whole long day without warning and would come home with a strange, different face that frightened his mother. I would catch the look of fear in her eyes, but the Doctor wasn't afraid of him. He would tick him off soundly. Once I heard him say: "That's all very well. You may have felt you had to be by yourself, but your mother was counting on you to look after Michael while she got on with her baking." And when Martin announced one day that he didn't want to go to church any more, the Doctor took him off to the surgery; they were closeted together for a good hour and at the end of it the Doctor to my great joy had won. Not that I thought church mattered, but as I told Francis, "It would do Martin good to be taken down a peg."

Francis of course didn't agree. He said that Martin didn't want to go to church because praying was a private thing.

"That's a silly thing to say."

"No, it's not, it's true."

"So you're going to give up church too, I suppose?"

"No. We're both going. Martin has decided to do what his father wants."

"I should jolly well hope so. A kid like that! Why can't he be like other people? Who is he, after all, to think himself different from everybody else?"

"He doesn't want to be different, he just is."

"If you mean that he has such a good opinion of himself that he can think of no one else, I agree."

"That's not fair, Babs. He loves his family awfully, you know he does. He's always helping at home with the washing up, he does all sorts of things for his mother, and he helps his father in the surgery every evening."

"Why shouldn't he? He's going to be a doctor and probably likes messing about with bloody bandages."

"Then after supper he always helps Edward and Kitty with their lessons."

"I help you, don't I?"

"Of course you do."

"Well, then?" But Francis was besotted about Martin. It was no use arguing with him. And it is easy to exaggerate the boy's strangeness in the light of later events. I wonder now if Katharine was clairvoyant. I am ready to admit that a woman may be so bound to her son that she will feel the warning of his fate in her entrails, but if Katharine was as close to Martin as this, then why, I ask, did she allow herself to be persuaded by her other children to take their side against him?

I remember a summer evening in the boys' bedroom. There are three narrow white beds, and Michael is sitting up in one of them in a striped blue and white night suit. He is two years old, Martin is ten, and he is telling a story. Edward and Kitty and Francis and I are sitting on the floor and Katharine is standing in the doorway. It is a true story of some noble deed of adventure, out of a history book or the Bible. Michael always asked: "Is this going to be about the real world?" And Martin would say yes, and then tell about Nelson putting the glass to his blind eye, or Joshua bringing down the walls of Jericho with a blast from his trumpet, or Daniel standing undisturbed in the middle of the lions' den.

We don't question the reality of these events, but Edward is only half listening, he is biting his nails, he isn't sure that this isn't all a bit silly. Pretty Kate is sewing on a dress for her doll; or is it one for herself? She has tied back her curls with a pink ribbon, and I wonder if she isn't already rather jealous of Martin? I catch a look in her bright eyes that is a little resentful. But Katharine in the doorway, her quiet arms folded, is monumental. One would say that she is as firm on her feet as a statue in bronze, and her faith in her eldest son as permanent as if carved in stone.

The Doctor doesn't appear in this picture. I can see the others and the simple furnishings of the room, the enamel basin and jug on the washstand, Michael's toy soldiers in battle array on the chimneypiece and the garden through the open window all aglow with Katharine's flowers; but Jasper Merriedew isn't there. He would have been going the rounds in the hospitals of

Warrington, Greymouth, Crabbe Major, or rattling along a country road to usher some creature into or out of the world. He had no time to sit with his children listening to stories, the war was on him, he only had time to protect them from it and teach them to cherish their mother and fear God and keep the Ten Commandments He gave to Moses. A steady, hard-working, modest man, not a thinker, not a doubter like his eldest son of the established order, merely a servant of England and a good workman who asked for no recognition or gratitude from his country. I wish he had lived longer. Who knows? If he had not died so soon, Martin's story might have been quite different. Jasper Merriedew ruled his family, he exacted obedience from his children and got it, he saw to that, sometimes with the help of a strap. Not in Martin's case; he never as far as I know took a strap to Martin but he checked the boy's extravagant impulses, he brought common sense to bear on his intolerance of our poor doddering Vicar. Michael, of course, came in for more than one beating and Edward, in my opinion, could have done with a few more.

I may be wrong about Martin. It may be that no one could have deflected him from his purpose. But looking back, I say to myself that I might have known Edward would become a religious prig, Kitty a vain little snob, Michael the conventional British officer with all the usual prejudices of his type. At the same time, I am certain that they would not have turned against Martin as they did in the end had Jasper Merriedew been alive.

But I had of course no such foresight. I was the misfit of the party, I was jealous and carping, but I wouldn't have been left behind for anything when Francis went down to the Merriedews', and when he said he thought they must be the happiest family in the world, I didn't disagree. I liked being with them almost as much as he did and I awfully wanted them to like me. So I would put up with Edward and Kitty when Martin and Francis disappeared together. I would even offer to look after

56

Michael if Katharine was busy, or spend the whole of a Saturday afternoon working with her in the garden. But one thing worried me. I suspected the two boys of talking together quite a lot about God and I knew that if Bertha Crouch or my mother ever got wind of this all our cosy days with the Merriedews might well come to an end. Nannie would panic immediately and Charlotte would be shocked. For God, in Charlotte's view, must be strictly confined to church save for five minutes at bedtime when it was the thing to say your prayers; any greater intimacy was quite improper and I was definitely on her side in this, but I kept my suspicions to myself.

Chapter Four

I

BERTHA CROUCH would never admit that Martin was in any way exceptional. Though Katharine was our friend, she did not approve of our going so much to the Merriedews', but she put up with it all because knowing them acted on Francis like a strong tonic. The difference in him was so evident after a few weeks that even Charlotte noticed it and stopped one day in her rush of war activities to ask what had come over him.

It was a bright blustery day in October. There were vans at the front door; men in leather aprons were carrying iron bedsteads up the stone steps, and my mother in shabby tweeds and an old green pullover was directing operations from the terrace when she saw us go past. I was riding my bicycle with Francis on the handle-bars. She shouted; we pretended not to hear, but she shouted again: "Stop! Come back, you two"; so we had to. Francis jumped to the ground as we wheeled to face her.

"And where might you be off to?" she asked, leaning over the stone balustrade, high above us. She was without a hat and her face was red.

"We're on our way to the Merriedews'."

"Oh, you are, are you? And where's Nannie, where's that Worthington creature?"

"We don't know."

"And do they know where you are?"

We were both a little frightened, but there was much at

58

stake, so I decided to brazen it out. "I don't suppose so. We've given them the slip."

I was not quite certain, but I thought she said, "Well, I'm damned!" It was something like that, half under her breath. Then she beckoned. "Come here, Francis. Come close. I want to look at you." So he went and stood under the terrace and stared up, while she stared down. "What's happened to you?" she asked, after a moment's scrutiny. "Since when have you taken to riding round on your sister's handle-bars and playing truant?"

"It's the first time we've played truant." Francis was rather breathless. "But Babs often takes me on her bike, it's quicker, and Nannie lets me. She's seen me do it heaps of times."

"But what's the hurry?"

"Martin is waiting."

"How do you know?"

"We arranged yesterday."

"But kept mum about it?"

"Yes."

"Why?"

"We were afraid Nannie might say no, not two days running."

"I should think she very well might. And I ought by rights to send you straight back to her now. Don't you agree?"

Francis didn't answer, but his face reflected so painfully the conflict between his recognition of the rightness of this and his longing that I put my oar in. "You could tell her instead of us, and say you gave us permission."

She looked at me then out of her round jolly blue eyes. "That's an idea," she said, "so I could; and I think I will. Well, then, be off with you!"

She was shouting directions again to the van men as we wheeled away.

This encounter had a number of consequences, not all of

59

them pleasant. Francis was due to go to his prep school in a year's time, and Charlotte was determined that he should. I had thought he wouldn't go until he was nine, and when I heard this I went to her. "What's to become of me?" I asked, desperate at the prospect of being left alone at Crabbe with Miss Worthington. But what was to be done with me didn't seem to matter. She hadn't thought about it. A boy, it appeared, must go to school when he was eight, especially a mollycoddled boy; but a girl needn't go at all, and even if she did, ten was too young. Charlotte didn't know any good girls' schools that took them at ten, unless they were orphans; but when I blurted out "Well, I would be almost an orphan," she added that if I liked I might move to town and go to a day school. How would that suit me? I said I didn't think it would suit me at all, but if I could take my own pony along it might not be too bad. Well, she said, bored with the subject, we'd see. In the meantime, something must be done about Francis, to get him ready. He would show up so badly at school if he didn't play games.

Charlotte, though she gave her son apparently only the most casual attention, had a fixed idea about Francis; and the idea was to make a man of him, not a man like my father, for whom she had such an illogical fondness, but the sort of man she admired and would have found quite impossible to put up with as a husband. A powerful man, proud, self-confident, ruthless, a leader of men; the type of man she would have been had she not happened to be a woman. He must be brainy, of course, but above all he must have a commanding presence, and the basis of that was physical strength. Francis promised to have brains of a sort, but he was a shrimp. The cure was games. He must be made into an all-round sportsman; and even if he never was good at games, he must be taught to appreciate sportsmanship. How else could he ever hope to understand and rule the British race?

So far the boy and circumstances had combined to defeat

her. All this Nannie business, as she called it, was ruining him. She couldn't pack Nannie off because he might get bronchitis at any minute, and then where would she be? Miss Worthington didn't know one end of a thermometer from the other. She was good enough at Latin and Greek and English; too good by far at the piano; the village schoolmaster was already bribed to come up three afternoons a week for maths, and modern languages could wait. But what about games? The poor shrimp had no one to play games with but me. Mr. Spink was a hundred and blind as a bat. Where was she to find a resident games instructor with this war on? Every cricket blue was being swept into Kitchener's army. Not an able-bodied young man was to be found free and fit to lift Francis out of Nannie's lap and turn him into a sportsman.

It was too exasperating, too discouraging. Francis went on mooning about like an old woman, playing the piano, painting pictures, pressing flowers in albums; he'd take to knitting next. But now something had happened that gave her new hope. That Merriedew boy had done it. Well, let him get on with it! He must quit the village school and do lessons with Francis. In exchange for this privilege, he must coach Francis in cricket and teach him to box. An hour at the nets; half an hour with the gloves; a bit of target practice now and then; competition, that was the thing; Francis must develop the competitive spirit.

But Martin, it appeared, didn't play cricket; he didn't care for games, not even tennis; and nothing would induce the Doctor to let him share lessons with Francis. Charlotte's bullyings and blandishments had no effect. The only concession she could wring from the Doctor was leave to put the proposal to the boy himself. I was there when she and he discussed it, so I know.

"You will let him decide?"

"Yes."

"And not attempt to influence his decision?"

"I've no need. We see eye to eye on most things, and we will on this."

"You seem very sure of him."

"I am; he's a sensible lad."

"He won't be if he turns this down." But when we left she said to me: "Mind, not a word of this to Francis; I'll choose my moment."

She chose it one day when we had pursuaded Martin to come bird-watching down by the lake, and met her in the stableyard on our return.

"What have you three been up to? Heavens, what a mess you are in!" We explained, and made for the old harness room, where Jim let us keep our treasures, but she stopped us. "Just a minute; I want a word with Martin. How are you, Martin?"

"Quite well, thank you." He had got rather badly scratched scrambling through a thorn hedge, and wiped a trickle of blood off his forehead with a dirty paw, then faced her gravely.

"I've been talking to your father, and have a suggestion to make. How would you like to come every day and share lessons with Francis?"

Francis gasped "Oh!" then held his breath and waited; for Martin was silent. He was thinking, and while he thought was looking steadily up into my mother's face from his distance. The suspense was dreadful for Francis, but Martin's look of serious concentration kept him quiet, and presently the boy asked: "You mean only me?"

"Of course; your brother and sister are too small."

"What does my father say?"

"He says that you must decide." And then, because the boy was again keeping her waiting: "Come, say yes for Francis' sake. Think how nice it would be for him."

"I am thinking about that, and I think it would be nicer for him to come with me to my school."

"But, good gracious, why should he?"

62

"Because we are friends."

"Can't you be friends here?"

"Yes, but not school friends." He spoke slowly. "Not quite such whole friends." He frowned, puzzling it out, with his clear eyes steadily looking into hers. "You see, I have my own family to think of, and my own work to do in my own home."

"Nonsense, I'm not taking you away from your family, only from that stupid village school, full of dunces. Thirty of you in one class, I know all about it. You'd get on much quicker with Francis."

He pondered again before answering, then at last he said: "It's not that I like my school very much. I don't. But I belong in the village."

"So you want Francis to belong in the village too, is that it?"

"Yes."

"Well, I'm blessed." My mother had flushed; she made an impatient movement as if to turn away, but Martin hadn't finished and he held her.

"I am afraid you don't understand. I don't belong here, but Francis could belong anywhere."

"I see. Well, I don't propose to have him belong to your stupid village school. Come along, Francis, get rid of that mess and go straight up and change."

I was surprised that Francis wasn't more disappointed. He only asked Nannie once if she didn't think going to a village school was better for a boy than having lessons at home, and when she said, "Not with those Larnigan brats with their dirty talk and snivelling colds in their heads," he left it at that. I think he knew, just as I did, that Martin would never have agreed to my mother's proposal, he had only had one instant of hope. I, of course, was very pleased to have him to myself for lessons; and my mother dismissed the episode from her mind. A more sensitive woman might have smarted under such

63

a rebuff and have retaliated; but Charlotte had a wonderful way of ignoring unpleasant facts if she couldn't get the best of them. She never wasted her energy in regret, and she wasn't petty or mean. She didn't refer once to Martin's attitude, and made no move to interfere with our constant visits to the Doctor's house.

What she did do was undertake to prepare Francis for school herself. She was no good at the nets, so cricket was out, and she didn't propose to put on the gloves; but she was a first-class shot, and there was nothing in the way of horseflesh she couldn't manage, so Francis should shoot, and Francis must learn to like horses. The fact that Francis hated shooting and horse exercise made her all the more determined.

But Francis wasn't merely nervous of horses, he was desperately afraid of them. Their teeth terrified him. The effort to hold out his hand with a lump of sugar and wait for the big leathery lips to come down on his palm made him quite sick; and the thought of killing pheasants and rabbits was horrible to him. He couldn't help it. I told my mother so, but she wouldn't believe me. "Rubbish, of course he can help it. Rabbits are a pest and what's to become of all the pheasants if we don't shoot and eat them? The next thing he'll refuse to eat chicken or mutton."

She would push him into the loose boxes: "Don't be such a sissy, Francis, the mare isn't going to bite you!" She would come striding into the schoolroom in her riding breeches immediately after luncheon: "Come along, we are going for a gallop on the downs. Nonsense, Nannie, a little rain never hurt anybody"; or early in the morning: "Good heavens, boy, haven't you finished your breakfast? It's past eight o'clock. We've time for half an hour's target practice before lessons. Then this afternoon we'll take your pony over the jumps in the paddock."

He didn't mind rifle practice, but go out with a gun after rabbits he would not do. "I can't, Mummy, I can't!" She gave that up in disgust, but she would put him through it in other ways: running and jumping was one. It was horrid to me to see his white face, set mouth, wobbling legs, and my mother standing by with a watch and a tape measure. He couldn't run for nuts. He couldn't jump — broad jump or high jump. He would stumble and fall. But the paddock was the worst. Luckily for Francis she didn't persevere for long at a time. Something would interrupt, a row with Matron, or a conference of the Red Cross, or my father would need her in town and she would forget about Francis, then be furious when she came back to find that he had failed once again to put his pony over the jumps.

"What's the matter with you, Francis? Look at Babs. Your pony's quite as good as hers. Just give him his head. Give him his head, I tell you. Don't drag on his mouth. Oh, lord, must you hang round his neck? I never saw such a duffer. Here, Jim, give me that whip; now then." It was the whip from the pony cart with a long lash, she would crack it like a ringmaster in a circus and off they would go, my mother running for all she was worth; and Francis, white to the lips, would come off like as not at the first hurdle. But that didn't stop the performance. What was a toss? Nothing. "Up you go; if you don't do it now you'll lose your nerve for good." And perhaps he would manage to stick on this time; but usually he didn't, and I once saw her give him a smart cuff on the ear when he had made a special ass of himself, as she called it.

He wasn't a crybaby, but sometimes after a couple of hours of this sort of thing he would drag himself up to the nursery and fling himself into Nannie's arms, sobbing with exhaustion and despair.

What made it all so painful to watch was his intense desire to do what she expected of him. It exasperated me. "Why don't you refuse? Why don't you stand up for yourself?"

"I can't, Babs. I must try."

65

"I wouldn't, if it made me feel sick at my stomach. Would you, Nannie?"

But Nannie only snapped her mouth shut. There was no satisfaction to be got out of Bertha Crouch when it was a case of discussing her Ladyship. She could be kind, especially after baths, when she would read aloud to us with Francis in her lap, his thin arms round her large waist, his eyes half closed, and the long silky lashes casting bluish shadows on his white skin. He was so light and thin that it hurt me to look at him. I know she felt the same, and I suspect that she took my mother to task privately more than once; but she wasn't going to criticize a mother to her own son. That wouldn't be right.

As for old Tillie, as we had come to call Miss Worthington, we had grown quite fond of her. Even Nannie had relented, and would take her knitting to the schoolroom and keep the poor thing company after we were in bed; but she remained "a poor thing," we would never have thought of her as an ally, and were greatly relieved when she fell in love with one of the visiting surgeons and made friends with the Tripp sisters at the post office, going down to have supper with them once a week and do table turning; because now that she had a secret romance and friends of her own we needn't feel sorry about leaving her out of things.

And I daresay it was natural enough that Francis should have tried so desperately hard to please. Charlotte might be impossible, she was still his mother.

Martin was the antidote to this obsession, not a rival as yet. If a conflict of loyalties was already set up in my small brother's mind he wasn't aware of it. Nor did it occur to Charlotte at this stage to be afraid of Martin's influence. She was content to accept the obvious and profit by it. Martin Merriedew was an obstinate brat, but he wasn't a mollycoddle, so good luck to him.

Then Francis caught a bad cold; it settled on his chest, de-

66

veloped into pneumonia, and everything was frightful. My father came down, and was utterly miserable for five days; so helplessly miserable that I had to do something about him, and would drag myself away from my place on the floor in the corridor outside Francis' door to go down and work with him at his stamp collection. This cost me a great effort because I was persuaded that I was helping Francis to get well by crouching in the upstairs corridor with my eyes shut and my fists clenched. And he did get better, thanks to Nannie and Dr. Merriedew. Perhaps even old Tillie's prayers helped a bit, I thought. But no, she was too utterly futile. What earthly good could have come from her loping across the park twice a day to pray for Francis in our sleepy old church? God wouldn't pay any attention to people like Matilda Worthington and me. She was too silly and I was too wicked. I was so aware of being wicked that I hadn't dared pray while I watched by my brother's door and I didn't think He would listen to Mr. Nightingale either if it came to that. And if my mother — but I couldn't imagine my mother driven to her knees by fear for her son's life. She remained consistent and confident, kept out of the sickroom and went about her own business as if nothing were so wrong that it wouldn't come right.

But she had had a shock. Though she never admitted, I believe, even to herself that she was in any way to blame, she had been badly frightened and after talking to the Doctor changed her mind about prep school. What were schools, after all? Why should her son be put through a sausage machine? The British system for reducing its members to a pattern was all very well for the middle classes. Let her boy stay at home until Winchester and do what he chose to do. If this meant playing the piano and being fond of birds and flowers, why not? Arthur Balfour played the piano. Edward Grey knew a lot about birds. A man with a great name and great acres could afford to be odd. Well, let Francis be odd. When spring came and he was out and about again, she washed her hands of him and gave herself up to enjoying the war.

She was rather bored by this time with her hospital but she had other scope for her energies. As regional commissioner of the British Red Cross she was continually dashing about the county and running up to London for conferences or to see my father. He had taken on a modest job in the Ministry of Agriculture and was often obliged to stay in town for the weekend, obviously he couldn't be left to look after himself. What with one thing and another we had only the briefest glimpses of both parents for the rest of the duration.

Children are brutes. They come tumbling blindly into the world and immediately start yelling for what they want. What we wanted most was to be left alone with the Merriedews. So we were quite pleased with our parents' activities but we were not much interested in the war and kept away at first from the wounded men who were carried in and out of our front door. The wounded, according to Charlotte, were things you never had enough of. We would often hear her clamouring for more over the telephone. Every week or so she would ring up Warrington and make a fuss. "Here I am with sixty beds and half of them empty. I've turned my house into a first-class surgical hospital at great expense and trouble to myself. I've a matron and eight fully qualified nurses on the place eating their heads off and you haven't sent me a fresh batch of wounded for three weeks. Nonsense, it's only forty miles, you can easily stop the train from London at Crabbe Major. If I don't get some more cases by Friday I shall get onto the War Office.

It was true that she had taken a great deal of trouble. The whole of the ground floor was given over to the hospital, excepting the library and my father's cubbyhole, but our own quarters were unaffected and we could play hide and seek on rainy days through the galleries and corridors upstairs without disturbing anyone, as Matron had insisted on putting the of-

68

ficers downstairs. No nurses, she declared, could be expected to look after their patients in a series of rooms at the top of an enormous staircase, and Mrs. Trumper had agreed with her. Mrs. Trumper too had been lent to the Red Cross. She looked after the hospital commissariat and had a handsome navy-blue uniform with brass buttons, like Charlotte's except for the tabs.

We went most often to the Merriedews' but sometimes, if the weather was bad, Martin would come to us and it was he, I think, who suggested that we might visit the patients, but perhaps it was Francis. It was on a wet Saturday afternoon, I remember, and I fancy that I was bored, so I said yes; and the three of us went down and rather timidly peeped into the ballroom. What I saw wasn't at all what I had expected. The gramophone was on. There was a fire blazing in the chimneypiece. There were vases of chrysanthemums, and the patients all in blue and white flannel jackets like Michael's pyjamas were laughing and smoking in their beds and looking at picture papers. Two in warm dressing gowns were up and were playing draughts by the fire. One had his arm in a sling and the other had a bandage round his head, but they grinned cheerfully when we turned up and indeed all the men seemed quite pleased to see us, so we made a habit after that of paying them a visit on Saturday afternoons.

We would take flowers or cigarettes or cakes supplied by Mrs. Trumper (this was Nannie's idea), and Francis would chat away quite happily about our doings to any who seemed to want to talk to us. I daresay they were all pretty bored and glad enough to hear about our childish affairs. Sometimes they asked questions, and Francis would tell them solemnly about Henry VIII with his many wives, and how badly he had treated the monks who used to live here, and how some people said there was a ghost in a cowl who haunted the Monks' Walk, though we were sure there wasn't. But Martin found nothing to say. He would move from one bed to the other beside **Francis**, quite silently shaking hands until he came on one who was evidently very bad, then he would stay with him.

One, I remember, was a captain, he was in the end drawing room and had a bandage that covered his eyes. Only the bottom half of his thin face was uncovered. His jaw was sharp and his nose pinched. We knew that he was blind, and he didn't seem very sociable, so Francis and I would slip past his bed; but Martin would stop and say "Good morning, sir," and the Captain would move his long pale hand to take hold of Martin's; and Martin would stand there beside him, looking down at the blind hidden face, until we called him. Then he would say "Goodbye, sir, I must go now," and the Captain, without speaking or moving his head, would let go of his hand and he would join us. I don't think they said much to each other. I never heard the Captain speak or saw him make any movement but that groping one with his hand. And Martin never spoke about him. But he would be white when he came away, and his eyes would be dark as children's eyes do go dark when they have been cruelly and unjustly punished.

I don't pretend to understand what this episode signifies in the way of some special gift, but I think it proves one thing, that Martin was more vulnerable than Francis and I to pain. He had one skin less than we had. He was hurt by the blind man's suffering and his reaction was direct. He didn't avoid him as we did.

It was like the case of poor half-witted Gus. Martin loved Gus, and I believe he loved the blind Captain. Gus was faithful and could be trusted to watch over young Michael as our Nannie could be trusted; but Francis said Martin loved Gus most because he tried so hard to talk and couldn't, and he loved the Captain because the Captain was alone in the dark and frightened. It would not have been difficult, you may say, for a small boy to understand what it is to be frightened in the

70

dark. The fact is that Francis and I tiptoed past the blind man's bed, but Martin went up to him. He tried to help both the Captain and Gus. He wanted to heal them. He couldn't obviously do anything about the Captain's eyes, they were gone. What comfort the silent man got from the boy's presence I don't know. He was taken away to another hospital and we never heard of him again.

What Martin possessed as a boy was not the power but the will to heal. When Francis was so ill, he came to see him every day, as soon, that is to say, as he was allowed to. That was almost immediately after the crisis, because Francis kept asking for him, and worked himself into a state when the Doctor and Nannie told him he must wait; he wasn't well enough for visitors. "But Martin isn't a visitor, he's my friend. He won't make me sicker, he'll make me better. He won't talk or anything. I don't want to talk to him. I don't have to. I just want him." So they gave in.

He would come after school, and sit for a quarter of an hour by Francis' bed, never saying a word, then go away. And Francis, Nannie said, would fall asleep while he was there. "Blessed if I know what to make of it. Mad for a sight of that boy. Watches the clock as if he was counting the minutes and they couldn't go fast enough. Then no sooner he's there than the poor lamb goes off to sleep, and so sound, he don't even notice his friend's gone again — just goes on sleeping till it's time for his supper."

II

I think there is no doubt that Martin's presence in the sickroom was good for Francis and that in that sense he helped to heal him, but when I put together with this understandable fact the tales that were told twenty years later of the miraculous cures he was supposed to have performed I think of Gus, for he willed to heal Gus and he failed.

71

He was already worrying his father about Gus when we first got to know him, and he went on badgering him for three years. Dr. Merriedew would become exasperated.

"I have told you, Martin, that I can do nothing for Gus. He has a defective palate and the mind of a child of three, that is to say of a stupid child. Even if he were to undergo an operation and it were successful, he would still remain a child, but very probably not be a happy one. He is happy now as he is. We must leave well enough alone."

"But he wants to talk, Father. He tries to talk to me, and he does talk to Michael. He has quite long talks with Michael, and Michael and I understand him. We do really talk to each other and Gus is most awfully pleased. He grins all over his face. But when Michael gets bigger he won't understand him any more than you do, or Mother."

Gus was very useful in the garden. He was clumsy but very strong, and reliable. Once when he and Michael were digging away, they came on a snake. It wasn't a poisonous snake, but Gus couldn't know that, and he had Michael up high in his big arms quick as a knife, and the snake under his great foot. It was quite wonderful, Katharine said (she was hoeing potatoes), he was as quick as lightning. Even the Doctor was impressed. He said something about reflexes, and was puzzled; but Martin said it proved Gus was much more than a child, and went on worrying about teaching him to talk.

"Let me try, Father."

"I have told you, Martin, there is a defect, it is at the back of his throat. You must study these things — and you will in time — but you must wait."

"But I feel that I could do it."

"Very well."

At last, he was ten at the time, with his father's permission he set about trying to teach Gus to talk and I watched him. He would take Gus's great fingers and place them to either side of his own throat, then speak slowly and distinctly, look-ing up into the other's heavy face. "I am your friend, Gus. I am your friend. You understand, don't you?" And Gus would nod his big round head. "Then say it, Gus. Say 'I am your friend.'" And Gus would try to say it, and strange sounds would come from his wide, loose mouth. Then Martin would say: "Not bad, but not good enough. Try again, Gus. I am your friend." And Gus would try again. Or Martin would say: "Michael. You know Michael, you love Michael. Now say his name." And Gus would grin and mouth "Michael."

But a day came when Martin was obliged to recognize that he had failed. Gus didn't mind. He would never learn to talk; he had only learned to love Martin and follow him about like a dog. But Martin was heartbroken. We didn't know what had happened, but we knew there was something, because Kitty saw him rushing across the fields. It was Francis who found him, late in the afternoon, lying on his face in a wood, sobbing.

"I was wrong," he said. "I had such a strong feeling that I thought I must do it, but I couldn't. I didn't know enough. Oh, poor Gus, poor Gus!"

III

It was during the winter of 1915 that we met Albert. No one knew how old he was. He seemed never to have had any family except the Blundles but had finished school and worked at the Chariot. Martha Blundle was supposed to be his aunt and em-ployed him as potboy, perhaps out of kindness, but more likely, Miss Molly said, because he made the customers laugh. He was just three feet, four inches tall and he seemed to like to show off and make you laugh. If he caught you looking his way, he began immediately to do handsprings or stand on his head. But that, Martin said, was because he expected us to laugh at him, and wanted to give us something more to laugh at than just himself. He was always like that with strangers. It was a pity.

73

Strangers couldn't hurt you, Martin said, only people you loved. Albert knew he was quite safe at their house. All he needed to make him feel comfortable was for people to treat him seriously, as if he were like anybody else; so after that we were always serious with Albert, and we came to like him very much. He was really a cheerful person when you got to know him, and very clever. He had his own room, he said, at the Chariot, high up under the roof, and he spent a lot of time reading. He was a great reader, and we used to lend him books, but most of our own books were too young for him. He didn't care for fairy tales, even Christie and the Goblins. What he liked best was history. *Lays of Ancient Rome* was one of his favourites. And the Bible, especially the Psalms. He knew a great many of the Psalms by heart, and would recite them for us, if we asked him to, sitting in Michael's small armchair by the drawing-room fire. Katharine often asked him to tea. She didn't mind him a bit, but Nannie said no when we suggested doing the same. You had to draw the line somewhere, it seemed, and she drew it at Albert.

And now I ask myself a plain question, searching my memory for an answer: was there anything about that boy Martin Merriedew, did he do anything, did anything happen when we were children that proves him to have been different enough from the rest of us to be called abnormal? But I cannot answer. I am not certain. It would all be so simple if one could write him off as unbalanced; if it were merely a case of not enough thyroid or too much, but I can't settle for that. Nothing that I remember or have been able to find out about his youth reveals him as irrational, as queer or doomed. There was no mark on his young forehead. He was a strong healthy boy with a great capacity for happiness, and he was only different enough from other boys to be laughed at for a fool by the village nitwits.

They laughed at him one day because he wouldn't hit back

74

when Fred Larnigan, the school bully, went for him. Fred was a foul-mouthed brute, half a head taller than Martin, with a shock of red hair and big red fists. He must have weighed at least a stone heavier than any of the others and, according to Edward, enjoyed making the little ones blubber. Edward gave him a wide berth, we gathered, but Martin had stood up to him more than once, so the thing must have been working up for some time. Martin, it seemed, wasn't popular in the school. The little ones looked up to him as their protector, but he didn't like dirty stories or bad language, so Larnigan's gang called him a sissy. Then one day it all boiled up, over the hunchback Jeremy Green. Jeremy in those days was a miserable little creature, very clever at lessons and, I should think, quite intolerable, but Martin had taken him under his wing and when he found Larnigan in the yard, holding Jeremy by the hair while he kicked him viciously in the pants, he walked up to him and ordered him to stop, whereupon the bully dropped Jeremy and turned his attention to Martin. School had just broken up, the bully had the whole lot for audience, and he gave himself up to it with enthusiasm. Francis and I were at the Doctor's waiting for Martin to come home and we could hear the noise from the garden but we didn't of course know what it was. The jeers, catcalls, yells of derision rose to a piercing crescendo. Teresa must have been there and yelled no doubt as loud as any, egging her big brother on. The spectacle sent them wild with excitement, for Martin stood quite still and took what was coming to him without attempting to defend himself. Blows to either side of the head, between the eyes, on the mouth, kicks when the lout had him down on the ground. Then Martin got up again and waited for more, with blood streaming from his nose and mouth, and they yelled louder than ever, splitting their sides with laughing. Edward was horribly ashamed of his brother that day. It was he who came home sobbing and told us, but Martin a few minutes later walked straight past us into the garden and put his head under the pump. And when I asked him after he had cleaned himself up why he hadn't fought back he said: "Why should I? I didn't want to hurt him — and I knew I wasn't afraid of being hurt but I had to prove it to myself."

The affair didn't add to Martin's popularity at school. If he had fought back and taken his licking like a man, he would have been something of a hero; but to stand still and allow himself to be kicked and knocked about was — well, no one could understand it. Poor Mr. Spink came hurrying along on his skinny old legs to apologize and explain how it was that he had been out at the back when the trouble started and Bill Trumble, our village constable — it was he, it seemed, who had put a stop to the business — came to report that he'd seen to it that Fred Larnigan got a good hiding from his pa, but they were both uncomfortable about the part Martin had played. Indeed Mr. Spink told Francis and me, when we broached the subject the next time he came to us for maths, that young Merriedew was a good lad and exceptionally clever, quite brilliant in fact when he cared to be, but if we would excuse him, he would rather not talk about what had occurred, and even the Vicar, it seemed, was nonplussed when he heard the story and said: "Dear, dear, how very strange." It was Tillie who told us this. Tillie was on our side, I say our side because, though I would much have preferred it had Martin gone for Fred Larnigan with his fists, I could not but stand by him when all the village thought him queer. And I was glad that Tillie agreed with us that he had been very brave. Unfortunately she was rather a fool, so she didn't help much. As for Nannie, she simply dismissed the whole matter by saying she wasn't a bit surprised at anything those Larnigans would do and how did Francis feel now about going to such a school?

We didn't realize it at the time but I can see now that our duck of a village was never very fond of Martin Merriedew. His looks told against him in the early days. Bessie Holt's mother said he was too good-looking by half and would come to a bad end. Martha Blundle called him a stuck-up piece of goods; and it was true that he sometimes had an air that was distant and proud. As for Mrs. Green, Jeremy's doting mother who took in washing, she wasn't in the least grateful to him for deflecting the blows and kicks from her precious son. She was downright spiteful. Even the two old maids at the post office, though they seemed to dote on him, didn't prove themselves very staunch in the end. They were not at all heartbroken when he came to grief. They didn't close up shop and go after him when he disappeared. They let the "young lord" do that and remained in their cosy cage selling their stamps, their boiled sweets and their picture postcards of that famous Old World public house, the Triumphant Chariot, while they nodded their sentimental grey heads and pursed their grim puckered lips over our great village scandal. They were very shocked indeed when they heard that he had gone off with Teresa; they clasped their fat little hands in distress and repeated the story to everyone who came in. "Martin Merriedew? Such a lovely young man! Who would have believed he would do such a thing?"

No, he didn't have many friends in the place — at any time. In fact, as a small boy, he only had Gus and Albert and Francis and me, if I can call myself a friend.

Chapter Five

I

WHEN I married Charles I was so wildly in love that I felt we must be immortal. This life wasn't long enough nor this world big enough for us. And Charles, because he too was in love, didn't snub me when I said I was going to prove to my brain that what my heart told me was true. But he would look up from the brief he had brought home for his evening reading and smile rather ruefully from his side of the fire to see me deep in some book by Whitehead, James Jeans or Eddington; knowing that I was counting on these great scholars to prove beyond shadow of doubt the existence of God in the Universe and that I would be disappointed.

"If we could be certain about God, Charles," I would say, lying with him in the trembling dark, "we would be safe." And he would answer: "We can be certain of nothing. There is, there can be no echo in the infinite to the cry of a man's heart; so let us not cry out, my love, nor complain, nor spend our lives asking questions that cannot be answered. Let us put our minds to enjoying the little time that we have together."

That was long ago. We have been married now for twenty-six years and the problem of immortality no longer seems a burning question. We are still very good friends; but I don't feel it a matter of desperate importance that we should live forever. I fear that we might be bored by such a long tête-à-tête. I am sure that he would be.

All that I ask now is not to lose him for as long as I live. The thought of going on here without him is unbearable, so I dismiss it. Sometimes when he comes in very tired, I notice how thin and grey he is, how slowly and languidly he puts his umbrella in the stand and hangs up his hat, and I have a moment of panic; but I shut down on it quickly. I help him off with his coat but I don't put my arms round him, we stopped that sort of gesture years ago, he would be startled and puzzled if I did such a thing; so I turn away from his courteous face and say to myself: "He's only sixty; what's that? he's got years to go yet, I'll get Jane to come round, she'll cheer him up, and he can rest over the weekend; we won't do a thing all day Sunday." I snap out of it; I cover up; I make myself busy. I look at my engagement book and say: "Tomorrow, lunch with Camilla; at three, the hairdressers; tomorrow night the Edringtons for dinner and bridge; a full day and a nice day tomorrow, and there will be hundreds just like it. Charles will come home tomorrow just as tonight, preoccupied, rather weary, with a bitter twist to his lips as if he had a bad taste in his mouth, but his face will smooth out when he sees his Rowlandson drawings on the panelled wall. He will give them a friendly glance, go and wash his hands, then come after me up to the drawing room and say: "Well, my dear, had a good day?" and stand in front of the fire, fiddling with his watch chain, ruminating, not really interested in my answer, but relaxed, and very considerately waiting in case I should have something to tell him before he goes downstairs again to his study.

I know better than to give an account of my doings. I merely murmur, "Yes, quite a good day," and hand him a glass of sherry; but sometimes I wonder what would result if I demanded his full attention, broke through the silence, the distance, the calm order of the familiar room with its softly fluttering fire and the rain pattering gently against the windowpanes. I don't. I am careful to preserve what we have left, the tacit acceptance of our bond and our difference; for what we have left is decent and precious to me, it must not be destroyed.

79

We are safe, I tell myself nowadays, if I do nothing and say nothing to spoil it. There is no end to the familiar, the known, the safe tomorrows I can count on if I am careful of Charles; and though I know I cannot count on a single one, I do. How else could I live?

Charles would pity me if he knew that I was afraid to die, or to live without him. He is very detached. He no longer regards life as dangerous, he doesn't expect it to surprise him, has a poor opinion of mankind, including himself, and no curiosity about the hereafter. He accepts the fact — it is for him indisputable — that there is none. He sleeps badly, but he doesn't dream. He turns on his light and reaches for a book. Though we have separate rooms, I know that he sometimes reads through half the night; I can see the light under his door; but I can't go in to him to be comforted when I wake from a nightmare.

His favourite bedside book is his schoolboy copy of the great Greek Tragedies. Sometimes, tidying his room in the morning, I find bits of paper on which he has been scribbling, his own translations of favourite lines; but they are always crossed out, he is too fastidious to be pleased. In his opinion the Greeks reached the summit of human achievement in the fourth century B.C., and we have been going downhill ever since. The thought does not disturb him. He seems to derive from it a certain satisfaction, and considers all reformers public nuisances and fools for their pains. He was made a judge in '43 and is of an impeccable integrity. We spent five years on the Western Circuit, and he is now at the Court of Appeal. He takes for granted that most men are liars, but that this is none of his business save when on the bench. He reveres the law, believes in his calling, and has no use for the Church, but went through the conventional ceremonies of marriage and baptism with me and the children to save trouble.

When we were married he was recognized as one of the

coming men at the bar, and his career, if not brilliant, has been distinguished. He is fifteen years older than me, and looks like a monk, but is in fact rather sensual and was an exciting lover. I don't know to this day why he chose me. My mother took a dismal view of my chances as a girl, and was relieved when I elected to go to Oxford instead of doing the London season; but I was lucky enough to meet him and take his fancy during my first year at Somerville, so I promptly abandoned the pursuit of knowledge to marry him.

My life at Crabbe ended in 1919. Francis went away as soon as our first world war was over, to a crammer at Folkestone to get ready for Winchester; and I went to Paris for a year, then Munich, then Florence. Charlotte said languages were of great value to any girl and I needed all I could get in that way, more than most; but neither she nor I thought the result likely to prove a great social success, so I spent six months in London with old Tillie working for my exams, and managed to pass. Charles, however, was never impressed with my brains. His pleasure in women has little to do with the mind, it is on a par with his very cultivated taste for good wine. He was first attracted to me, he said, by the way I moved, he sensed the tiger inside, then fell in love with my voice. The passionate years have left sweetness behind, if one can use the word in speaking of such a dry man as Charles. Why not? Though we are not quite so easy together as we used to be, there remains his exquisite courtesy. We never mention Martin Merriedew's name.

II

Charlotte had decided at the end of the war that Francis had had enough of Martin Merriedew. The Doctor's boy had served his purpose and saved her a deal of trouble but now she had no more use for him, and he was to be liquidated together with Nannie Crouch and Matilda Worthington. Her son was no

81

longer a child, and must cut loose from his childish habits; she confidently expected that once he had settled down at Winchester he would make new friends and forget the old ones. But things didn't work out that way.

I know now that Francis and Martin had already settled on a combined plan of life before he went to his crammers and were preparing for it, because Francis told me so afterwards when it had all come to nothing. It was quite definite, they were going to spend their lives together in some arduous effort for the good of their fellow men, and on the day that Francis left for Winchester they sealed a solemn pact to dedicate their joint lives to the service of humanity. Nothing was to be allowed to come between them or deflect them from their purpose and all through their schooldays they kept each other up to it. It must have taken some doing, for Martin was left behind at Crabbe: they only met during the holidays, and my mother managed to fill the house when Francis was at home with young people of a very different type from Martin. She knew nothing of course about her son's plans for the future, he kept those very dark, but she was aware, one couldn't not be, that the two boys were as thick as ever. Francis would leave his guests to me to look after and slope quietly off to the Merriedews' most afternoons, he insisted on including them in every festivity and, though Martin always refused these invitations, Kitty would come sometimes with Edward. And all Charlotte's efforts to persuade Francis to join me abroad for a part of the summer recess were met by a blank refusal.

My father, as I remember, didn't share her views. He said the Doctor's boy was a good sort of boy and why ship Francis off to Europe if he wanted to stay at home? But I seem to have been willing to enter into a conspiracy with her to keep the two apart. We both failed. Though I wrote often and at great length, hoping to lure him with the brilliance of my foreign horizon to join me, he has admitted that he found my letters very dull and when I came home, as I did each year for Christmas and Easter, I made the mistake of running down the Merriedews. He didn't tell me in so many words, that my years abroad were doing me no good, but I know my fault-finding only made him think more of the Merriedews and less well of me.

In my Paris letters I described, I remember, the Cathedral of Notre Dame, the Louvre Museum, and the Château of Versailles in great detail, painted what I flattered myself were witty portraits of the stuffy French family I lived with, and went into ecstasies over Sarah Bernhardt and the cream cakes we devoured in a shop in the Rue Royale. When I moved on to Munich, the second year, I discoursed at length on the opera. Finally from Florence I announced that I had suddenly come to realize what wonderful pictures there were at Crabbe. We had never, I informed him, appreciated Crabbe or the things in it. Would he please send me the name of the Italian woman painted by Bronzino, the one in green brocade with pearls in her hair. There was a Bronzino just like her, here in the Uffizi. Ours might be a copy — what a sell if it was. But the greatest of all painters in the Contessa's opinion was Giovanni Bellini. I was in charge of the Contessa and when I told her we had one at home she nearly fainted. What else had we got, she wanted to know, and I couldn't tell her. I only knew about the Bellini and the Bronzino because they hung in the drawing room. Most of the other good pictures were in the gallery and when I confessed I'd never really looked at them, she said she hoped God in His mercy would forgive me, so would Francis please send me a catalogue of the picture gallery if there was one, and make a list if there wasn't, as we did seem to have been a couple of idiots.

Francis didn't answer half my letters and when he did was brief. He knew he would hate Paris and my French family. Munich he thought must be nicer because of the music. "A pity, old thing, that you are almost tone deaf." But he was more interested when I wrote from Florence. He had checked up on the Bronzino. Ours was the same lady as in the Uffizi but quite genuine. The artist had painted her half a dozen times. Charlotte had been furious when it was suggested that ours might be a copy. He enclosed a list of the paintings in the gallery. The Filippo Lippi, Charlotte said, had cost my grandfather a lot of money. He had been had over the supposed Giorgione. The experts were divided but it probably wasn't one. Mrs. Merriedew sent messages, so did Kitty. Martin was working hard for his scholarship. Edward wanted to take Holy Orders and Martin was against it but the Doctor and Mrs. Merriedew thought it a good idea. Michael was a fine chap but not very brainy and always in trouble at school.

Francis chose to assume on my visits home that I was as happy as ever to be with the Merriedews. He would say, "Come along, Sis, Kitty is longing to see you," and we would go down to tea or supper as we always had done. But each time I came back from Paris or Munich, the house seemed smaller, shabbier, and more untidy. Mrs. Thimble had passed on, was that the reason? And poor Gus was dead, he had been run over by a truck. The door still stood open but the rooms lacked the exhilarating light and air of the old days. They were dimmer. And though the pram had disappeared from the front hall it was more crowded than ever with large-size boots and bicycles. It is distressing to confess but, though I still thought of the Merriedews as great friends, I didn't find them after a year in Paris quite as delightful as formerly.

The Doctor wasn't an old man, he can't have been much over fifty when I married, but he had gone very grey and moved heavily, as if with a weight on his shoulders. Katharine too was heavier, not in body — she hadn't changed much in looks; there was no sign of white in her dusky hair — but in spirit. She didn't hum to herself now over her cooking, and when she

84

forgot, as she still would forget, what she was doing, Kitty, who was supposed to help with the housework, wouldn't run laughing to rescue the pots that were boiling over, but would wail: "Mother, I do wish you would concentrate. Just look at the mess on the linoleum!" And Katharine's eyes would be quite frightened for a moment and she would say, "Oh dear, I'm so sorry, I'm afraid I was thinking of something else," and go down on her knees to mop it up.

She wasn't allowed to do this sort of thing when the Doctor or Martin was about, but the Doctor was out more than ever. I think he was finding it difficult to meet the expenses of his growing family; he was never very good at collecting his fees; Martin was away all day at his grammar school in Crabbe Major, and it almost seemed that her other children were too much now for Katharine.

She was the type of woman, I told Francis, who should always have an infant in her arms but didn't know what to do with children when they stopped being babies. Kitty was no use at all to her mother. She pretended to dust and tidy the boys' rooms, but she only pushed their shoes under their beds and then went and curled up by the fire with a novel. She was as luxury-loving as a cat, very sweet and affectionate, no doubt, though I did hate being pawed and called darling. And she was going to be a beauty. She would be quite lovely now without that plate in her mouth, but she was eaten up with envy. As for Edward, he was too tiresome. Michael was all right but Edward was quite horrid.

I said all this to Francis one Sunday morning during the Christmas holidays. I think it was in my Munich year. We had been to church with my father and had left him to go back with the Merriedews to see Martin. Katharine, Edward, Kitty, and Michael had all been in church but not the Doctor or Martin. The Doctor had been called out on a case, Katharine explained, and Martin had stayed at home to work, he had been at his books since six in the morning and it was high time he was interrupted. Her smile suggested that it was a pity the boy had to work so hard, but if he must he must. Edward had then made a scene. He couldn't understand his mother. She didn't seem to mind a bit Martin's working on Sundays instead of coming to church. Martin never came to church any more. "That's not quite true, Edward." Well, hardly ever, and people noticed it, they said things, he'd heard them. Young Michael fired up at that in defence of his elder brother. He was eleven at the time.

"What does it matter what people say? And what's it got to do with you, anyhow? If you'd do your own work instead of sneaking upstairs to Martin to get him to help you, maybe he would come to church with us."

"Shut up, you're only a kid and know nothing about it. Everything Martin does is perfect. That's what you think. But I know better. I know why he doesn't go to church even if you don't. I heard him telling Francis he hated the Church. 'I hate these professional priests who are paid to say prayers.' And then he said, 'Jesus of Nazareth would have had a tough time among the college of Bishops.' Didn't he say that? Aren't those his very words?"

"Edward! Be quiet. Martin couldn't have said such things. You misunderstood him." Katharine was very distressed but Martin, appearing just then, laughed at Edward, swept us all into the drawing room for a glass of sherry, and said to his mother: "Darling, don't worry. He'll be a bishop himself one day, in spite of me."

I asked Francis on the way home if Martin really had said these things.

"Yes — something of the sort."

"Poor Mr. Nightingale."

"Oh, he doesn't mind old Nightingale. He merely has no

use for him." Francis dismissed Mr. Nightingale with a flick of the hand.

"You are pretty intolerant, you two, I must say."

"Are we? I daresay we are. We don't like humbugs if that's what you mean."

"He's not a humbug. He's just a lazy old man."

"All right, all right. No one cares about old Nightingale. It's Edward who matters."

"I shouldn't think he did, in the least."

"He does to Martin."

"He can't, not really."

"I matter to you, don't I?"

"Frightfully."

"Well, then?"

"It's not the same thing. Edward's quite horrid about Martin."

"They're brothers all the same, and awfully close. They all are. That's one of the difficulties."

"Whose difficulties?"

"Martin's."

"What on earth are you talking about? Martin isn't responsible for Edward as far as I know."

But Francis wouldn't explain. He seemed to feel that he had already said too much.

I saw little of Martin himself during these visits, but I was aware of him in the background, and it was as if he were standing behind Francis when I talked to my brother. I was convinced that he was interfering with my brother's life at Winchester but I didn't say so to Charlotte. I couldn't give Francis away even though I agreed with her, but I was worried and exasperated.

"Do you like your life at school, Francis?"

"It's not bad."

"Who are your special friends?"

"I don't know that I have any very special ones. You see, I don't play games, so I lead my own life."

"What does that mean? Music?"

"No, I don't mean music. I'm learning to play the organ; but I wasn't thinking of that."

"What, then? What else do you do outside lessons?"

"I read a lot, go for long walks."

"By yourself?"

"Usually."

"But why, Francis? Don't you like any of the boys?"

"They're all right; I like them well enough; they're quite good chaps, most of them. I like best being alone, that's all."

"You're not getting religious, are you? Oh, Francis, you mustn't."

"Why not? But don't worry, I'm not thinking of going into the Church like Edward. What we — what I want to do is quite different." He frowned, as Martin used to do, stood thinking, kept me waiting, and there was a touch of arrogance in the lift of his head as he said at last: "I'm afraid I can't explain. You wouldn't understand."

"How do you know? You might at least try. You are being quite maddening."

But he wouldn't tell me. And he wouldn't join me in Italy during my last summer abroad. He and Martin went instead on a two weeks' walking tour through the English Lake Country. And when I came home very pleased with myself, having tracked down the lesser Masters of the Cinque Cento whose works had glowed from the walls of Crabbe before my indifferent eyes, ever since I was born, and began to hold forth on our possessions, he ticked me off smartly.

"Aren't you being rather vulgar about all this, Babs?"

"I don't think so. Why?"

"There's nothing to be so smug about."

"I'm not in the least smug, only excited. Dad is really too extraordinary. To have all these treasures and not even look at them."

"How do you know?"

"Well, he never seems to."

"Perhaps it's only that he doesn't buck about his things as you, my girl, seem likely to do. You'd be surprised at how much he knows."

"Then why didn't he make us care?"

"You might ask him."

"I did — yesterday. He just mumbled about there being a lot of books on the bottom shelf in the last alcove on the left in the library if I was interested."

"Poor Dad. We never gave him a chance and I think now that he has a guilty feeling."

"About us?"

"No, I should think he asks himself if any man has a right to keep so much, just for himself. I daresay I shall ask myself the same thing in time. We were talking about it as a matter of fact the other day. But then Mum butted in and called us a couple of fools. She says the Bellini might one day keep me out of the poorhouse. But I'd never sell it. That I've quite made up my mind about. You can't make money out of a priceless thing you didn't earn; it doesn't really belong to you. I shall give it back."

"Who to?"

"The nation."

"What nation? Italy?"

"No, England, the National Gallery."

"Then why not give back the whole works: house, lands, everything. You didn't earn any of it."

"The house is different. The trustees of the National Gallery will look after the Bellini quite as well as I can, but I'm afraid the house — still, I might, you know — only — "

"Only what?"

"Well, there's Dad. He's counting on me to look after Crabbe. I would hate to think he was disappointed in his grave."

"Thank God for that much. If you want to know what I think, I think you are crazy."

"Yes, Sis, you would think just that."

I was exasperated, but rather impressed. He had grown up. He was more mature than I now. He had passed me by. Was it Winchester or Martin Merriedew, I wondered, that had done this?

III

I was married at Crabbe. My father gave me away, Mr. Nightingale managed to get through the service without too much fumbling, and all the village came to the wedding including the Merriedews.

Francis was in his last half at Winchester and at the spotty stage. Martin had won his scholarship, he was about to start his medical studies in London and I recall noticing with a pang, through the haze of my own excitement, the contrast between the two boys; and thinking how maddening it was that Martin too shouldn't have spots. He was half a head taller than Francis, he had been going all out, I knew, to win his scholarship, and was helping his father at the same time. He had been nowhere, seen nothing, had no relief from the humdrum grind of his home and his school and here he was, as vital, as glowing, as beautiful as ever. And he held himself with the old air of unconscious authority that I knew so well. Francis had grown quite a lot, but he would always be on the small side. He was slender, he moved with such easy grace that no one would suspect that he had ever had anything wrong with his legs, and he had charm, he was gentle and sensitive, with a heartbreaking smile that should have made him a host

90

of friends, but he seemed to have only one and that one dominated him. Martin Merriedew at eighteen was absolutely glorious and to me quite maddening.

But Charles, strange to say, didn't notice him. He wasn't aware, when Martin came up for trial nearly twenty years later, that he had ever seen him before. Why? he asked when I told him he had been at our wedding, should he have noticed a young country bumpkin dressed up in his best country suit? The church had been full of them.

"But he stood out from the rest, Charles. I can see him now. It was after the service, we had gone back to the house. He was standing in the dining-room window with Tillie. They were drinking our health. The sun was on his head, he was laughing, and Tillie was blinking up at him with an adoring expression that was quite idiotic. Nannie was on the other side of him. Don't you remember Nannie?"

Yes, Charles remembered Miss Bertha Crouch, who had come up for the wedding from Bournemouth in a handsome new bonnet to tell him he'd have his hands full with that headstrong Barbara, but he didn't remember a young man who looked like a Greek god. And when Katharine said that she hoped I would bring Charles to see them on our next visit, I decided it was better not. And I never did take Charles to the Doctor's house. He wouldn't have cared for the Merriedews.

I did my best to keep in touch with Francis while he was at Oxford, and went up several times to see him. I couldn't ask him to stay with us in London, because we were living in the Temple and had no spare room. And I had no idea that he sometimes came down to spend the weekend in London with Martin until I ran into the two of them one Sunday morning in Regent Park. They were feeding the waterfowl and were quite pleased to see me in a casual way. I only found out later that it was by now a habit with them to pass their nights on these weekend occasions in Martin's lodgings in Bloomsbury,

91

comparing notes, searching their hearts, and renewing their vows.

I asked them to lunch or dine on several Sundays after this but Martin never came and though Francis did, occasionally, he and Charles had little in common and Francis always hurried away after the meal to rejoin his friend.

I lunched with the two of them once in a Lyons Corner House, Martin's choice presumably, and once had tea with them in his lodgings. Dismal lodgings and the tea was very black and bitter. They said they made it strong because they meant to stay awake all night, they had so much to talk about. But they didn't take me into their confidence; they were extremely secretive, and they seemed to me from my vantage ground of a married woman very young and pathetic.

I only heard of their schemes later and there was much Francis couldn't bear to tell me even after their final rupture, but he told me a little. "Perfection" was a word he let slip, Martin held to the very simple notion that to do good in the world one had to be good, and to get anywhere near the real thing one must aim at perfection. As to the kind of work they would undertake, they agreed that it must be exacting and ungrateful, but differed as to what form it should take. Francis' choice was to go to the lepers in India, but Martin said our own people had first call on their services, there was plenty to do in England; and anyhow they weren't ready. They had a lot to learn first. "Self-discipline" was another word Francis used. Martin knew by this time, Francis said, that he could heal, he had the gift in his hands; but he wasn't certain that he wanted to give his life to healing men's bodies, he was more interested in their minds and hearts. He thought he might specialize in mental disease. On the other hand, he wanted to work with children. Children could love with all their hearts. No one else could. They must be, he and Francis, like children if they were to do anything worth doing. They were not yet twenty-one at this time, but Martin expected to be free in four years for what they thought of as their great adventure. Then they would decide what work they would undertake.

Francis didn't say anything at home about his plans, fearing our parents would object. He was right. My mother would certainly have kicked up a fearful row had she known.

She was by this time profoundly alarmed by what she called their morbid friendship. She had consoled herself in her early disappointment over Francis with the hope that he would stand out as a gifted eccentric, but he was not considered odd, and he didn't seem to be very gifted. He had given up his painting, didn't seem to care much even for his music, and as far as she knew hadn't a single picturesque hobby. At Oxford it was much the same as at Winchester. He in no way distinguished himself. Not only was he not in the right set, he was in no set. He was just a dim figure who went for long solitary walks and sat up until all hours reading books on strange subjects like Oriental religions, or morbid psychology. She blamed Martin for this. She said Francis' obsession with Martin was ruining his life. He was as besotted as a girl in love. Finally she asked me outright if I thought they were lovers?

I denied it passionately. I do so now. Charles would have said yes, it was obvious, and would have thought nothing much of it. He might even have referred me to his precious Greeks; but then Francis wasn't his brother. Charles takes a curiously serene interest in sex aberrations. He finds them funny, and is amazed at my violent intolerance of such things; but he wouldn't be at all amused if his son developed homosexual tendencies. He simply never cared enough for Francis to try to understand him. But I knew that my brother's relations with Martin Merriedew were much stranger and more complicated than a love affair between two young men. Francis is naturally a rather timid, conventional man. He was afraid of my mother. If what she suspected had been true, he would

93

have made an effort to conceal his feeling for Martin. He did the exact opposite. When Charlotte taxed him with caring for no one else on earth, he said: "Yes, in a sense that is true. Compared with Martin no one else counts. I would give my life for him!"

Charlotte is tough. She can take a good deal, but when she discovered that Francis was spending his weekends with Martin in London, she came to me.

"You must tackle this, Barbara. You must find out what they are up to, those two. I know there is something. When your father talks to Francis about his plans for the future and suggests his taking over the management of the estate and relieving him of at least some of his bothers, the boy is nice enough, and seems interested. They spend hours over the books and going round the farms together, but Simon can't pin him down. And you know what your father is, he just leaves it. He was quite shocked when I said he ought to insist on knowing what Francis and Martin were hatching up between them. Prying and meddling, he calls it. And I daresay it wouldn't help. So you must get at Martin, get hold of him, make him tell you. Ask him to lunch or something."

"I have asked him. He won't come."

"Tell him it's about Francis and important. Put your cards on the table. Put it all down to me, if you like."

I didn't want to be bothered. I was in love, I was happy. I didn't want to take Martin on. I funked it and I knew Francis would resent it very much if he knew. But Charlotte was distracted and I gave in. I wrote Martin asking him to lunch with me alone, anywhere convenient to himself, on any day he chose, and he rang me up the following morning. He would rather not lunch, if I would excuse him. But would I care to take a walk? He often walked on Hampstead Heath in the late afternoon. If I would join him he would meet me next day

94

at Hampstead tube station at five o'clock. He couldn't make it earlier, he had lectures.

His voice sounded so young and friendly over the telephone that I was greatly relieved. I thought: "What nonsense it is to get in such a fuss! I'm two years older than he, why should he make me nervous?" But I was nervous. And when I got to the top of the escalator in the tube station, I couldn't find him. I didn't see him until he spoke my name. "Barbara!" he said. And there he was in front of me. I had almost bumped into him.

"Martin! I didn't see you."

"I know. I was experimenting." He laughed. "I didn't mean you to."

"Making yourself invisible, were you?"

"Yes, just for fun. It can be done, you know. In a crowd of course."

It wasn't much of a trick, I thought. He looked like all the other young men who were hurrying past, just as an overworked medical student should look. He was bareheaded and had on a brown mackintosh, too short in the sleeves. His face was bone thin and his long sensitive hands were red with cold. I felt rather sorry for him.

"Have you had tea, Barbara? There's an A.B.C. shop just along here."

"Don't let's bother about tea, unless you want it."

"Oh, no, I had mine at three, and very nasty it was. I could do with a pint of mild and bitter, couldn't you? But we must wait for that, so come along."

It was a dull raw April day. We walked rapidly up the hill and presently were in the open in a fine drifting mist. The heath was rather ghostly.

"Nice, isn't it?" he said. "I see that you have on stout shoes."

"Yes."

"I come up here to breathe and get my blood going. Tell me if I walk too fast."

We swung off shoulder to shoulder across the rough grass, and were silent for a bit, then he said: "You want to talk about Francis?"

"Yes."

"What is it, Barbara, that you want to know?" His voice was rather diffident; he said my name softly but slowly, as if it meant something. He was moving beside me with long easy strides, his hands in the pockets of his raincoat, and his head up. He didn't look at me, but straight ahead.

"I want to know what you are doing to him?"

"I am saving his life." He spoke quietly but quite firmly.

"He isn't dying, as far as I know."

"He will be soon, if you have your way with him."

"Isn't that rather insulting?"

"No. It's a simple statement of fact."

"I don't accept it. I don't begin to know what you mean. I don't even know you. Come to think of it, you and I have always been strangers, but I do know Francis. He's my own brother, after all. Next to my husband, I love him more than anyone in the world."

"Yes, but you are his enemy."

"How dare you say that?"

"I say it because it is true."

"It's not true. It's a lie. You are insufferable and arrogant."

He didn't answer or look round. We walked on in silence, then he said, still without turning towards me: "You should not be angry, Barbara. We both love Francis." Then after another silence: "Did you notice your fellow passengers in the tube?"

"Not particularly."

"Look at them on your way home. You will see that their

96

eyes are sad, their eyelids heavy, their mouths droop. Only the young are beautiful — and alive."

"Old people are tired at the end of the day."

"Eternal youth, eternal life — there is such a thing. Every day at the hospital I see life, struggling to renew the youth of tired men. We tend it, we watch the flicker, hurry with our stimulants lest it go out, our needles of caffeine, our digitalis, our oxygen cylinders. We fight for it. We call on all the wonders of science in our battle, and everywhere it is the same: armies of trained men and women, engaged ceaselessly in a war with death. And when we win a battle we send the patient home; but what is the use of it? He is already dead, he has never lived, not since he was a child. Not since he was a child has he known what it is to be gloriously alive."

"What has this to do with Francis?"

"Everything. He has the gift, the divine spark, call it what you like. Eternal life. Eternal youth. Innocence. Or, if you prefer more modest words, let us say that he has a pure heart. That is the secret; and he has it. You know it. That is why we both love him. But you would have killed him. I shall save him."

"Ha! ha!" I flung my laugh at him. "So you are out to save his soul?"

"No, his life. I am a giver of life. I know it."

"What about Gus? Did you save Gus? Isn't he dead, the poor half-wit? Wasn't he run over by a truck? What did you ever do for Gus? You couldn't even teach him to talk; but you thought you could, didn't you?"

Martin had stopped and stood now, looking down into my face. His own was very white.

"Yes, I failed with Gus, and I have failed since, only last week in hospital. It did no harm to the patient. She was dying, they said, but I believed, I felt, that I could save her. I felt compelled to attempt it as I did with Gus. I was only a

97

kid then, but I remember the feeling of compulsion, it was the same the other day. It was so strong that I thought it meant the power to save; but I was wrong. The woman died. And I am not talking now of power when I speak of Francis. I have no power, and want no power, over Francis." He stopped. He seemed to have difficulty in speaking. He was very distressed, unduly, uncomfortably distressed. "Believe me, Barbara. I can give Francis life because I love him, and I only want to give. But I see that you will not listen or understand." And with this he turned and started back through the mist the way we had come.

"Wait, Martin; don't walk so fast; I'm sorry."

It was difficult to keep up with him. He was speaking again, but I couldn't catch all he said.

"To give life, that's what we mean to do, Francis and I; but we have much to learn. It is very hard. But I won't hurt him. He needs me. We need each other. Don't let your mother interfere. Don't allow Crabbe, that great dreadful house, to fall on him. Edgar Allan Poe wrote a story, *The Fall of the House of Usher*. Francis must escape with me. Leave him to me, Barbara. He will be safe with me."

I don't remember any more. I didn't repeat the conversation to Charlotte or mention it to Charles. Had she guessed what was afoot she would have gone to extravagant lengths to prevent it; but she wasn't obliged to. My father and Dr. Merriedew died; Francis came home to take over the estate, Martin to support his family; and the plans of the two young idealists had to be postponed.

Chapter Six

MY father died quietly, without fuss, as he had lived. He seemed in his coffin to be surprised at finding himself there, and rather sorry, even ashamed, that it was finished and he had done so little. I wept when I saw the look on his dead face and realized that I had never known him or shown him any special affection. He left me his stamp collection with a note in his rather crabbed hand: "Dear Barbara, you once showed some interest in these stamps, so you may like to have them. But I daresay you'd rather have the money. If you decide to sell, the collection should bring, so Kellaways tell me, not less than seven thousand pounds. Let them deal. They are as honest as any." I did what he expected, and Kellaways got ten thousand for the collection, I bought this house with the proceeds.

My mother missed him, I know, very much; but bereavement didn't soften her. *She* was more strident and bossy than ever, and concentrated her energies on Francis.

She rang up one day some months after the funeral to say she must see Charles at once, so we asked her to lunch. But what she wanted was to get Charles to help Francis spoof the Inland Revenue, so the lunch wasn't a success.

She was very excited and angry with the authorities and the world in general. She talked a great deal. Everything, she said, was being sold to pay death duties. The house in Charles Street was already gone; it was being turned into a club. That was of no consequence, it was a white elephant anyhow. Francis was selling the Bronzino, Filippo Lippi, the portrait of the third

Earl by Gainsborough, the three Canalettos, and twenty thousand acres of good arable land, but still had the best part of a quarter of a million to find in death duties. It was outrageous, perfectly outrageous. But the library would do it and more. If he sold the library he'd be left with a nice little nest egg and everything paid. All the booksellers were mad keen to get hold of it. She'd had a man down and he'd said the First Folio Shakespeare alone would fetch twenty-five thousand, the Caxton another twenty. Then there was the Codex, you know, that old thing there was so much fuss about when they found it in Baghdad, or was it Babylon? No matter. Francis was behaving like a fool and being generally tiresome. He had asked her politely to mind her own business. But if he let the remaining farms go he'd have no land left and might as well emigrate. The pictures would go up at Sothebys' in six weeks' time, and he'd thrown in the Sèvres and the collection of snuffboxes. She didn't mind that. What were snuffboxes? It was land that mattered. A big house without land was a monstrosity. He was leaving the Bellini to the National Gallery and refused to sell the library. He said if he sold the books they'd be lost to England, whereas the land would remain whoever owned it. And he refused to do anything or try to do anything that was what he called tricky, so she had come to Charles; there must be ways —

Charles was perfectly civil, but made it clear that she had come to the wrong quarter. To begin with, he had nothing to do with the estate, save indirectly as it affected me. There was a charge on it to my benefit that would bring me a thousand a year, and he had no doubt that Hurst, Hurst and Blackwood, the family solicitors, would see that I got it. He was equally certain that they would refuse to lend themselves to a conspiracy to defraud the Treasury, and he presumed she knew this as well as he did, since she had come to him. Just why she thought him more likely than Hurst, Hurst and Blackwood to meet her wishes he couldn't make out. A family connection was not, in his view, a sufficient reason for indulging in professional dishonesty of a high order, and he warned her that what she wanted to make Francis do would land him in jail if he tried it. So she went away in a huff saying she didn't believe him, and if what he said was true, well, then, Francis must marry money.

We didn't see her again for some time, but got wind of smart parties at Crabbe. There were photographs in the picture papers: Francis was entertaining for the Hunt Ball; a shooting weekend included royalty. Always in the list of guests were the names of lovely young women with money. I would look at these sheets at the hairdressers' and say to Charles in the evening: "Big doings at Crabbe. Charlotte will have him married off in no time. Poor Francis!"

I often said "Poor Francis," but he didn't write, and nothing seemed to come of my mother's matrimonial efforts, so I didn't worry about him. I was house hunting. I had Jane and James and Charles to look after. Charlotte told us to come down to Crabbe when we liked, but Charles liked to sleep in his own bed, so we stayed in London most weekends. I wanted Francis to marry, naturally, it was necessary that he should; but I didn't want him to be pushed into it by my mother. He would be so dreadfully unhappy if he married the wrong sort of girl. I never gave a thought to that shy gazelle, Kate Merriedew. If I had thought of her I would have said she hadn't a chance against Charlotte. Nor did it occur to me that Francis was only marking time until Martin was ready to launch their long-promised joint enterprise. Poor Francis, he thought that marrying Kate Merriedew would fit in beautifully with her brother's plans.

Charlotte put me wrong. She would come bouncing in to kiss the children and wash her hands on the way somewhere and give me the news from Crabbe. Francis was very fit, and up to his ears in estate business. The house was to be open two days a week to the public; a bore, but it would bring in some

101

shillings. He refused to take a flat in town. Greymouth had wanted him to stand at the next election against the sitting member, that rich middle-class Socialist chap, Gideon Fish, and he could have won the seat, no doubt of it. Family influence still counted for something, thank God, in places like Greymouth, the cathedral town where the Church was the principal landlord. But Francis was being tiresome about the Lords. He was quite ready, he said, to take part in any useful way in the county but he wouldn't go to London. "No interest in politics," Charlotte said. "Worse than your father ever was." But he was rather taken with the Elkin girl. She'd been down twice: quite well mannered and not at all bad-looking; a bit on the thin side, but then they all were nowadays. No bosoms or bottoms, all neck and eyes. But she was healthy enough, and there was wads of money. Francis was silly about that, he shied off the minute she mentioned it, seemed to have a thing about it; said the Merriedews had never had any, and look at them! "I said it was no good looking at the Merriedews. He had to look at Crabbe. How was Crabbe to be kept up without money? Scientific farming was his answer and nursery gardens — as if cabbages would pay to repair the roof!"

Oh, yes, he still saw the Merriedews. Not on quite the same terms — how could it be? He still went down there every now and then, he and Martin had started a children's brigade or something of the sort in the village and he took an interest in some clinic or other Martin was opening with Fothergill, the Crabbe Major medico, but all that old nonsense was over. Both too busy; a poor country doctor with a widowed mother and a sister to keep, and two brothers, one to put through divinity school and the other through Sandhurst, had his work cut out for him.

Jasper Merriedew had left nothing. Katharine had a few hundred a year of her own, about enough to keep a roof over their heads. The rest was up to Martin, and it took him all his time, thank God!

I asked if he ever came up to the Minster? No, never came near the place. "Shouldn't think he's got such a thing as a dinner jacket. I ask him, mind you. I ask the whole lot when we have a dance, and the girl comes with one of the other brothers, that stick Edward, or Michael, if they are at home. Michael is the best of the lot. But why break one's back," Charlotte asked, "to send such a harum-scarum through Sandhurst? It was your father who got the boy into the regiment. The Doctor asked him, and he dropped a line to the Colonel. But how sensible middle-class people like the Merriedews can ruin themselves — Not that Martin is keen on it. Quite the opposite, I'm told. Has no more use for the Army than for the Church — Where's your face powder, my dear? Nor can Katharine Merriedew be called sensible. A more futile woman — Much too dark, this powder. You may be a gypsy, I'm not."

She went on for some time about Katharine, but the impression she gave, though she didn't put it in so many words, was that the whole situation was eminently satisfactory. The Merriedews had sunk back into the rut where they naturally belonged, and Francis and Martin were now moving in circles that only touched in the village. "Such a relief, Babs. You know how worried I used to be." Charles agreed when he heard this. Charles said: "We can be grateful that's over." They were both wrong. They couldn't have been more mistaken.

II

My father predeceased Jasper Merriedew by over two years. The old Doctor managed to live just long enough to give Martin time to take his medical degree, and Francis spent the time at Crabbe while Martin was still away, falling in love with Kitty. All that is straightforward enough. But I have never understood what happened in the Merriedew family when Martin came home to take his father's place as breadwinner and head of the house. Something went wrong, but what? I see Katharine at work in her garden, Kitty pedalling off to a party on her bicycle with her pretty skirts tucked up, her slippers in her pocket, and Martin in his surgery doing apparently with a light heart what his father had done before him. Is the clue to his cruel conduct to be found in Kitty's pretty eyes, or Edward's frown? I cannot believe it.

They were, after all, a devoted family; not especially selfish or opinionated and no more tiresome to live with than the average. Martin had loved them. Did he stop? Did they get intolerably on his nerves? He had loved Michael to excess, and Michael had adored him. Now there was this difference between them about Michael's chosen profession and Edward's too, for that matter. But it can't have been an intolerable cause of friction. Martin in the end had accepted the situation, with at least enough grace to set himself to earning the money his brothers needed, and Edward and Michael were at home very little, he had only Katharine and Kitty to put up with most of the time. Katharine certainly did not interfere with him; she looked up to him and trusted him blindly. As for Kitty, on the rare occasions when I saw them together he seemed more amused than annoyed by Kitty's young men who took her to parties, Kitty's new dresses, Kitty's longing to be asked out in the county.

As for Crabbe village, opinions were divided but the community on the whole was ready to accept young Dr. Merriedew. He had been a bit queer as a youngster but he had turned out a nice young fellow, the men said; it stood to reason you wouldn't expect a lad of his age to be as steady as his old man. There was no harm in his dropping in at the Chariot of a Saturday night for a pint and a game of darts with the boys. Champion he was with the darts! And no harm either in his picking Albert up and swinging off with him on his shoulders. Albert was a good little chap; not a bit of harm in the young Doctor being keen on Albert.

I took Jane and James to Crabbe for a long weekend in the spring of '32 while Charles killed salmon in Scotland, but I didn't see Martin to talk to. I only saw him once on the Saturday morning marching through the village at the head of a comical procession of children, but I called on Katharine and looked in on the sisters at the post office, so I heard the gossip.

Francis had told me on the Friday night that he would be out most of Saturday. He was off for the day with Martin and a pack of kids from the village. If I cared to take Jane and James down in the pony cart at about eleven, I could see them start. It was quite a sight, he said. It was.

Martin led the procession, he was in grey flannels, bareheaded, and had a skinny little white-faced brat on his shoulders; the child, I learned later, was a cripple. Albert came next, swinging a walking stick in the manner of a sergeant-major, then the band. Penny whistles, toy drums, tin cans, a couple of trumpets; there were twelve in the band and they made a considerable amount of noise but they were drowned out, for all the rest of the procession, there must have been thirty or more, were singing "John Brown's Body" at the top of their lungs. Francis brought up the rear.

Martin saw us and waved, but no one else in the procession gave us so much as a glance. Eyes straight ahead, mouths wide open, faces serious and feet keeping time, they marched with packs on their backs containing sandwiches, Francis explained, and bottles of pop and bathing suits and towels. They were off to the river, and a more motley crowd I'd never seen, for some were very shabby indeed and some very neat and some had good boots and some no boots at all. And some were quite big boys, and some of the big girls wore hats, but Francis had two tinies each clinging to one of his hands and both had to run and skip to keep up, but Albert carried one and he carried the other, he said, when they got tired.

Jane and James were very excited. They clamoured to get down and join in the procession. I was half laughing, half crying. I didn't know why I didn't allow them to go along with that crazy, ridiculous, happy band. Too slow at the uptake, I suppose. Too stupid to seize the flying moment, the glorious, fleeting, vanishing chance for fun. I wiped my eyes and turned the pony cart round through the park gates, promising a row on the lake instead.

Great changes, the Tripp sisters said when I called on the Monday, twinkling mournfully through their eyeglasses. So very sad about the old Doctor! Such a good man, and so greatly appreciated. The funeral was wonderful, it was indeed. Half the county had come to it, and the flowers! Master Martin would have his work cut out for him if he was to take his father's place. Not that he wasn't working hard, mind. Three days a week at the hospital in Crabbe Major; a new clinic being started with Dr. Fothergill, and out all hours. Oh, they hadn't a word to say against Dr. Martin. They'd always had a soft spot for Martin Merriedew since he was so high. What some didn't seem to like was his newfangled ways with drunks and others, hypnotism, and such like; though there were those who thought the world of him. That Bessie Holt was daft about him, poor creature. Miss Molly and Miss Sally just didn't know what to think. It was wonderful about Bessie, quite a miracle; but there were some — and the Vicar was one of them — who thought it wasn't right, and no good would come of it. And that Jeremy was a queer one; some said he shouldn't have taken on that Jeremy in his surgery. There were plenty of able-bodied young men looking for jobs, he'd no need, they said, to pick out a hunchback to help him. It gave Martha Blundle quite a turn, she said, when he looked down her throat.

Oh, yes, Master Martin had a wonderful way with children,

Miss Molly agreed when I mentioned the jolly procession of Saturday morning. But jolly, Miss Sally said, was a nice word for a noise to split your ears. An orchestra, they called it. Well, she supposed there was no harm in it, though some didn't hold with their children going off like that for the day with the poorest and dirtiest in the place, and only allowed it because of his Lordship. They couldn't very well stand aside with his Lordship lending himself to the doings, now, could they? But Edward, Miss Molly said, was the serious one of the family, and the most thought of at the vicarage. The Army was making a fine man out of that wild Michael, and Dr. Martin would settle down, no doubt, in time; but Edward was the one his mother would be proudest of in the end, the Vicar said. He'd go a long way in the Church, the Vicar said, and Miss Sally was inclined to agree. So very earnest; you'd never find Edward in the bar at the Chariot, cracking jokes with those Larnigan boys. "And so very nice to see him," Miss Molly said, "walking to church on a Sunday morning, with his mother on his arm; and then again in the evening." The devotion of a son to his mother was a lovely thing, wasn't it?

Personally I found Edward's attitude to his mother quite exasperating, but I couldn't say so to the Misses Tripp. If Edward insisted that Katharine do no cooking on Sunday, and give them nothing but fish on Friday, the neighbours weren't supposed to know that. According to Kitty, the Doctor during his last weary days sat down to a cold Sunday lunch as well as a cold supper unless Martin was there to pop the roast into the oven, and scramble some eggs for their evening meal. "And you should have seen Edward's face, Barbara," Kitty said, "when Martin brought Father a hot whisky at bedtime. We wouldn't have had a drop of drink in the house if Edward had had his way."

It isn't difficult to understand how Edward felt about his elder brother. Edward was logical, single-minded, quite without humour, and a coward. He had made up his mind what he wanted, and he meant to have it. He wanted to be safe and respected. The Church offered him safety and a career that was eminently respectable, so he joined it. Doubting himself, pursued by demons, he wanted to belong to a great organization that would cover him with its authority, take his responsibilities from him, solve his problems, and forgive him his sins. So he took Holy Orders and he would have been a happy man in his calling had he been capable of happiness. Unfortunately, he was not. He was aware in himself of passions and impulses that filled him with fear and disgust. He aspired to holiness — was not holiness the summit of respectability? — but he couldn't attain it. He had his guide, the English Prayer Book. Not the Bible. He would be lost if he studied the Bible too deeply; but the Prayer Book, and those extracts from the Holy Scriptures which were admirably expounded in the orthodox textbooks. He was not obliged to think, he need not know in his heart that the Scriptures were true, he had the authority of the Church for it; but there were dreadful bits that he did know in his heart were true, the bit, for instance, about Adam and Eve and Satan in the Garden of Eden. He knew in his whole priggish nerve-racked being that Eve was the mother of all evil, and he fled from her to the Church and found there almost everything he needed: rules, books of words, methods of treatment for the sick mind, ready-made prescriptions for the sinful heart, magic formulas to exorcise the devil; in a word, protection from life, from the world that was full of women, and above all from his brother, who was illogical, inconsistent, incomprehensible, and terrifying.

But Edward does not provide the clue to his brother's behaviour. Martin did not run away from Edward. Edward was a small man, Martin a giant beside him. No, I do not know why Martin abandoned his family. The enigma remains.

It was during the last week in August 1933 that Francis wrote asking me to come down to see him. He wanted particularly to talk to me on matters of importance to himself. Charlotte was away. She had gone to her villa in the South of France, and could I leave Charles and the children for one night? He hoped he didn't seem rude; but he would rather like to have me alone. If I would choose a day, and make it soon, he would be grateful.

I had felt more peaceful of late about Francis, and more kindly towards Martin. They had seemed to be settling down so satisfactorily, side by side, each in his own proper place. But I knew I was wrong immediately I read the letter. Francis was in trouble. It couldn't be money, his money troubles were public property, nor a scrape with a woman, Francis wasn't that kind; it must have to do with Martin.

Charles was rather cross about my going. "Why can't your precious brother come to see you? Who is going to look after me? Suppose the children go sick? I noticed this morning that James had the snuffles."

"He hasn't, Charles. They won't. They mustn't. I don't know why Francis didn't come up, but he didn't. He wants me down there. I really must go."

"What about Frinton? Have you forgotten?"

Of course I hadn't forgotten that we were taking the children to Frinton for a fortnight. "Today's Tuesday, Charles. I'm only going for one night. I'll be back on Thursday. We don't go to Frinton until Saturday. It couldn't be simpler, do be reasonable."

But I didn't feel reasonable as I boarded the train. I was nervous and apprehensive. It was a long hot journey, and my book bored me. My thoughts kept jumping backwards and forwards from Francis to Charles, Charles to Francis. If only

Charles were fond of Francis, but he wasn't a bit. Charlotte was the one he liked. Quite unscrupulous, he called her, but a realist; Francis was a weakling and a dreamer.

It was a year since I had been to Crabbe. He had seemed happy then. We had talked quite happily about Martin and the children's brigade, and I had felt more kindly towards him than I had felt for years. But now something had gone wrong. Francis wanted me. What could it be? I was in a fever before I reached my journey's end.

He was at the station to meet me, and when I saw his fair narrow red head and thin, darling, smiling face coming towards me, I felt I had been a fool to get so worked up.

We kissed in a perfunctory fashion. "How are you, Francis?"

"Not too bad. Good of you to come, my dear."

Francis was driving and we didn't talk on the way home. The hood of the car was back, the sun blinding, a heat haze hung like a fog over the fields. Much of the corn was already gathered in. He gave me his sunglasses and I took off my hat. I didn't feel that I could question him. His rather strange profile with its long nose and the silky hair blown back from his high narrow forehead looked strained and stiff like a pointer's. He was leaning forward over the wheel as though in a desperate hurry; but he didn't accelerate. I began to worry again. There was something unnatural in his pose. His fine wide lips, drawn down in a curious grimace, were bloodless. He had lost weight and was painfully thin, but was sweating. His long hands were wet on the wheel, and sweat was trickling down the side of his neck.

Old Bowles, who had been with us since I could remember, beamed from the front steps. A footman in livery took my case. Another waited at the foot of the great staircase.

"Tea indoors, I think, don't you, Babs? It's too hot on the lawn. And you'd like a bath, I expect. Shall we say in half an hour?"

We went up. He had put me in what we called the Abbot's

Parlour in the North Wing, a large, rather gloomy apartment with a high-canopied bed and a painted ceiling, because it was cooler, he said, on this side of the house. I would find him in the French drawing room if I would come down when I was ready. But I wasn't to hurry. We had plenty of time. We needn't start until seven, it was now only five. He ought to have told me, the Merriedews had asked us to supper and he had said we would go. He hoped I didn't mind? Edward and Michael were both at home. It would be a reunion. Kitty was making quite a thing of it.

He said all this rather jerkily, leaning against the high carved chimneypiece, while a brisk young woman in starched cap and apron unpacked my modest belongings and held up the one dress I'd brought with me. It was yellow, yellow linen, and I had thought it rather nice. Charles liked it, but it badly needed pressing. I had packed in a hurry, with Jane and James making themselves a joyous nuisance while I did so. Charles was taking them for a picnic tomorrow on the river. But the dress would do well enough, I thought irritably, for the Merriedews, even if the new and very superior maidservant sniffed at it.

There was certainly no visible sign of change and decay in the house, I said to myself when Francis had left me. Even Mrs. Trumper, who had departed long since to enjoy her pension at Eastbourne, could have found no fault with the arrangements. Two footmen to support Mr. Bowles's tottering footsteps, half a dozen housemaids — how many in the kitchen? I wondered. And what had I expected? I might have realized that my mother would see to it that Francis lived in splendour even as a bankrupt. And he wasn't that, of course. He was a long way from that. And you couldn't have smart house parties and not do things properly. They were gambling, that is to say, Charlotte was. She was still gambling on landing a large fat fish for a daughter-in-law, a beer baron's daughter or something of the sort. She had said so, hadn't she? Was that what was making

Francis ill? Had she pulled it off and put it across him? But he had looked self-conscious just now when he said Kitty was making a thing of our coming to supper. It was really too bad of him to send me an S.O.S. and bring me all the way down to Crabbe in the sweltering heat just to take me out to supper at the Merriedews'.

It occurred to me as I got into my nicely pressed yellow linen that he hadn't mentioned Martin. What did that mean, if anything?

The house seemed very empty as I made my way along the north corridor and down Inigo Jones's beautiful staircase. There was no one about. Not a sound. It had never seemed so empty. "What obtuse egoists children are," I thought. "Francis and I never felt like this when we were young." The front door was wide open, the sun was dazzling on the marble tiles of the hall, and I could hear now in the distance the pleasant throb of a harvester. They would be threshing on the home farm. I would get up very early and go to see them.

I stopped a moment in the doorway of the Spanish drawing room. It is the first of three that open into each other, forming a lovely composition. The blinds were down on this side of the house, and in the filtered light the rooms seemed to be swimming as if underwater. I have often had a sense at Crabbe of the whole light harmonious building moving gently and smoothly through space, but it was stronger that strange afternoon than ever before. I could see Francis in the distance. He was standing quite still with his back to me at the end of the long vista of polished floor and delicate panelling. His hands were in his pockets, and he seemed to be looking down at his feet, to be lost in thought; but the play of light on dim gilt and bronze, the rippling reflection in a mirror as a blind fluttered, gave the eerie impression that he was being carried away out of reach by magic. And then I heard a tiny sound, like a bell in a fairy cave. It was only the tinkling of crystal pendants on a chandelier, but I hurried to him, almost running and a little breathless.

He didn't notice. "Had your bath, Sis?"

"Yes, thank you."

"Then let's have tea. Will you make it? I told Bowles we would look after ourselves. There's so much to talk over."

But when we had sat down he was silent. His face had a livid tinge. Was it the half-light? To break the silence I asked: "How is Martin?"

"Very well. Very busy. He's had some remarkable cures. You remember that girl Bessie Holt?"

"The paralytic?"

"Yes. Well, she's riding about on a bicycle."

"Sounds like a miracle."

"It was. A miracle of patience, perseverance, faith between patient and doctor, and applied science. It took the best part of a year, but to hear her mother talk you'd think Martin had ordered her to pick up her bed and walk the first day. If you were staying on, I would take you to see her, and to visit our new clinic."

"What's that?"

"A new clinic we've built, for nervous diseases. It was opened only last week."

"You say 'we'; you haven't set up as a doctor, I take it?"

"No. It's Martin's of course, and the county's. The chaps at Crabbe Major are very keen. You know, at the County Hospital. They've got nothing like it. Martin and I are in it as partners, but they are all welcome to avail themselves."

"Meaning, I suppose, that you put up the money?"

"That's about it. But I take an active part in running it. I would love you to see the place, Babs. We've every sort of contraption. We do shock treatment, everything." His face was alight now. "You would never have believed I'd be any good at

113

electricity, would you? Well, I'm not at all bad. We have a trained man, of course, but in an emergency — "

"Where did you find the money, my dear?"

"I sold a few things."

"I see."

"Now, Babs."

"I was only wondering what things?"

"The drawings, if you must know."

"Not the Leonardos Daddy was so fond of?"

"The same."

"Oh, Francis, how could you?"

"And why not? I've sold them to the Victoria and Albert. They're safer there than here."

I pulled myself together. This wasn't what he had brought me down for. He was happy about this. I would never learn what troubled him if we quarrelled over this.

"Well, if it's done it's done. I shan't make a fuss about it. But I wager Charlotte cut up pretty rough."

"She couldn't. She doesn't know."

I had nothing to say to that, and presently he got up and walked away from me and, pulling up the blind on a far window, stood looking out. I waited. I knew now that it was coming, and thought I knew what is was.

"I'm going to marry Kate Merriedew," he said at last. But why did he look so tragic, so appealing, so awfully young and frightened? He used to look like this when he was quite small and was being driven out to the paddock to put his pony over the jumps.

"Do you love her?"

"I do, very much."

"In that case, darling, I don't see why you shouldn't."

"I'm glad you feel that."

"How else could I feel? Aren't we friends? Haven't we always been?"

114

But he didn't answer, he didn't come nearer, he didn't look much relieved. It must be Charlotte. Well, he would have to stand up to Charlotte.

"You are afraid to tell Charlotte, is that it?"

"Oh, I've had it out with Charlotte. That's why she has cleared out."

"You mean she's not coming back?"

"She says not."

"Well, what of it? She wouldn't stay on afterwards, anyhow, whoever you married."

"No. Of course not. And it isn't as if she didn't have the Dower House. That's waiting for her. I'm having it done up. And she knows she can take what she likes from here, within reason. I don't want you to think I'm being mean."

"You're incapable of that, my love."

He took a turn round the room, stepped out the open window onto the terrace, then came back again. "I thought we might go out, but it's stifling. I think we're in for a thunderstorm." He was still unhappy, still strained.

"What is it, Francis?"

He came back on that, sat down near me and, leaning forward, beat his hands softly together as he stared at them. Then he looked up and said: "It's Martin."

My heart missed a beat. That is the phrase, I believe. Anyhow it thumped.

"What has Martin to do with it?" I tried to be casual.

"A lot. More than you know."

"You mean to tell me that Martin is against your marrying his sister?"

"Not exactly. Well — yes, he is."

"What on earth do you mean, not exactly? And why should you listen to him?"

"Don't, Babs. Don't be cross, I beg of you. I want you to

115

understand. I want you to help me. If you can't, then no one can. There is no one."

"Then tell me quietly. I'll listen. And I promise you I'll help if I can. I do want to, Francis."

"I know. We do trust each other, don't we? We always have. We had no one else, did we, before Martin came, except Nannie?" And at that my brother stretched out his long nervous hand and took hold of mine, clutching it tight. "You see, Martin is my world. He has been for years. Years ago we promised each other to spend our lives together, and I've been waiting for him. We were going away together. We had a plan. We were going to lead the good life. Don't laugh, Babs. It may sound silly, but it didn't, it doesn't seem so to me. And we were going to do it together. It meant giving up a lot, and being pretty uncomfortable, all that, but it was wonderful to me, because Martin was wonderful, and he is, Babs. Believe me, he is the most wonderful man on earth. What he is doing here is nothing to what he can do and will do."

He stopped. He let go of my hand and, taking his handkerchief, wiped his perspiring face. "Then I fell in love with Kate and she in love with me. Martin was still in London, and we kept it a secret. It was nice having it secret. But I thought he'd be glad when he knew. We didn't tell him at first when he came back. Dr. Merriedew's death confused things. Mrs. Merriedew was ill afterwards, you remember; Kitty nursed her, so we waited. Then we told him. It was only a few weeks ago."

Francis stopped again. The silence lasted so long that I had to break it.

"Well, what happened?"

"Nothing happened. He just said that Kitty wasn't up to it, that she wouldn't fit in."

"Fit into what?"

"Into our scheme of life."

"But he has settled down here. You've just built him a new

116

clinic. You said you were partners. Why can't you go on as you are? Marrying Kitty wouldn't make any difference surely?"

"He doesn't mean to stay much longer in Crabbe."

"Not stay, after all the expense — ?"

Francis interrupted with an impatient gesture. "That's not the point, Babs. The clinic will remain and be useful. It will be taken over by the hospital. The point is that when the moment comes Martin will go away. And I was to go with him. I must go with him."

"Where? When?" My brother's intensity was contagious.

"I don't know where, and I don't know when. Presumably when Edward has taken his degree and Michael has finished with Sandhurst. In a year? Two years? All I know is that I must be ready, ready to go at a signal. And I'm not ready." He groaned, let his face fall on his hands.

"You mean because of Kitty?"

He shook his head, still keeping his face covered. "It's not only Kitty." The words came through his fingers. He sounded as if he were choking, there was a gulping noise. Then he flung his head up. "He makes conditions, one in particular."

"You are telling me that Martin Merriedew consents to take you with him on some wild-goose chase in search of the good life on certain conditions? What are they?"

Francis got to his feet again, seemed about to walk off, but wheeled to face me. "He says I must give it all up."

"Give what all up?"

"This. This house, this life, Crabbe and everything that it stands for."

"But you can't. You couldn't if you wanted to. It isn't yours to give. It's only yours to hold, to take care of. We talked about this before. You spoke about Dad counting on you. You said you would not like to think he was disappointed in his grave."

"I know. I remember. I still feel the same. That's the trouble. I am very unhappy, Babs. If I gave Crabbe up — "

117

"And who, I'd like to know, does your precious Martin suggest you are to give the place to? Or does he want you to sell it and give him the money for a bigger and better clinic?"

"Don't, Sis! Stop! I forbid you."

"Sorry. But really, I never heard such fantastic nonsense."

"But it isn't nonsense, it's sense, in the real meaning of the word. For me, I mean. The effort involved, the cost to me. Don't you understand? Can't you see? It isn't the house and the things in it. It's not the library, or the money. You know that. I could do without money. I meant to. I was ready to. I only meant to hang on to just enough to keep the place from going to ruin. It would be hard on Kitty. She would be so perfect here, in this setting. I often see her in imagination, pouring out tea, walking in the rose garden in a large floppy hat with a basket on her arm. And she loves the place. I don't mean that she is worldly, she isn't. I know she would be happy with me anywhere. Martin is wrong about that. He doesn't know her as I do. What I want to say is that she loves the place as a part of me, and I — Well, I love it too but I didn't think that it mattered so much to me until Dad died and it was mine. Then I understood what he felt. You see, he talked to me a bit towards the end. He said I would have to sell some of the land, and when I did he hoped I'd give the small men a chance. He talked a lot about the land and the village. I'd best let the village people buy their houses if they wanted to. We had no right, he said, to hang on to them. We had no rights of any kind, only responsibilities. His were mine now. He hadn't counted for much as a man, but he hadn't shirked and I mustn't. That was the last thing he said, and now I feel the same."

He hesitated, and I broke in. "I should jolly well think so. What of the family? The past? Your public position? What of England, if it comes to that? Don't you stand for something? Don't you believe in what you stand for? Do you propose to abdicate? Run out on it all? Martin can't understand."

"Martin does. It's the whole point. He says if I don't cut loose I won't put my heart into the other thing. I'll be no good to anyone; most certainly not to him."

"And who is he?" I cried out. I too was on my feet now. "Who is Martin Merriedew to lay down the law and tell you what you should do?"

Francis answered quietly: "He is the man I love with all my soul."

"You can't! It can't be true! I won't have it. You mustn't say such things."

"But I do."

We glared at each other, speechless, like enemies. And the lovely room with its delicate panelling, its faded rugs, its old brocades and satins, its spindly tables of polished wood — all its precious intimate contents of silver and gold and crystal that we had treated so carelessly for so long and its bowls of fragile roses with petals dropping, seemed to be revolving round us. There was a tinkling like laughter. Was it the crystal pendants of the great chandelier hanging over our heads, or were there small devils scampering about among the painted cherubs on the ceiling to mock us? I took Francis by the arm to steady myself. I waited till the giddiness passed. Then I said: "And Martin expects you to do this?"

"Yes."

"Then he's mad." I hissed the words.

"Yes." Suddenly he pulled away from me, backed away from me. Suddenly he was shouting again. "Yes, that's what they'll say of us if I go with him, that we are mad. And of him if I let him go alone. They will say he is mad. But he is right, he is reasonable, he is speaking the truth. He is right, I tell you, to ask it of me." Francis was almost sobbing. "Only I cannot do it. I cannot do it."

I was frightened. I felt I must put a stop to this, so I spoke sharply. "Well, he's not gone yet, and if we are going to him for supper we'd better make a move. But I must first see the rose garden. Come, show me. You know you are very proud of your roses, Francis."

And at that he started laughing, more than a little hysterically. "When a man's soul is in peril," he giggled, "make him show you his rose garden."

It was Bowles who appeared in the doorway to save us from further frenzy.

"Will your Lordship be taking the car this evening?"

"No, Bowles, we'll walk."

"Then I'll have it put away."

"That's it."

"Any special orders for the morning, my lady?"

"Tea, please; at seven!"

"Your train isn't until ten, my lady."

"I know; but I'd like tea early all the same."

"Very good, my lady."

How could I have known that I wouldn't be leaving next morning? But I daresay I might have known.

Chapter Seven

WE were late at the Merriedews'. If I was to face Martin after all this, then Francis, I said, must give me time to pull myself together. But need we go? Why couldn't we both cry off? Or let him go without me. If I went I should probably be rude. But Francis' poor sweaty face looked so stricken when I said this that I gave in hastily, and said, "There, there," as one would to a child. "But I must have a cold shower and an iced drink." So we each had a gin and tonic (I had two) before we started out across the park.

We had been asked for seven-thirty, and it was after eight when we arrived at the Doctor's house; but it didn't matter, it would have made little difference had we been hours late, for Martin never turned up.

We waited until nine o'clock, then sat down to supper without him. Katharine said he must have been kept, but it was unlike him not to ring up. Kitty said he knew we were coming, they had been talking of nothing else ever since Francis got my wire, and she had reminded Martin of the fact that very morning; it was really too bad of him. Michael said: "The poor chap leads a dog's life. He was pretty white round the gills when I saw him at breakfast." Edward didn't agree, he had never seen Martin better pleased with himself; and I saw Francis wince.

Luckily, it was cold food. Melon, I think, and cold chicken and salad, followed by a gooseberry fool; I can't quite remember; but I recall a nice Chablis that I recognized as coming from my father's cellar. There were champagne glasses as well at each place, and the table looked very festive. Katharine had done one of her flower pieces for the centre and had lighted candles in her four tall silver candlesticks. I sat on the right of Martin's empty chair with Michael opposite, then Kitty between him and Francis.

Kitty was enchanting in cool billowy white muslin. Her small dark curly head was as lightly poised as a flower on her long slender throat. Lovely arms and hands, tender little breasts: yes, she would look very well at Crabbe. The tinkling laugh, the caressing voice, the big dark shimmering sentimental eyes — perfect, perfectly suitable. If you hung her in the gallery as she was now in her snowy muslin, you would never know — but the mouth was a pout, the big eyes kept sliding sideways at Francis, questioning, puzzled, a tiny frown was suggested by the delicate eyebrows. Were they waiting for Martin to come home in order to announce their engagement? Was that the meaning of the champagne? Francis must have sent it down with the Chablis for the event. But I hadn't known that the little party was to be an occasion, and the scene of the afternoon hadn't prepared me for a celebration. Well, if it were to be so, let it be so. She would be kind to Francis, and gentle and clinging; it would be a nice change from Charlotte, and he loved her, even if he was wrong in thinking she would be happy with him in a garret. "So stop finding fault, my girl," I said to myself, "and drink to the health of the happy pair with a good heart."

Not that Francis looked in the least happy. Katharine was remote and serene at her end of the table; Edward was only a shade more peevish than usual; Michael was talking a lot of nonsense about what was going on in Germany; but Francis seemed to have nothing to say to his ladylove. He hardly seemed aware of her, but kept looking at Martin's empty chair as if Martin were there.

Michael rattled on. They didn't seem to think much of Hitler at Sandhurst, but in his opinion the man was dead right to get rid of old Hindenburg, go for the Communists, and kick the Jews out of the soft jobs they'd got for themselves. He'd met a chap who had just come back from Berlin, he'd been there for the opening of the Reichstag; he said he'd never seen anything like the enthusiasm.

I only half listened. With the doors and windows open it wasn't really very hot; but Francis' face glistened with sweat. He would wipe it with his handkerchief, then turn to Kitty and smile; but his smile was uncertain and his eyes always went back to the empty place at the head of the table. Mine would follow. It was quite idiotic, but I too became gradually obsessed with the idea that Martin was there. I almost imagined that I saw him leaning forward to smile at his mother as he lifted his glass. Drat the man! He knew perfectly well that Francis couldn't hand over Crabbe. Who to, in God's name? And what for? What was the point? Perhaps he didn't expect him to. Perhaps he was bored with Francis, and had done this to be rid of him. "And he probably has run out on us now," I said to myself, "because he doesn't want to meet me. But he'll have to. I'll wait all night if necessary." Watching Francis, I became only more determined as the minutes passed to have it out with Martin. But Francis seemed to be afraid of his friend who wasn't present, his eyes were sick, he had difficulty in swallowing.

They were all worried by the time we had finished supper, when Martin still hadn't come. Michael lapsed into gloomy silence, Edward kept pulling out his watch, Kitty was cross. I saw her touch her empty champagne glass with the tip of a slender finger and look a sharp question at Francis. Then, when he shook his head, she turned abruptly to her mother.

"Francis seems to think we ought to wait until Martin comes before we have the champagne, but I don't want to wait. If he is so inconsiderate of us, I don't see why we should consider him."

Katharine remained calm; her voice was gentle. "I think we might wait just a little, darling, if Barbara doesn't mind. Martin can't be long now. We can have coffee here instead of in the drawing room, then when he comes we can sit with him. Michael, perhaps you would bring in the tray. It's all ready, and the coffee is on the back of the stove." She stopped and turned to the open window, her face suddenly radiant. "Listen! There he is — I hear his car." So we listened; but the car went past, the sound of it died away. "What a pity!" she sighed. "But it's not so very late, surely?" she added, brightening up again.

"It's past ten o'clock," Edward grumbled.

"Is it?" Katharine was quite unimpressed. Her smile was dreamy. "Your father was often kept later than that, as I remember. Sometimes it was midnight before he came home. At least I think so. I was always a little vague about the time, as you know; and the kitchen clock didn't go very well, it had a way of stopping."

"But the champagne," Kitty broke in. "You don't suggest that we should wait until midnight before we drink — " She broke off; Francis had laid his hand firmly on hers, and I saw her go scarlet. "Before we drink Barbara's health," she finished lamely.

Michael came in on that with the coffee tray and the news that Jeremy Green was in the hall.

"What does he want?" Edward's question was sharp.

"He wants Martin. He says Martin didn't take his surgery at six; he took it for him, but there was a case he wasn't happy about. He thinks it may be smallpox. It was the youngest Larnigan brat. Jeremy sent for the ambulance and the child has gone to the fever hospital in Crabbe Major, but he wants to consult Martin. He says if there is smallpox in the village — "

But the hunchback was there in the doorway. With his wide

leathery lips drawn back in a nervous grin, he seemed to be sniggering, but his bright little eyes were frightened and his sudden appearance added something miserable and mysterious to the general gloom. He was neatly dressed and was holding his cap in his hands. His sharp gaze was inquisitive, and greedy; his manner to Katharine unnecessarily humble.

"Excuse me, Mrs. Merriedew." His soft high voice had a singing lilt. "But I wonder if you can tell me where to find Martin."

"I'm afraid not, Jeremy; I don't know."

"Then maybe you don't know when he's likely to be back?"

"We know no more than you, Green." Edward's antagonism was obvious. "When did you last see him yourself?"

The hunchback seemed to cringe, but his eyes slanting up were bright and vindictive. "It was this morning, Mr. Edward, at nine o'clock, and he was in a hurry."

"Didn't he say where he was going?"

"No, he didn't say."

"Nor when to expect him?"

"He would do, normally."

"But he didn't this morning?"

"No; nor give me any address in case he was kept; just pushed off, like it was urgent."

"And he gave you no idea of where he was off to?"

"No, he didn't say anything. Only to phone Dr. Fothergill if there was anything serious."

"You mean at the hospital?"

"That's right. I thought it a bit queer at the time."

"Why? Wouldn't it be the natural thing for you to do?"

"Not if it was his day at the hospital. Then I'd telephone him direct, I'd have no call to speak to Dr. Fothergill. This is Wednesday and Wednesday's one of Martin's days, leastways of a morning. Young Larnigan hadn't come in by the morning, but I called the hospital just to make sure, and he wasn't there.

Then when he didn't come home this evening, I got to worrying."

Michael jumped to his feet. "Why in hell didn't you tell us before? I'll ring them up now. Even if he didn't come in he must have left word."

"Yes, dear, do. They are sure to have news for us." Katharine sat quiet, but she had gone rather pale.

The telephone was in the hall and we could hear Michael quite clearly through the open door.

"Hullo. Is that Crabbe 330? This is Michael Merriedew speaking . . . Yes, Dr. Merriedew's brother. I wonder if you could put me on to whoever's in charge? . . . Yes, the night sister would do . . . Hullo, yes. It's Michael Merriedew, Sister . . . Yes, his brother. We are a bit worried . . . Yes, Martin hasn't come home and we wondered if he was at the hospital by any chance? We understand that on Wednesdays — . . . You haven't seen him? You don't think he's been in today? . . . Yes, if you could . . . Yes, I'll hang on."

Jeremy had slipped out into the hall. I could see him standing close to Michael, and I heard his loud whisper: "Smallpox. Ask about my query smallpox."

Michael, covering the mouthpiece with his hand, said: "Yes, yes, in a minute." Then to us: "She's gone to find out. She thinks he hasn't been in all day, but she's gone to make sure." He turned back to the phone. "Yes? Hello, yes? . . . He's not been in? You are sure? . . . I see. What was the message? Can you tell me? . . . Just to say he wouldn't be in. Nothing more? . . . You are sure of that? I'm sorry. But you can understand that my mother — Yes, I'm sorry . . . Yes. Thank you . . . Yes, if you do, we would be grateful." He started to put up the receiver, but Jeremy, with a frantic gesture, stopped him. "And I say, Sister, one minute! Just one more thing. We sent you a patient this afternoon, a youngster." Jeremy was dancing with irritation. "My brother's assistant saw the child, and thought it might be a case of smallpox . . . Yes, I know. Yes, but if it were smallpox — . . . I see."

He hung up. "It's not," he told Jeremy. "If it were, we'd have been notified, or you would. She says it's chicken pox."

He came back to the dining room. "You heard, didn't you, Mother? They haven't seen Martin all day. They know nothing. They had just that one message to say he wouldn't be in. She got shirty towards the end, said she was too busy to go on talking, and it was all most irregular; how did she know I was Dr. Merriedew's brother? I might be anybody; they weren't supposed to give information over the telephone — all that rot! But she did promise to ring up, or that someone would, if they had any news."

Jeremy had followed Michael back into the dining room. He had been snubbed over his query smallpox, but he still had a part to play in the family drama and he meant to play it. They weren't going to keep him out, however much they disliked him. He was responsible to Martin, and for Martin in his absence. He knew much more about this than they did. I daresay I am reading into his attitude on that harrowing night what I learned from him later on. I couldn't have realized at the time how wretched and angry he was with Martin. He was Martin's devoted, trusted assistant, and Martin should have warned him. But he wasn't going to tell the family all he knew. He waited, turning his cap round in his skinny hands, until Katharine gave him her attention.

"Well, Jeremy, I'm afraid all this is not very helpful, but we can be glad there's no question of smallpox in the village."

"Yes." His sigh sang on the air. "You'll be ringing the police now, I expect?"

"Certainly not." It was Francis who spoke. "There is no need for that, I assure you, Jeremy. Martin would be annoyed if we did so. Had there been an accident, Mrs. Merriedew would have been informed immediately."

"Thank you, Francis." Katharine rose and put her hand on my brother's arm. "Shall we go into the drawing room, children?"

Jasper Merriedew's widow was very grand at that moment, and Jeremy recognized it; he ducked his head. "Then I'll be going," he said, as she swept from the dining room. She paused in the doorway to smile. "Poor Jeremy," she murmured. "Yes, there is no need for you to wait; you must be very tired. Sleep well; don't worry. You'll find Martin quite as usual in the morning, I promise you."

II

Francis and I stayed on until about one o'clock. It was after midnight when Katharine consented to Edward's ringing up the police; and a half hour later when Michael discovered Martin's car in the garage. Jeremy Green hadn't told us that fact, though he must have known. It was Michael who thought of looking, in order to prove Edward wrong. For Edward's pent-up rage and disgust burst out of him after he had rung up the police.

Kitty by that time had collapsed on the couch and was snivelling in the crook of Francis' arm; and Katharine was lying back in her old chair with the crimson velvet, her eyes closed. We had, or rather they had, talked themselves to a standstill. I had contributed no suggestions. I couldn't have had I wanted to. I didn't know whom or what they were referring to when they said he might have had an urgent call from old Isaacs; or perhaps he had gone to London to hurry up delivery of his new apparatus and had a breakdown. But then, they said, he would have rung up or sent a wire. It always came back to that. It was so unlike him. He always rang up if he was going to be late. He was, Katharine said, so very thoughtful. She must never wait up, he wouldn't allow it. She was to leave a tray, and he would make himself a cup of cocoa; so she did. She would leave the

128

tray on the dining-room table; there was a spirit lamp in the pantry; he could make himself cocoa quite easily. He had always liked cocoa, ever since she could remember. Didn't they remember? When he was quite a small boy — but they were too young, of course, they wouldn't have noticed. It was Martin who had looked after them, so dependable, such a help always; washing up in the scullery, putting Michael to bed, helping his father clean up in the surgery.

Poor Katharine had maundered on until Kitty couldn't bear it any longer. "Stop, Mother, stop! I can't stand it. He's dead, he must be dead! Oh, I know he is dead!"

"Be quiet, Kitty." Francis had hushed her. They had all agreed that it couldn't be true, and had begun again to reason it out, pursuing the imaginary trail of this possibility, then that; but at last they had no more to say, and Katharine had consented to Edward's ringing up the police.

Michael and I could hear from our miserable perch on the window seat that Edward was insistent on the phone; but he had closed the hall door, so we only caught a word now and then, and a name. "Feathers" was one. Then I imagined I heard him asking about someone called Teresa, but I decided I must be mistaken; whoever Teresa was, she could have nothing to do with Martin's disappearance; Edward was simply trying to find out if he had been picked up and was lying somewhere dead or unconscious.

"Nothing!" He spat out the word when he came back. "No accidents are reported, and they would have been. You can be certain of that, Mother. If your eldest son had crashed into a truck or bogged himself in a ditch, you would have been told."

He stood a moment in silence in the centre of the room, his long legs straddled, his big bony hands placed lightly together and pointing upward, his head bowed; it was almost as if he were praying; then he lifted his head and spoke distinctly.

129

"But Teresa Larnigan has been seen in these parts, just as I thought. Teresa was observed in the High Street at Crabbe Major only yesterday."

"And what do you mean to imply by that?" Michael broke away from me, he was shouting suddenly. They glared at each other; Edward's face began to twitch. His nostrils dilating, then pinching, in out, in out, gave him a strangely savage appearance. He spoke through his teeth.

"You don't deny, do you, that Teresa Larnigan is thick with our precious brother?"

"Yes, I do," Michael yelled. "Yes, I do deny it. And no one but a foul-minded sanctimonious prig would say or think such a thing!"

"They were seen together, I tell you, in the High Street yesterday. They went off arm in arm to a public house, the Three Feathers; she was picked up dead drunk last night by the police, and discharged this morning."

"You're a liar!"

"How dare you?" And with that Edward hit Michael hard across the face with the flat of his hand. It was a slap, not a blow, but the boy, who was much stronger than Edward, staggered back, stared an instant at his brother, his face going crimson, gave a strangled sob, then rushed out the open door into the garden; and we heard him floundering and crashing through the dark.

I had forgotten Teresa Larnigan. Now I remembered a skinny little girl who had appeared long ago at the bottom of the Doctor's garden, wheeling two dirty infants in a homemade pram. She had stared at me out of a pair of monstrous blue eyes and given me cheek. I had never seen her again. She must have left Crabbe. Hadn't there been something about incest? A baby born dead? I wasn't certain; but I could see her quite clearly, standing with one hand on her bony hip, watching me with an impudent grin.

130

The woman conjured up now by Edward didn't much resemble that ragged waif. "Picked up drunk by the police." Yes, that could easily be my cheeky little devil, grown up, grown full-bosomed and blowsy; though not too blowsy to go arm in arm with Martin to the Three Feathers. But the creature Edward had flung into Katharine's drawing room, and was now staring at us like one demented, was no jolly wench of the streets, who didn't know when she'd had a drop too much. She was sordid, squalid, enormous. She had no face, no shape, no substance; but she was bestial, and she seemed to be crouching at Edward's feet, prowling round him and purring like a great cat, while he stood shaking and spat at her, mouthing words like "Filth — lust — obscenity!" But he was quite incoherent.

Katharine cried out at last, holding out her hands like a suppliant. "Edward, be quiet. Edward, I beg you, stop, unsay what you have said. Go and find Michael. Go and bring him back to us. You didn't mean what you said. Go and bring Michael in. We must wait for Martin quietly and together. When he comes, and I pray he comes soon, you will see how wrong you are, how wickedly you have misjudged him; and all will be well. Only go, I beg of you, to find Michael, for if you don't, perhaps Martin will never come."

But Edward paid no attention to his mother. He went tramping insanely up and down the room, muttering to himself; and Kitty went on weeping. She was positively howling now, with her arms round Francis' neck. Suddenly I felt sorry for Martin. Francis must have misunderstood him.

"My God," I said to myself, "what a fuss! What a life the man must lead in this family! Can't the poor chap have a night out if he wants one? Cocoa! Good Lord! What he needs is a jolly roll in the hay with his Teresa, and I hope he's having it. It would serve them right if he never came back."

That thought arrested me. On that thought came another; they were frightened of that very thing. That was what was

131

the matter with them; they were scared, not for him but for themselves. They knew quite well that he wouldn't go off for a night's fun with Teresa or any other woman. Even Edward knew it. If Martin was absent of his own volition, if he was not lying dead somewhere in a ditch, then he had gone for a reason, and it wouldn't be a small one. It would not be for some trivial purpose or from some petty annoyance; it would be big, and it might be final. That was what they were afraid of. He was the one who paid, who forked out the money and settled their bills. If he dished them, they were for it. Edward wouldn't be able to take his degree. Michael would have to leave Sandhurst and give up the Army. Michael was more decent than Edward. He wasn't prepared to cover his brother with slime because he was scared; that he wouldn't do. But he was in a panic all right. And so was Katharine. Katharine was more afraid than any of them, perhaps because she suspected the truth. She was white as a ghost, her eyes were unnatural, they were turned up, the whites showing. With her hands clasped in front of her she seemed to be praying. Perhaps she was, but in terror. Yes, that was it, she was putting her trust in God because she couldn't trust Martin.

Kitty was the only one who was behaving quite naturally. Kitty wasn't really scared, she was only hysterical, she had only caught the contagion. She didn't have sense enough to be frightened, she thought she was safe. Martin didn't threaten her life. She had Francis. She had him tight round the neck, and with him she had Crabbe Minster.

But now at last Francis had had enough. He firmly loosed Kitty's hands, and got up. Ignoring Edward, he crossed to Katharine. His manner was quiet, rather formal.

"Good night, Mrs. Merriedew. It is useless, I fear, for us to wait any longer. I will ring up in the morning for news."

"But the champagne!" whimpered Kitty.

The loud laugh was mine. She certainly had a one-track mind, that girl. Francis ignored me. He was looking at her pretty face, all red with crying, as if he were sorry for her. "It's too late for champagne, my dear. And you will never bring Martin back this way." He turned to me. "Come, Babs."

It was then, as we were leaving, that Michael came in to say that Martin's car was in the garage.

III

It began to rain as we turned in at the park gates. We hadn't noticed the thunder. We each had a lantern, but we hadn't brought mackintoshes or umbrellas; and the storm hit us as we passed the lodge. We were drenched in two minutes. Heads down, clinging to each other, we struggled home, in silence. Impossible to talk, thank God, against the black wind and the lashing rain. I'd had enough talk for a lifetime.

Francis' teeth were chattering when at last we let ourselves into the front hall; well, so were mine.

"A hot bath for you, my lad, and I'll make you a toddy when I've got out of these things."

"Better ring for someone," he said, and started up the great staircase. He was on the landing where it divides when the front door flew open, and the wind rushed in like a pack of hounds. We had forgotten to lock and bolt it. The lights flickered, there was a snorting, snuffling noise; the rugs lifted, hangings bellied out. Francis came leaping down the stairs, he slipped, almost fell. We flung ourselves on the door. As we did so there was a crash. "Hell and damnation, what was that?" We managed to close the door, locked and bolted it this time, then, switching on the lights, went to see.

One of the chandeliers had come down in the French drawing room; the crystal pendants lay scattered.

"How on earth? Everything's tight shut in here."

133

"Wires frayed, I expect. There's nothing we can do, all the servants are in bed. Come, you'll catch your death. We'll pick up the pieces tomorrow."

It took me quite a while, after I'd rubbed myself down and got into a dressing gown, to find my way to the kitchen, put the kettle on a spirit lamp, collect whisky, lemon, sugar; and when at last I went up with my tray to Francis his room was dark, he didn't answer when I spoke, so I left and drank the toddy myself. I don't know if I should blame myself for that. Anyhow, he was in a raging fever next morning, and naturally I couldn't leave him. So when I'd got Fothergill at the hospital at Crabbe Major, I telephoned Charles. He wasn't too nice about it. He said he was sorry, but my brother did manage to make himself a damned nuisance. Why couldn't I leave him? He had his doctor friend to look after him, hadn't he?

"That's just it, he hasn't. Martin Merriedew's gone."

"Gone where?"

"I don't know."

"For how long?"

"I don't know that either. Nobody knows. No one knew he was going, he just went. That is to say, he didn't come home."

"You sound very odd."

"I feel it, it is odd, it couldn't be more so; but if you don't mind, we'd better not talk about it. The telephones in this house — "

He left it at that, but then wanted to know what he was to do with the kids. Should he cancel our rooms at Frinton?

"No, Charles, don't do that. It's only Thursday. I may be able to join you on Saturday. It may be only a chill. Martin may be back by tomorrow."

Suddenly I felt I must go to Frinton with Charles and the children. Suddenly I was frantic to get away to my own family. But I didn't go, of course. Fothergill came about teatime. Query pneumonia, query typhoid, a distressing nervous condition.

He'd send nurses, one tonight if possible, but it might be difficult. Could I manage? Yes, I could manage.

We spent a dreadful night. No nurse turned up. Francis kept flinging off the bedclothes, and talking to Martin.

"Martin, listen. Martin, wait! You didn't give me time. I didn't know you were going so soon. If I had had more time — Martin, listen, look at me. You can't do this!"

He was quiet by morning, and the nurses arrived, but Fothergill took a grim view. Lungs not too bad, no serious congestion, but his head seemed to trouble him. Anyway I couldn't very well leave my brother alone in a great house full of servants with two hospital nurses ringing for tea all day and night. Someone had to give orders. Bowles was past it. John, the first footman, was helping himself daily to the port, I had to sack him in the end for insolence, and the kitchen had a thing about nursing sisters. "Nothing but stomachs and horrors," Cook said. "I know them. Give themselves airs as if they were quality, and tell each other stories at breakfast about other people's insides fit to make you go queer. You ask Fred, he waits on them, but all they say to him is 'I think I could manage another grilled kidney,' and 'What's for dinner?' "

Miss Brown, the day nurse, was a pleasant creature with golden hair and blue eyes. She fell in love with her patient, so gave me no trouble; but the night nurse complained. Would I please come and look at her tray? Sardines, a stale bit of cheese, and a peach. She would have thought in a house like this — There was soup, I pointed out, in a thermos, and coffee in another; but she never touched coffee and didn't care for soup. Nor cold beef and pickles. She couldn't digest cold meat in the night, it gave her heartburn. We fell back on eggs. With two new-laid eggs, and a saucepan and spirit lamp on which to boil them, a new loaf, a large pat of butter, just one or two ripe tomatoes and some of those nice purple grapes she'd seen in the greenhouse, she thought she could manage. She did. She was a large, fat woman when she came, she was larger and fatter when she left.

I wanted Charles to bring Jane and James down to me since I couldn't go to them. Francis, I knew, wouldn't mind, he needn't know the children were in the house. But Charles wasn't at all keen on the idea when I rang up to suggest it. He would come himself if I needed him, but if Francis was as bad as that, the children had best stay at home, since Frinton was off.

"How bad is he?" Charles said.

"I don't know, Charles."

"Are you worried?"

"Yes, I am."

"And you want me to come?"

"Yes, I do."

"Then I will, of course."

But I could tell from the sound of his voice that he didn't want to, so I added quickly: "I'm not actually . . . frightened. The doctors say they don't think his condition is really critical; it's only — "

"In that case I don't see what good I could do by coming. Your brother certainly doesn't want to see me."

"No, I don't suppose he does."

"But you really do want me, is that it?"

Oh, Charles, my dear Charles! I should have said yes, I should have made you come; but I didn't. I was hurt. I wanted you dreadfully, and you didn't want to come to me, you didn't see the point. Why should you have the sweat and expense of a long journey just to come and kick your heels outside a sick-room, when you could stay comfortably at home and sleep peacefully in your own bed?

Talking on the telephone can be the very devil. I couldn't explain to Charles over the telephone about Francis and Martin. I was too harassed to write more than a few lines each eve-

136

ning. Impossible to describe our distressing supper party at the Merriedews', or the excitement and wicked glee in the village when it was discovered that Martin had disappeared. I never did tell him about it. By the time I got home I had decided it would be hopeless to try, he would only scoff and think Francis a fool. But if I had insisted then on his coming down simply to be with me, then I would have told him everything; and he would have been involved in spite of himself in the Merriedew drama and would have refused to take the case when Martin came up for trial. But he didn't come. He stayed in London with Jane and James; and my impression was that the three of them were having a riotous time.

I would be sitting with Francis when I'd be summoned to the phone. "I say, Babs, Jane says she is always allowed to read in bed for half an hour after she has said her prayers. Is she pulling a fast one, or is that correct? And James says you think chocolate ice-cream sodas as provided at Selfridge's are good for boys in hot weather. How about it?" Or: "We went to the Zoo and rode on elephants, but when we got home James had a nosebleed, so I put him to bed, and we had a row about this. Yes, I know we have a menial in the house called Jenny, but it's Sunday, and Jenny was having what Cook calls her half-day; and the fridge is out of order, so there was no ice . . . Yes, quite a lot. Jane says it's the biggest and best nosebleed he's ever had. . . . Not in the least. Sound asleep. Nothing to show but a basin of gory towels in the bathroom."

Then Charles would ring off and I would go back to Francis, to be met each time by the same question.

"Any news?"

"No news. That was Charles."

"They must have heard something. Have you asked?"

"Kitty promised to telephone."

"But have you asked?"

"Yes. She is downstairs now. Would you like to see her?"

"No, oh, no, not yet."

Kitty came every day. I would find her in a heap somewhere waiting, hoping to see him, always hoping that he would ask for her; but he never did, and at last when he was definitely well enough to see people if he wanted to, I told him I was getting bored with telling Kitty lies. It was really too hard on the girl.

"You're engaged to her, after all."

"I am."

"And love her — or don't you?"

"I do, very much, but I can't see her until I have thought this thing out."

"What thing?"

"What I'm going to do about Martin."

"But Martin has gone."

"I know."

"So it's finished."

"No, it's not finished, not for me. When I'm well again I am going to find him."

"Do you know, then, where he has gone?"

"No, but I think I know where to look."

I was appalled. I wanted to shout at him: "For God's sake, pull yourself together. He's dished you, and not only you but his own family; he's a rotter; he's no good to you or anyone, never will be; and you'll be no use if you don't snap out of this." But I had to keep quiet. Francis was a sick man. His face was wasted to nothing, his hands were claws; only the long golden-red hair on the pillow about his high narrow forehead seemed to have any vitality. The wraith in the bed had me at an immense advantage.

"Be a good girl, Babs," he smiled, closing his eyes. "Give Kitty my love, and ask her to be patient just a little longer. When I get out of bed she shall come to tea, and I will explain."

I talked to Fothergill. I liked the brisk unemotional little man, with his snapping black eyes and quick clipped speech. Why shouldn't I talk to him? He knew Martin, they were colleagues. He had had a lot to do with Francis in connection with the clinic, and was devoted to him. He must have seen the two together often, and I had to have someone to talk to.

"My brother worries me, Doctor. He's obsessed with this mystery of Martin Merriedew's disappearance."

"Yes, I know."

"What do you think of Merriedew?"

"In what way?"

"You've worked with him, you know him. What is your opinion of him? Please tell me."

"Very well, I'll tell you. Martin Merriedew is a brilliant chap, and I should say exceptionally gifted. He has done interesting work here, and is particularly successful with nervous cases, hysterical women, that sort of thing. But he is unreasonably sure of himself, he is very daring, and his methods are not always orthodox. I don't disapprove of hypnotism. No one but a fool would deny that there is such a thing as the gift of healing. Merriedew has something in his hands, and autosuggestion is a useful weapon against mental troubles. Naturally I admit that a medical man is right to encourage faith in himself on the part of his patients; it helps; but to demand it and to make that faith a condition, well, there is a point beyond which none of us has a right — Don't misunderstand me. I liked young Merriedew; and he is young, don't forget that. Twenty-six or -eight? Not more. But I confess he frightened me sometimes. I had begun to wonder if he wasn't a little unbalanced before this happened."

"What's your explanation, Doctor?"

"Of his going?"

"Yes."

"I have none."

"The gossip is that he has gone off with a woman."

"I should say that was nonsense."

"But you don't really trust him?"

"How can I, now? He had responsibilities, as we all have. Many of us would like to get rid of ours. We can't do it."

"Francis intends, when he is well, to go after him."

"That's bad. Let your brother talk of Merriedew as much as he wants to, don't choke him off, but don't let him go. He will get over this — shall we call it an attachment? Whatever one calls it — and I am speaking as his physician — it wasn't morbid. It wasn't Merriedew's going, remember, that brought about this chest trouble, it was a thunderstorm. He will get over both. But don't let him run out on us. We can't spare him. We can do without Merriedew in this district. One country doctor more or less is no great matter; but no one can take your brother's place in this county."

I stayed at Crabbe just over a fortnight. Charles was quite sour at the end of it; then Francis let me wire for Charlotte, and she came and took over.

Chapter Eight

I STAYED on for twenty-four hours after my mother's arrival in order to give her the picture; but it was evident that she was far from satisfied with my bald account of the situation and was going to bustle about the village in search of further data with a fine disregard for the Merriedews' sensibilities. She had brought us up to feel that gossip was a low form of amusement, but she wasn't going to miss the fun of a first-class local scandal. Martin's disappearance was the breath of life to her and suited her book perfectly. She could say what she thought of him and take his family under her wing while she did so.

"Now, then, what's it all about? Family row? Trouble with the police? A woman? I can believe anything of that young man. I hope this has cured Francis."

"I'd go gently with Francis if I were you; there was no family row that I know of; the Merriedews seem to have had no idea that Martin was going away."

"Chucked them, has he? Just like that! Well, I never did believe in that mother-and-son situation. Katharine spoiled him outrageously, I always said so. Michael's worth ten of him; not Edward, Edward's too pious; but Michael's got guts, and one could make something of Kitty."

It was evident that she would be quite prepared to make something of Kitty if Kitty agreed with her about that dreadful brother of hers. An alliance between Charlotte and Kitty was a development that I had not foreseen, but it might be a happy outcome for Kitty, and was in any case none of my business. My business as always was Francis. He was still, I said, very weak and nervy. He was worrying about money, and had given half the staff notice.

"Why didn't you send for me sooner?"

"He didn't want me to."

"You mean he didn't want *me*."

"If you care to dot your i's."

"Why not? He never liked me, nor did you. Not that it matters. Children always detest their parents. You think yours are fond of you. Just you wait, my girl. But let's get back to this Merriedew business; what do you make of it?"

"Nothing."

"What do the family say?"

"My only informant is Kitty. According to Kitty, they thought for some days that he had had an attack of amnesia and had wandered off not knowing what he was doing. They asked Fothergill and he said it might be so. Edward then insisted on calling in the police; but their enquiries led to nothing. The stationmaster at Crabbe Major thought he remembered seeing him get on the ten-o'clock train that last morning, but couldn't swear to it. Dozens of people popped up after that to say he'd been seen in the most unlikely places; you know, like a man hunt in a murder. One thing they did find out, he didn't go near his London hospital or call at his old lodgings. So the family gave up the search and, when the gossips got properly going, bolted the door."

I had called on Katharine, once; decency seemed to demand one visit, though not two; I saw no one else that day and came away with nothing more definite than a sense of emptiness and stagnation. It was like talking to a drugged woman in a deserted house. Her words were dictated by old habits of courtesy, but her mind was asleep. She enquired after Francis and my husband and children. She said the weather was very warm for September. She didn't mention Martin, and made no reference to the drama that had set all the village by the ears. Though her manner forbade sympathy, it was not stiff; her eyes were not cold, but blind. She sat quiet in her accustomed chair with her hands folded, and turned her calm face to mine, gently, but she didn't see me. She hadn't pulled down the blinds, there was no death in the house; she had simply closed the door that had always stood open, because someone had gone out, and until his return no one was welcome. In the meantime, the air in the once vivid rooms had gone stale.

I do not pretend to understand Katharine's state of mind, nor her subsequent behavior. If she was expecting Martin to turn up each day, as Kitty believed, she gave me no such impression, nor does she seem to have confided the hope to her other children. But perhaps this was simply because she knew that they didn't feel as she did. Kitty mentioned her silence. "She hardly says a word all day. She moves about the house like a sleepwalker; it gets on our nerves. If only she would break down, we could do something. As it is, she doesn't answer if you ask her a question; and Edward has the greatest difficulty in getting her to take any decision or even approve of what he has decided should be done."

Edward had received, it seemed, a notice from the bank that the balance in his brother's account had been transferred to his name. It amounted to four hundred and sixty pounds. "So we are all right for the moment," Kitty said. "But of course we can't make any plans, and if we don't hear soon and Martin doesn't come back before Christmas, I don't know what Edward and Michael will do. Edward says Martin can't have planned to stay away long because he had so little money with him. He only drew twenty-five pounds out of his account and that, Edward says, won't get him anywhere. But Michael says it's no good reasoning in that way where Martin is concerned. Martin, Michael says, is quite capable of starting out on a world tour without a bean, and it was jolly decent of him to leave all that money behind. Michael won't let us say a word against Martin, even now when he's left us in this ghastly fix. He says we took for granted that Martin was going to go on sweating blood over a lot of whining ungrateful patients just to pay for us, and why should he? 'If you ask me,' Michael said yesterday, 'I don't blame the chap for clearing out of this place. Of all the foul-minded evil-smelling holes in the ground, this village takes the cake. Nothing he did was good enough for them. If he cured a girl like Bessie Holt, it was a phony, some dirty kind of hanky-panky. If he didn't cure old Ma Hawkins of her double pneumonia, he was a bad doctor and next thing to a murderer. And do they pay their bills? Not on your life. You ask Jeremy Green how many people there are in the village, and in the county too, who've never paid Martin one cent.'

"That's the way Michael talks, but Edward says it's all very well; even if what Michael says were true, and it isn't, what's to become of us? Martin took on the responsibility of seeing them through and looking after his mother, did he or didn't he? He knew quite well that Edward had a year to go before he could get his degree, and that Michael couldn't stay on in his regiment without the allowance he had guaranteed. Of course it is true that he had been against Michael's soldiering. But he accepted it in the end, so I don't see that there is any excuse for him."

Charlotte was interested in the financial side. "You say he took only twenty-five pounds with him?"

"So I believe."

"And left them a balance of four hundred and sixty?"

"Plus the car, that old Morris 8; he left that in the garage with instructions to sell it and keep the proceeds. There was a note tucked under the windshield. It won't fetch much."

"No other message? No letter or anything?"

"They haven't found any."

"Pretty hot that, I must say!"

144

"Yes."

"What's the local verdict?"

"I gather the general opinion at the Chariot is that he has gone off with Teresa. Who, by the way, is Teresa? Is she the Larnigan girl?"

"Yes. A slut who used to live in a broken-down hovel in that bad quarter back of the Chariot. No end of a nuisance, that girl, always has been. She's the oldest of the Larnigan brood; was raped by her father and had a baby born dead when she was thirteen. An impudent hussy if ever there was one, used to walk round the village with a stomach like a watermelon. I gave the Doctor — the old Doctor, you know — a piece of my mind, and we put her into a home in Greymouth. Then he got her a job there in a decent family. That didn't last long. She was had up for stealing from the shops; sweets, trinkets, she took anything she fancied, before she'd been with them three months. And there was some story about the son of the house. Jasper Merriedew took it very hard, but I told him it was no good. Bad blood, I told him, you can't do anything with bad blood; and I was right. She ran away twice from that reform school in Warrington; you know the place. The last I heard of her she was on the streets. That was three years ago."

"Where does Martin Merriedew come in?"

"I haven't a notion, but I mean to find out. Even Francis, besotted as he is, wouldn't stand for that sort of thing. Now that you ask me, I believe she came back a year ago for Pat Larnigan's funeral. Yes, I remember now. That pair of old tabbies at the post office were all agog over her fine clothes and the presents she'd brought home for her young brothers. I wouldn't put it past our precious Martin to have picked her up then. Yes, that must be it."

"What does she look like?"

"How should I know? I didn't see her when she came back. Haven't laid eyes on her for years."

145

"I'm asking because I believe I saw her the other day, when I called on Katharine."

"Where?"

"At the Merriedews'. I saw her at the surgery door as I crossed the green. She was trying to get in; but it's closed. Jeremy Green has closed it down and gone to work at the clinic. There was no one there. She had given it up and was coming away when I got there; we met at the gate."

It had come to me as I talked to Charlotte. I hadn't known who she was, but she had seemed to know me. She had stopped to allow me to pass, and I thought for a moment that she was going to speak. A slight woman with fair hair and big blue eyes, fringed by black lashes. I remembered now the contrast of those thick dark lashes with the wisps of silvery hair hanging down over a child's dirty face, and the rather flat nose, the full wide voluptuous lips. An impudent child, with an old vicious face.

"What's your name?"

"Barbara Patche."

"Mine's Teresa, Teresa Larnigan."

We had stared at each other, as we had done long ago. Yes, it had been Teresa at Martin's door. Not impudent now, not the other day, but distressed and angry. The enormous blue eyes had been defiant, yet frightened. An animal face. She wasn't made up, the skin was soft and fair. There was no rouge on the heavy sensual mouth. I wouldn't have taken her for a tart. She was cheaply but soberly dressed in something dark blue, rather shabby. There was a pink rose in her hat. The silvery coil of her hair was neat under the brim. She was pale; she might have been crying. She had wanted to speak to me, then had thought better of it. When she stood back for me to pass, her face had gone sullen. If it was Teresa, and I was sure of it, her presence proved at least one thing: the village was wrong.

I said so to Charlotte; but she would have none of it. She

146

liked her solution of the Merriedew mystery. It would take more than my story of a woman knocking at a closed door to shake her. I was as fed up with Martin as she was. It seemed to be true that he had been carrying on a squalid affair with a trollop; Edward's horrid suspicions must be founded on something, and the bit about the Three Feathers had had the ring of truth; but I didn't tell Charlotte about that; I saw no point in adding such spicy bits to the story she found so enjoyable, because of Francis; and I had found it from the first difficult to believe that Martin had gone off with a woman.

I ask myself now if I had, even then, a feeling of uncertainty. I had thought Francis mistaken about Martin. Did I wonder now if we were all mistaken, Francis excepted? It seems highly improbable; and yet what makes me feel that it may have been true is the recollection of how irritated I was by the way the village smacked its lips over his disgrace. Not that I went foraging, as Charlotte would surely do, among the dustbins. I refrained; that is the point. Had I been quite convinced that my brother's friend was a vicious cad I would have welcomed every proof of his caddishness, wouldn't I? But I didn't. The Misses Tripp made me quite sick. "Master Martin, such a lovely young man! Who would have thought he would do such a thing, and for a woman like that?" Miss Sally leaned forward, clasping her lumpy hands on the counter. "But there, you never can tell about men, can you?" Miss Molly counted the number of words in my telegram to Charles and looked up, twinkling merrily, through the bars of her cage. "Martha Blundle says she knows for a fact that the girl did a year in Warrington Jail. That'll be one-and-fourpence, my lady; one shilling for the telegram, fourpence for stamps; and I do hope his Lordship will be about again soon."

And the Vicar. Poor Mr. Nightingale would come every few days to enquire after Francis. I would catch sight of him trotting across the park, peering this way and that at the clouds. the trees, the pretty birds in the trees, all God's creatures; and my heart would sink, for he bored me exceedingly, but I felt I must see him because I remembered how he and my father had enjoyed pottering about together in the library, or among the tombs in the crypt of their lovely old church. So I would give him tea, or a glass of sherry if he came in the morning, and he would sit with his fat little legs just reaching to the floor, and mumble happily on about the shocking affair of young Dr. Merriedew and Teresa Larnigan.

"Very sad, so very sad! The effect on the community is quite distressing. I hear them, you see, after Matins. They linger, they chatter. I have even been asked to preach a sermon about him; but that would hardly be seemly with his mother, perhaps, in the congregation, though she hasn't attended of late. Not that I blame her, oh, no. But I would like to have been of some comfort, if only she would allow me. But it seems she sees no one, and perhaps after all it is for the best. I might possibly find it a little difficult — one could temper the wind — even so — Luckily, in God's mercy, she has another son to comfort her, Edward, a most remarkable young man. Yes, thank you, just a drop if I may. Such excellent sherry! I remember your father always fancied a glass at this hour. But as I was saying, I have felt for some time that young Dr. Merriedew was most misguided, quite dangerously misguided. Indeed, I warned both Mrs. Holt and her daughter Bessie. 'Beware, dear friends,' I said to them, 'of the Powers of Darkness.' But they wouldn't listen. I even ventured to speak to the Doctor himself, but he only laughed at me. He had such a bright face when he laughed. Quite beautiful it seemed, like the face, I used to say to myself, of a fallen angel."

"So you think, Vicar, that Martin Merriedew is in league with the devil?"

But at that the old fool was quite frightened. "Oh, no, dear Lady Barbara, I wouldn't say that! That would indeed be a shocking accusation. I would rather put it — how shall I put it? I had best refer you, perhaps, to the Scriptures. It is St. Paul, I think, who puts it most clearly. I will look up the references and send them to you. The passages I am thinking of deal unmistakably with hypnotism, spiritualism, all such questions, and I believe that you would be interested. Perhaps even your brother — I do hope he is well on the road to recovery? Please convey my regards. I pray each day that he may be restored to us in good health. I have written him. I wrote him only last night, but alas, I seem to have forgotten the letter. It contained a receipt. I will post it this evening without fail, but perhaps you will be so kind as to tell him that his cheque has proved to be more than sufficient, and assure him that the work carried out on the altar is really quite excellent. Forgive me for keeping you; I have stayed, I fear, an unconscionable time." At last he shuffled away.

II

I didn't report this little talk to Francis, and Mr. Nightingale didn't send me the references from St. Paul. Perhaps he forgot, or perhaps when he came to look them up the poor old muddlehead found that the passages did not, after all, throw much light on the modern practice of psychotherapy. But I did ask Francis about Martin's relations with Teresa Larnigan.

Sister Brown had just brought him his breakfast when I went in to say goodbye on my last morning. She was adjusting his pillows. "There!" she said. "What do you think of my patient? Doesn't he look a poppet in that blue woollie? And don't make faces, please. You're to eat every bit of that toast."

The tray looked inviting: coffee, a boiled egg, toast, and honey. She had put a posy by his plate. A nice creature.

"Would you like a cup of coffee, Lady Barbara?"

"I think I would."

"I'll just fetch another cup and bring in the flowers, then I'll

149

leave you." She bustled away, to come back with my cup and a vase of quite lovely red roses. "Aren't they beautiful? Miss Kitty brought them last night. She's coming to tea today, and we are having our hair cut."

We chatted awhile, quite cosily, after she had gone. I said I was glad that Kitty was coming. He said he was afraid that he had been selfish, he hoped Charles hadn't been too annoyed at my staying so long. Then I said: "Tell me, Francis, do you know Teresa Larnigan?"

"I do. Why do you ask?"

"Because I saw her the other day."

"Where? Are you sure?"

"Yes, outside the surgery."

"Did you speak to her?"

"No. But I felt I had better tell you, because it proves that what Edward thought isn't true."

"Did you need proof?"

"Yes, I did. It's all over the village. You can't imagine — but never mind that. Just explain to me why they were all so ready to believe that she and Martin had gone off together. Did he see a lot of her?"

"He did."

"And you?"

"We were not intimate."

"Where did you meet her? Of course I know she lived here as a child; but I mean afterwards."

"Two years ago. I was in the surgery. We were looking at plans for the clinic when she came in."

"She came as a patient?"

"Yes, that first time. She had syphilis."

"Sounds rather horrid."

"Does it? I daresay it does." He was on the defensive.

"I loathe the whole subject of venereal disease."

"Most people do; so we had best not discuss it."

"Please, Francis! Not that tone — not with me. I deserve something more, surely, than a snub."

"I'm sorry, Babs. What is it? What are you driving at?"

"I want to understand. A woman of that type seems such an odd sort of person for you to know. You said she came as a patient the first time. What happened afterwards? Did she come back? Did Martin cure her, or what?"

"She did the cure he advised. She went into hospital. Then she fell in love with him."

"I see."

"I don't think you do, Babs."

I got up, crossed to an open window and stood looking out. The sun was shining, there was no wind. How beautiful and still it was! Mid-September; the air was fresh and delicious; a fire of birch logs crackled behind me in the luxurious room.

"I want you to tell me," I said, "about Teresa and Martin. I would like to know."

"But why are you interested?"

"I thought her rather attractive, and she seemed so dreadfully disappointed. Tell me what happened."

He pushed away his tray, and leaned back on his pillows.

"She kept coming. Not to the surgery here in the village; she only came here once after that first time, for her father's funeral. She used to come to the clinic; and if Martin wasn't there, or wouldn't see her, she would wait for hours sometimes. Do you mind, Sis, taking the tray? Just put it over there on the table."

I did as he said, and stood by the fire where I could see his face. He was certainly ever so much better, and though still painfully thin and languid he did, as Sister had said, look a poppet. I could understand her finding him a romantic figure.

"Please go on," I said.

"She was very violent on occasion. She had violent passions, or pretended to have, where Martin was concerned. Fothergill considered her a nymphomaniac. Martin didn't agree. I wanted

151

to think Martin was right, but I never believed in her. I felt she was rotten through and through, mind and body; but she made out that Martin could save her. She said if only Martin would be her friend she would give the life up, turn over a new leaf. She used glib phrases like that. She was very common. It showed even more when she was on her best behavior, and after about a year she did behave better. But I was always afraid of her; I mean for Martin. I was always aware of the violence smouldering. And I felt she was making a fool of him, getting him talked about. The assistants at the clinic would snigger when she came. She didn't mind, she went on pestering him. She was as obstinate as a mule. Finally I exercised my authority as founder of the place — owner, if you like — and showed her the door, gave orders she was not to be admitted. It only made matters worse. She would hang round outside; and when he came out he would go with her, as like as not, to some teashop or pub. I begged him not to. I implored him to give her up, but he wouldn't. He said he must see her; she had come to him for help, he couldn't send her away. He wouldn't believe she was lying, that all she wanted was the animal thing. He said I was wrong about her. It wasn't only sex hunger. She was animal, yes, a natural savage, who had been abused and degraded by men, but she wasn't depraved. He used the word 'innocence.' He said it was still there; she still had innocence; the proof was that she could still laugh like a child when she was happy. 'She laughs when she's with me,' he said. And he used the word 'love.' He said she had the power to love. Though a slight creature physically she had great vitality. Her resistance was enormous, he declared, else she would already be dead. If she could learn to love she would be young and quite innocent again. 'Let her love me, Francis,' he said. 'Don't interfere.'

"I lunched with them once in a pub, and she laughed at lunch. She was describing Albert, 'My old pal Albert,' she called him, climbing up into a tree to see a procession go past, and she laughed till everyone else in the pub started laughing too."

"The pub was, I suppose, the Three Feathers?"

"Exactly; the Three Feathers. They give you a very good lunch."

I came back to my chair by his bed. His manner suggested that there was no more to say, but I wasn't prepared to be fobbed off with such an unfinished tale.

"So the Three Feathers became one of their haunts?"

"Yes."

"That must have given people something to talk about!"

"It did. It not only cost him a number of patients, it affected the clinic."

"Didn't he mind that?"

"He was sorry about the clinic, but he wouldn't give her up. He said that he didn't propose to hide with Teresa; that we must trust him."

"And did she get him in the end into her bed, or did she love him enough to reform?"

"She tried both and succeeded in neither. I believe she did take on a job for a bit as barmaid or something somewhere; but the last we heard she was back on the streets."

"So he failed."

"Yes."

"And now he has gone. Where has he gone, Francis, and why?"

"I don't know just where; and if I told you he had gone to learn how to breathe you would guffaw. Come on! I'm waiting for your loud laugh."

But I didn't laugh. Looking into his face, it didn't seem funny.

"You mean Yogi stuff?"

"You can call it that."

153

"And you still mean what you said? You are going to find him?"

"Yes."

I had done what I could. There was nothing more I could do. I got up. "Well, I must leave you or I'll miss my train."

"You've been very good to me, Babs; I'm grateful."

"Don't mention it, love." We kissed in our casual fashion. "Try not to row too much with Charlotte."

"I daresay we'll jog along."

I stood for a moment, my hand on the door. "It's rather pathetic," I said, "about Teresa. He might have told her that day. It was only the day before he left, you remember. But he didn't, for she didn't know. That's why she came. She came to find out what had become of him, but there was no one there."

III

If you have made yourself responsible for your family, then leave them suddenly to shift for themselves, and stay away for three years, you can hardly expect to be received with joy and a fatted calf when you come home. The story of the Prodigal Son is all very well; the chap in the Bible wasn't the bread-winner, and his father doesn't seem to have suffered materially when the boy went off to sow his wild oats. There was a fatted calf to kill, anyhow, and a fine coat for the dear one on his return; the Merriedews were up against a very different proposition, and my feeling was at the time that they behaved on the whole very well; but they bored me. Dear God, how glad I was to leave them behind me! As for Francis, if he wanted to go off on a wild-goose chase, I couldn't stop him. It was none of my business. I was going back to my own family. They might be nothing out of the ordinary, but they were mine. "Jane," I said to myself in the train, "will have started one of her bilious attacks, you can count on that. James has probably broken a leg or something. Charles will be demented by now between the two of them; and Cook, what will you bet, will give notice tomorrow? Never mind, it will be heaven to be at home."

It was. There had been no catastrophes. The house was still standing just where I had left it, the children rushed down the front steps and flung themselves on me with heart-warming shouts of joy, and Charles was very pleased to see me. He hadn't felt the need to bestir himself to come to me, but he was glad to have me back. We had been married nine years, I was as dear to him as his favourite pair of old slippers, and my presence in the house gave him the same sense of comfort.

It was not for me to disturb it. When he had said he was glad that Francis was better and Charlotte in charge, that was that. When I told him that Francis was engaged to Kate Merriedew, he said: "Who's she? Oh, the sister of that queer doctor chap." He seemed to have forgotten my mentioning over the telephone that Martin had gone away. The fact hadn't interested him, so I didn't refer to it. He said we were dining with Camilla, and he had work to do before dinner if I would excuse him. To insist on telling him the Merriedew story would, I realized, be a bore; and I didn't want to bore Charles, so I never did tell him what had happened at Crabbe.

I lost touch with them all after that. I think it was Francis who made it possible for Edward to take his degree and for Michael to stay on in his regiment; but I am only guessing about this. Francis left Crabbe in November and was away for a year; but he didn't break off his engagement to Kitty until after his return, so I assume that he provided the needed funds for her brothers as her future husband.

Even so, they seem to have been hard put to it. Charlotte reported during the winter that Katharine had tried taking in paying guests, but couldn't make a go of it in spite of her gift for puddings, because she was so hopeless about time. "So I have advised her to turn the surgery into a cake shop, and go in for those sticky spice cakes and sugary buns you all used to dote on. And for once she has listened to me. Kitty is teaching kindergarten in the Church of England school at Crabbe Major. She bicycles in and out, and has gone rather thin."

Charlotte, I realized, had acted in character and done a *volte face*. She knew when she was beaten. All she really wanted was someone to bully. Francis was out of reach, so she had taken on Kitty. I was amused, but there seemed no point in showing this letter to Charles. It was as well that I didn't, for some months later she reported that Francis was back, but was so impossible to live with that she was moving into the Dower House. "He has behaved very badly," she wrote, "to Kate Merriedew. The whole thing is off."

I only learned later that he had spent six months in the Middle East, then pushed on to India, but had failed to find Martin.

IV

It was a monstrous irony that Martin should have come up before Charles. If the Army hadn't washed their hands of him, he would have been court-martialled. Then, when they sent him home, he did one of his disappearing acts and was arrested in Warrington, so was tried at the Assizes instead of the Old Bailey. Even so, I could perhaps have persuaded Charles to refuse the case, but I did nothing, and though I paid for it, I am glad now that I didn't interfere.

The bare facts are that Charles never knew Martin, and that I had forgotten him. I had hated him for the way he behaved to Francis; I then made up my mind to forget him, and I did forget him. I wasn't interested in the vague rumours of his doings that reached me. A great deal of what more I shall have to tell I only learned at his trial, or found out afterwards, driven by my painful doubts. But for years before I saw him in court

156

I hadn't wasted a thought on him. I had my own life to lead and I liked it. I still like it.

We've been lucky, Charles and I. We have two satisfactory children, a few friends, and enough money when our taxes are paid to indulge our taste for small dinners, good talk, and old brandy. We survived the last war without too much discomfort. Except for Francis, it brought no acute personal anguish. James was too young and Charles too old to join up. James is soldiering in Germany now, he is twenty-two, and Jane is married, she is twenty-four; they have both gone off and left us, but that had to happen; Jane pops in most days, Charles dotes on her and my son-in-law is very nice to us.

James wants to stay on in the Army. If there should be a new war — but I refuse to think of it. Two wars is enough for one life. The worst of the horror missed us this last time. Even our house escaped with nothing more serious than shattered windows and a hole in the roof when the Blitz struck our London square. Atom bombs would be a different story; but we wouldn't know what had happened to us, so why worry? We sent Jane down to Crabbe in '39. Charlotte was in charge, Francis was in his Air Force cellar in London; but she didn't turn the Minster into a hospital this time. She gave it over to a girls' school, so that solved Jane's problem; and James's prep school wasn't affected. He went from it to Winchester, spent his holidays at Crabbe, and Charles and I joined them there when we could; but Martin had gone long before. We were in lodgings in London in '45 when we saw his name in the paper.

We were at breakfast, rather a nasty breakfast, I remember, smoked haddock, in a squalid sitting room, with faded cretonne, tiled grate, lithographs. Still we were lucky, I told myself, to find even these rooms in poor ragged London. I was cheerful. The war, thank God, was over.

Charles was reading the *Times*. He said from behind it: "Here's a fellow called Merriedew been indicted for treason at

Greymouth. Do you suppose it's that queer fish you used to talk about, who was once such a friend of your brother's?" And I said: "It might be. Let me have a look." He passed the sheet over. "Yes, it must be. Martin Merriedew, British Red Cross ambulance driver. How extraordinary!"

"Why extraordinary? From what you told me about him — "

"I didn't mean it in that sense. He was a doctor, and rather brilliant, I believe — a nerve specialist or something. What I was really thinking was of how long it is since I'd heard of him."

"Francis not mention him?"

"Hasn't for ages. How very odd. I've just realized. If it's at Greymouth, he'll come before you, won't he?"

"Presumably, would that distress you?"

"Not in the least. Why should it? I used to detest the man."

"Well, I'm off. How's the house going?"

"They've finished the roof and put back the front windows. It's mostly dirt now. I'm on the track of a char. With luck we can move back in a month or six weeks."

"We'll be on circuit in a month's time."

"Then when we come back. It will be nice to have our own things round us again."

"Yes. Well, goodbye for now."

"Goodbye, Charles. See you tonight."

"Tonight?"

"We are dining with Bill and Ann at the Berkeley Grill, seven-thirty."

"Not changed, I take it?"

"No, not changed."

Charlotte rang up from Crabbe before I went out.

"Seen the bit in the *Times* about Martin Merriedew?"

"I have."

"Not very pretty."

"No."

158

"Funny he should be coming up before Charles."

"Is it? I shouldn't say so."

"You know what I mean, awkward."

"Why? Because of Francis?"

"Lord, no; Francis is all right. I was thinking of Gideon Fish."

"What's he got to do with it?"

"Everything, my dear girl. He was with him all through the war."

"How do you know?"

"I've kept track of him. I make it my business to know things, if you don't."

"Gideon Fish never interested me."

"Well, he did me — until he went and joined up with that lunatic."

"What lunatic?"

"Merriedew, of course. What are we supposed to be talking about?"

Later I met Camilla at lunch in our favourite pub, the Scroll and Keys. We had the sort of lunch we like, cold beef and pickles, bread and cheese, lager. Her talk was spasmodic as usual. "How are you, ducks? Charles all right?" She had found a man on the pavement outside her house, playing the zither, and had invited him in. He was a Pole, and was starving. He must be taken up. She was going to give a party for him. Rodney said he would go off with the spoons but she couldn't see that that mattered.

Camilla is the woman I know best. We were at school in Florence together. She leads a multiple life because of Rodney, who has a job connected with the Diplomatic Corps and goes to a great many Court functions. Camilla goes when she must, then escapes to Bohemia or the East End. Playwrights, actors, musicians, and painters interest her as long as they are not successful. She works hard at her settlement in the East End, largely from political motives. The Communists, she says, are getting away with murder. One's got to stop them. One of her methods is being matey with taxi drivers, barmen, the tarts she runs into in pubs. Frankie at the Scroll and Keys is a great pal of hers. What she enjoys most is helping lame ducks, partly out of genuine benevolence, partly to score off Rodney's pompous friends. She groans when she mentions Rodney's activities, and sees no point in being faithful to him, "He doesn't expect it, ducks. As long as I make things look right he's perfectly happy." But she is fond of him. Her conversation is larded with groans and chuckles. She seldom finishes a sentence, but leaves it on the air with a sigh. You can't believe a word she says, but you can depend on her to stand by you if you are in trouble. She stood by me when Jane was born, then with James. If it hadn't been for Camilla, things would have gone badly with me and James. Then when I cut up rough about Charles she told me not to be a fool. She has been involved in almost everything that has happened to me since I was sixteen, we criticize and count on each other. She says that I spoil Charles. "A pity you are still so in love with him!"

"Why a pity?"

"Because it makes you unhappy. You aren't sure of him and you're scared, what of, God knows, he won't leave you, he's a creature of habit. But you never have any fun, ducks. Can't you forget about Charles just for a little before you are too old?"

"No, Camilla, I can't."

"Oh." The way she says "Oh" is entirely her own. When she says "Oh" the lift has come down to the ground floor with a bump. We then go up again and talk about Rodney, and she giggles. "Poor sweet, he's got that foreign Princess in tow. Her false teeth fell into the soup last night. He picked them out and gave them back to her without a smile. He didn't think it was funny."

Camilla is quick, thin and haggard, with humorous blue eyes

and hollow cheeks; not beautiful, but a lot goes on in her face. She amuses Charles, but he calls her flighty. She isn't. She has a strong stubborn streak and a lot of horse sense.

She mentioned Martin when we got to the cheese. She said she hoped Rodney wouldn't notice the paragraph, it would give him such a chance to say "I told you so," and he might stop her having the little chap with the zither. "Not that I ever landed Rodney with a real crook." She sighed. "It just shows, doesn't it? He looked so extraordinary that night."

"Who? What night? I don't know what you are talking about."

"Martin Merriedew, the night I went with him and Gideon Fish to that place down by the docks, the year before the war — don't you remember? I told you about it."

"No, I don't remember."

"But you must, sweetie. The Fascists broke up the meeting. He looked too extraordinary in that hall — Merriedew, I mean — like an eagle, or an archangel. Then they began to throw rotten eggs. One hit him in the face, so I asked Fish to bring him to see me. I asked you, but you wouldn't come. Don't you remember now? You said you weren't interested in Martin Merriedew. But I collected a lot of people, and then he never came. We waited hours, it was too awful; and then Gideon Fish turned up to say he was sorry, he had lost Merriedew in the tube. You can imagine!" Camilla chuckled. "Rodney was furious. He said Gideon Fish was a Communist — that I had no business — I had gone too far — all that. Let's have some more beer. Frankie!" she called over her shoulder. "Two more half pints, please, there's a good chap. So I never saw Merriedew again. He disappeared afterwards. But I didn't forget his face. Hypnotic. Rather frightening. Not evil, exactly. A little mad, perhaps. But one would never have suspected. Did you, when you knew him?"

"I didn't know him. Only as a kid. We never got on."

161

"But would you have said? Oh, I know how you felt, ducks, about the way he treated Francis; but this — well, this — You would think that a man who had this in him would smell, wouldn't you? And he didn't, I gather, when he was young, or did he?"

"No, I can't say he did."

"You hadn't a glimmer?"

"I didn't like him. I was afraid of his hold on Francis; but I didn't think he was evil. He couldn't have been in those days. Francis would have known, he wouldn't have stuck to him."

"As for that, my sweet, are you quite certain that those two — "

"Oh, for heaven's sake, Camilla, I've told you a hundred times; it was not that, Francis never — "

"All right. All right. Have it your own way."

Camilla called for the bill. We each paid half. "All the same," she said, getting up, "I hate beautiful men."

Chapter Nine

A FIREBRAND who set fire to nothing, a rebel
who launched no rebellion, a leader of men with
but one follower to stand by him in this court, the pretensions
of the man you see in the dock, members of the jury, would
be comic, save for this, that he has ended his inglorious career
by betraying his king and country to the enemy."

Counsel for the Crown in the case of *Rex* v. *Merriedew*
neatly summing up the failure of a life, invited us to laugh at
the prisoner and someone in the crowded gallery sniggered
but I stared with unbelieving horror at his inscrutable, un-
recognizable face while the Clerk of the court read out the
indictment:

"Martin Merriedew. You are charged in an indictment containing three counts. The particulars of the first count are that
on the fifth day of March 1943 and on other days afterwards
you, being a person owing allegiance to our Lord the King and
while a war was being carried on by the German and Italian
Realms against the King, did traitorously adhere to the King's
enemies in parts beyond the seas, that is to say, in Libya, Tripolitania, and in Tunisia in North Africa, where you were employed as an orderly in a Field Hospital attached to the 10th
Corps of the Eighth British Army, by engaging in traitorous
intercourse with wounded German prisoners entrusted to your
care and helping them to escape. In the second count it is
charged that you did forward information to the enemy concerning the condition and dispositions of our forces in those
parts of the said territories where they were waging war against

the enemy. And in the third count it is charged that you on the 24th and 25th December 1944 in the canteens and rest camps of his Majesty's Forces in Italy did suborn the troops and endeavour to persuade them to mutiny. Are you guilty or not guilty?"

The answer was so long in coming that the wigs of counsel bobbed and quivered, there was a hissing sound of indrawn breath through the court, and I saw Charles lean forward, but at last it came: "Not guilty." And the voice was one I knew. Though deeper than the voice I remembered, it was unmistakably the voice of my brother's great friend, who had been a young man of great physical beauty.

This man was dreadful to see. He was big with a powerful frame but he had no flesh. He wasn't old, he was ageless as a skeleton, or some awful immortal. The skull appeared bald and the shadow under the jutting bones of his forehead was so dense that there seemed to be nothing where his eyeballs had been but empty sockets. He looked at no one. Perhaps he was blind. Sweat trickled down into his mouth as I watched and the officer with him in the dock offered him a handkerchief but he didn't notice. Watching, for I couldn't but watch him, I felt that the crowded court was empty and he alone in it. The impression was solitude, silence, one man alone in the world, not dying, but already gone beyond reach.

What had happened to change Martin Merriedew into this stranger since I had forgotten him? I didn't know. I knew next to nothing about his life during the past thirteen years and what I had heard had given me no desire to know more. If rumour was to be believed, there had been some trouble with the police, he had been barred by the Medical Association, and had fallen out with the Church. None of this had surprised or interested me. Nor had his doings been reported in the London papers. He was only local news occasionally in our West Country provincial press. Hysterical women had written now and again to the Greymouth *Mail* to bear witness, as they put it, to his miracles of healing, but I didn't believe a word of such nonsense and had tossed the sheets away half read.

Why should I trouble myself about Martin Merriedew? I had believed Francis was done with him. I hadn't seen him when he came home to England after two or three years' absence — because, for one thing, he hadn't come home. He had gone straight to Warrington and had only come back the once, as far as I knew, to Crabbe village, a year later, for a few disastrous hours. He had made the headlines then for a day but even then I hadn't been interested. Had I known that Francis was there — But I had been out of touch with Francis. I didn't know what he was doing with himself at Crabbe. Charles and I were involved in a crisis of our own that seems to have absorbed all my attention.

It didn't amount to much in the end and it all seems very silly now, but I was frightened and extremely unhappy for quite a time. In fact, I lost my head, and I nearly lost Charles. It was the usual sort of thing: both of us growing old, Charles getting restless, another woman younger than me. It happens to most people; there was no couple of my acquaintance who were exclusively content with each other; and I knew quite well how I ought to behave. There was a recognized technique for such things. I must pretend that I didn't know what was going on, and that if I did it was of no consequence; but I found it very wearing to pretend to Charles and in the end I broke down. I made scenes. I raged. I treated him to storms of tears. I packed up at one moment and went away with the children, swearing that I would never come back, but I did come back, only to begin the old scenes again. Camilla was disgusted with me. "Laugh it off," she said. "Get a chap of your own — Anything but this, if you don't want to lose him." And I did very nearly lose Charles. I think there was a moment when it all hung in the balance. I don't know what happened. She was very attractive, the other woman. She must have done something stupid, or perhaps he merely got bored with her and decided he liked me best. Whatever it was, she faded out of the picture; and in the end I found that Charles and I had settled down again, almost as if nothing had happened. But I have been a little afraid of Charles ever since.

This, however, is not the story of my married life. I only mention the threat to it in an attempt to explain to myself why I was so absorbed in my own affairs that I even forgot to wonder what Francis was doing with himself all this time. It was just before the last war. When that started I discovered that he had been getting ready for it and had his pilot's certificate. Everything changed then, of course. Charles and I were bombed out of our house; Crabbe became a girls' school; Francis crashed; but life in wartime has no likeness to normal reality. The five years as I recall them stand apart; they are merely a piece cut out of our allotted time. We were neither better nor worse for them, Charles and I, nor closer together. We only seemed to be. When it was over we were back where we had been before it began, fond, friendly but not quite at ease with each other. And I suspect now that had I been uninterruptedly happy and confident I would have been equally intolerant of Martin Merriedew.

II

It was only a few months ago that I went down to Crabbe to find out what had really happened in '38 when he went back there. I had been to Warrington to see Teresa. Adding what she told me to the facts that came out in the evidence, I had pieced together a picture of the strange life he had lived in the dismal place, but the story of the riot in Crabbe village wasn't told at the trial; counsel for the Crown objected that it was irrelevant. Indeed a great deal that I wanted to know was left out as irrelevant. What I was looking for, after all, was Martin himself, the real man behind the scandal and the legend, not the glamorous being whom Teresa and my brother still loved — they were too prejudiced for my purpose — but the familiar man, the ordinary man with two legs and arms who had been taken for granted at one time by his neighbours as a decent citizen and member of a respectable family; and if this was what I was after, then the village where he had grown up was the place to go.

Many of those who had known him were gone. Katharine was dead; Kitty was a registered nurse on the staff of a hospital in Plymouth; Edward was curate in the slums of Warrington and Michael had rejoined his regiment in Germany, but the Misses Tripp, though retired now from Government service, still collected and dispensed village gossip from their cosy cottage; the Holts, mother and daughter, were there. I must see Bessie Holt, who had had a fright and taken to her bed for nine years then been cured by Martin Merriedew only to take to her bed again after he went away. And I might even learn something of interest from that poor creature Jeremy Green, who had gone to join Martin in Warrington but had found it all too much for him and come home after the trouble at Crabbe, to his mother.

My difficulty was Francis. We were still on speaking terms, but I knew that I was no longer welcome at Crabbe. And yet I couldn't very well go down there and not stay in my old home. That would mean a complete break between us and that I could not bear. But, again, I must go. How could I ever hope to be rid of my doubts or answer my own tormenting questions if I were afraid to face up to the facts? It was unpleasant to foist myself on Francis, it would be painful to be his unwanted guest, but no more so than this horrid uncertainty.

At last I rang up Francis and suggested coming down.

"What for, Babs?" He sounded even less pleased than I expected.

"Nothing special. Charles is fishing. I'm alone."

"Oh, very well then, come along; I'll tell Daphne."

"How is she?"

"Busy. She's cataloguing the books."

"Perhaps I can help."

"I shouldn't think so."

Daphne was in the front hall with a group of sightseers when I arrived. She left them to greet me, and said I would find Francis in the library. He was mending the broken back of a book, and his tools were spread out on a table. He apologized for not getting up. His artificial leg made his stump sore, so he didn't wear it, he explained, when he and Daphne were alone, he managed well enough on his crutches.

He looked not so much ill as strange. He made faces over his work, he fidgeted, he cursed the tourists under his breath, "the muck they brought in, the questions they asked." At last he tossed the book on the table and turned to me rather rudely.

"Well? What has brought you down here? What are you up to? Out with it!"

"I'm not up to anything; Charles is fishing; I was alone, as I told you."

"I know what you told me, old thing, and I don't believe a word of it."

"Very well, if you must know; I want to see people, and find out what happened the day Martin came back here."

"Why, in God's name?"

"I'm not satisfied. There was so much that didn't come out at the trial."

"Nothing came out: nothing but lies. But it's finished; it's all over; it's too late. You can't do any good now, if that's what's eating you."

"It isn't. I couldn't change anything if I wanted to. I'm not sure that I do. I only want to be sure."

"Of all the self-centred nosy parkers — "

Daphne came in on that and I tried to laugh off Francis' words.

"Listen to him! Do you call that a way to welcome a sister?"

But the big strapping wench was tired. She crossed to her desk (it had been my father's) and pretended to be busy with papers. "It's his leg," she murmured, without looking up. "Is it hurting you, darling?"

"No," he snapped. "It's not hurting, and if it was — Babs has come snooping, and I don't like it. You didn't believe, my dear, that she had come down just to see us, did you?"

"Snooping?" Her round eyes were foolish. "What is there to snoop about?"

"Don't you know? Have you forgotten? I once had a friend in this place, and he was tried as a traitor, and the Judge in the case was my brother-in-law. But my sister isn't quite satisfied; or perhaps she is gathering material for a book — yes, that must be it. She is going to whitewash her husband and write a life of Martin Merriedew at the same time. There's an idea for a best-seller! Wife of famous judge writes her memoirs — eye-witness account of a trial for treason — personal details of the traitor's early life."

Tea arrived, luckily, to interrupt him. Daphne poured out and Francis sulked while she asked about Jane and James. We were interrupted at tea by a mishap, small in itself, but the effect on Francis was so out of proportion that it made me quite sick.

The manservant, he was young and untrained, bringing in a covered dish of hot muffins on a tray, slipped; the dish went one way, the tray the other, and Francis leapt up.

"Goddammit! You clumsy fool! Can't you come into a room without tripping over your feet? Look what you've done. No, leave it alone! Leave it alone, I tell you, and get out!"

Francis' face was crimson. He was shaking. He reached for his crutches, and I thought for a minute that he was going to hit the boy, who looked scared as he backed away. Daphne and I picked up the muffins and the pieces of the broken dish. Francis after a minute sank back into his chair, dropping his crutch with a clatter on the floor. He went on shaking for some seconds. At last he said, "I'm sorry," and we went on with our tea.

He made an effort at dinner, but it wasn't a pleasant evening. The soup was lukewarm, the grouse very high, and the man-servant so nervous that he spilled the wine, luckily at my place. Francis and I played piquet for a bit after dinner, while Daphne got on with her cataloguing. I was glad to go to my room.

I spent a miserable night. Francis was out when I came down next morning and, though Daphne tried to be pleasant as I ate my bacon and eggs, I was not happy as I started out for the village. And yet why, I asked myself, should Francis hate my doing this? I wasn't letting him down. It was in the hope of finding again the Martin Merriedew we had both known that I was paying these calls. My first must be on the Tripp sisters. Then I would see Bessie Holt and Jeremy if he consented to see me. I must be prepared to listen patiently and carefully sort out the kernel of obstinate fact from the scandal and the legend. I was. But I was not prepared for the bald truth that met me almost before the bell on the Misses Tripp's door had stopped tinkling.

Martin Merriedew wasn't a legend in Crabbe; he was merely a disgrace. Miss Molly and Miss Sally made that quite plain. Crabbe village, not excepting its sentimental old maids, had, it seemed, a strong stomach. It could believe almost anything of anybody and wasn't a bit surprised that Dr. Martin, as they called him, had turned out to be a traitor and a lunatic. Not after the way he had treated his mother. That was the shocking thing. Left the poor soul to earn her living baking cakes, then went and set up in Warrington as a quack doctor and preacher. It was a good two years before he ever set foot in the village, and then didn't so much as knock on her door; and when she went all the way to Warrington to see him, he hadn't a word for her. Oh, yes, she had gone all the way in the train, everyone knew all about it, and rooms reserved for the night in the Temperance Hotel. And she had taken her two sons with her, Michael being on leave and Edward not yet moved to London; though some said it was all Edward's doing, and he had dragged the poor soul with him against her will, saying something must be done to put a stop to his brother, who was telling the workers to strike else there'd be a war and the end of the world. Every night in the week, or anyways most nights, he would hold meetings in a big hut they'd put up, and such crowds would come, so they said, that the police had their hands full keeping order. And even so there'd be fights like as not outside, with brickbats flying and heads broken, Communists taking one side, Fascists the other; and some said Merriedew's followers were Communists mostly, but perhaps it was the other way round. Anyway, it was no sort of place for a decent woman to go to, down as it was in the roughest part of the town, and Edward and Michael shouldn't have taken their mother. All the village was agreed about that, and she had had no heart for it, poor thing, but they made her go. And then, when they got to the meeting, they couldn't get in, so Edward sent in a note to his brother, telling him they were waiting outside, and it was handed up to him on the platform. A hundred people had seen the bit of white paper, and Martin Merriedew had stopped in the middle of his speech to look at it, and frowned, then shook his head and said: "I don't know these people; they are no friends of mine." So they had to come away without seeing him, and spend the night at the hotel.

"Leastways," Miss Molly said, "that was the story put about." Denied his own flesh and blood, said his own mother was no kin of his. Jeremy Green was there on the platform, and he said Martin knew very well Edward wanted to get him locked up in a loony bin and was only using his mother to get near him. But Martin, Jeremy said, wasn't to be caught by any such tricks. Next day when they called at his clinic he was gone out of town, no one knew where. And when Edward went to the police to complain, saying Martin Merriedew's mother had come a long way to see him and could get no news of his whereabouts, the police said they were sorry but they were afraid they couldn't help; this appeared to be a family matter and a misunderstanding, not a case for the police.

"So they had to come home," Miss Sally said, "without seeing him. They'd been all that way for nothing at great expense."

"His mother," Miss Molly said, "was very poorly afterwards, very poorly indeed. But it was the dreadful trouble when he did come back that nearly killed her."

"Tell me about that, Miss Molly."

But Miss Molly shook her head. "I'd rather not talk about it," she said. "Sally and me had words with Martha Blundle and we've promised each other never to mention it again."

"Was Jeremy Green with him that day?"

"Oh, yes — he came with him."

"Then perhaps he will tell me."

"He might — seeing as it's you, my lady, then again he mightn't. It all depends on that mother of his. She's so very bitter, you see, about Dr. Martin ruining her Jeremy's life. He wouldn't dare say a word if she was there. He's scared out of his wits of her. And it's true that he hasn't done a stroke of work since bar digging in their potato patch. When you think of the money she's spent on his education and how smart he was in the dispensary. Yes, it's great pity. Not that Hetty Green isn't partly to blame, mind, with her carrying on when he went off to join Martin in Warrington. Who was to give him his bath of a Saturday night and see to his food and his clothes? Dear, dear, the way she went on. And when he came back again after the trouble here, sending for Dr. Fothergill and telling the police her son was in no state to tell them anything. He came home, you see, in the middle of the night and took to his bed and no one knew for three days that he was back. But you'll not get much out of him about the trouble at the War Memorial, your Ladyship."

"You ask Mary Holt," Miss Molly put in, patting her hair-net. "She and Bessie will tell you. They're never tired of talking about it, those two. You'd think to hear them that Bessie was the heroine of the affair."

I decided to try Jeremy first and leave the Holts until the afternoon and I was lucky. Hetty Green was out and I found Jeremy lifting potatoes in the bit of garden behind their bungalow. He looked frightened when he saw me but in the end I induced him to take me into the kitchen and after he had washed his hands at the sink and put the kettle on to make me a cup of tea, I persuaded him to talk, and once he had begun, the words came out with a rush.

"I'll not say a word against him to anyone. When he went away that time without telling me anything, I didn't know what to do with myself. I was lost like, couldn't take any interest in anything, but after a bit when Dr. Fothergill offered me a job at the clinic I took it, not so much for the pay, he gave me ten pound a week, but because it was Martin's clinic, least-ways it had been. And I stayed on the job for three years, until one day I had a letter from him from Warrington asking me to come and work with him again. He said there would be no pay but he could use me if I wanted to come, so I gave a week's notice and went."

"How could you afford to do that, Jeremy?"

"I had fifty pounds in the bank, but it wasn't because of that. When I saw his handwriting on the envelope and the Warrington stamp, it was all up with me. I knew I'd got to go and I went."

"Hadn't he written to you while he was away?"

"Not a word."

"And you dropped everything and went as soon as he sent for you."

"Yes. You see, your Ladyship, I thought all the world of him. You remember that night when he didn't come home and you and his Lordship were there for supper?"

"Yes, I remember."

"You was all upset, I could see that, but it wasn't the end of the world for any of you; now, was it?"

"No, I can't say it was."

"Well, it was for me."

"Not exactly, Jeremy, since you found him again."

"No. But then I didn't really find him in a manner of speaking; he wasn't the same as he had been. Nothing was the same as I expected. We had a clinic and I had my work. It was doing dressings mostly — that was all right — and the people would come, crowds of them, and sometimes they'd go away cured of their eczema and their varicose veins and such, seemingly just from the sight of him. But none was allowed to pay anything. If they wanted to, he wouldn't let them. He wouldn't even have a box to put money in."

"What of the other expenses, light, heat, surgical dressings, and your own food? Who paid for all that?"

"I don't know. Gideon Fish saw to it. We were supposed to be beggars. It was queer, that's what it was. I couldn't make it out. Some days we'd be hungry, then suddenly he'd say 'Let's have a feast.' I couldn't make it out. I still thought a lot of him, but I was uncomfortable like. There was a lot of us sometimes and he wouldn't give us any rules for living. Only two in all. The one about money — the other about war. We was to own nothing and stand out against war. Otherwise we could do as we liked and live as we liked. But we weren't to organize, he wouldn't let us organize ourselves or call ourselves anything.

174

And we'd no proper roof over our heads — that was what got me down. It wasn't so much having no money — "

"But some of you had money of your own — you had your fifty pounds."

"Not when we were with him."

"You gave it into the common fund?"

"No. He wouldn't have none of it, he made us give it back."

"Back?"

"To our families or the places where we had earned it. I sent mine back to my mother."

"Then what did you live on?"

"Charity. We was supposed to be naked and, as I say, beggars.

" 'If you want to work with me,' he would say, 'you must be naked as when you were born.' "

"But where did you live if you had no community house and no money to pay for lodgings?"

"We were took in by the people he'd helped. Sometimes quite good people with good houses, but it didn't last long, ever. We'd no sooner be settled than he would say it was time he moved on, and off we would go."

"The whole lot?"

"No. He'd take one or two with him and leave the others behind in the charge of Gideon Fish. He was supposed to beg too — but he didn't, he saw it wouldn't work. So he took a house for us in the end — a big barracky place with a few sticks of furniture. Then things were a bit better."

"And did Martin live there with you after that?"

"He would come for a night or two but he never stayed long. There was no time, he said, he must be on the road."

"No time for what?"

"I'm not too sure as to just what he meant. To stop the war was one thing, and bring in the Kingdom of Heaven."

The hunchback's snigger might have been a sob; he had

175

been making tea as he talked and now gave me a cup.
"Poor fool," I said.

"No!" He shouted the word. "That's wrong. You must never
say that. He's — he — I don't know what he is, but he was
never no fool and he was never a traitor, I tell you, and he
wasn't out of his wits whatever they say. We've got him all
wrong. Every one of us has got him wrong and I left him because I was afraid for my life, that's why." And with that the
poor creature burst into tears.

III

I found Bessie Holt sitting in a wheel chair by the window.
She had been a plain girl and was now a plain woman with a
long peevish face and small shrewd eyes, too close together.
Her colourless hair hung down over her narrow shoulders in
two plaits tied at the ends with pink ribbon. She wore a soft
pink woollen bed jacket, ill suited to her sallow skin, and had
a cashmere shawl over her legs. She received me with a good
imitation of a patient martyr, then lay back exhausted by the
effort on the pillows heaped behind her back.

The room was crowded with furniture, china ornaments,
palms in pots, and bits of brass. It was stuffy but clean. Mrs.
Holt had changed more than her daughter during the fifteen
years. Her once mild face had a waspish look, and she couldn't
keep still. She had knitted the bed jacket, she told me, the
shawl was a present. So was the Toby jug on the chimneypiece
and the standard lamp with the pleated shade of cherry-red
silk. People were that good to Bessie. Too good if you had to
do the dusting. No offence meant, and the flowers I'd brought
were just beautiful if she could only find something to put
them in. There was Martha Blundle now outside, and she'd
dropped her glass vase only yesterday, smashed it to smither-
eens, Martha'd be sure to notice. But, no, she was not coming
in, she'd gone across to the butcher's to complain. Martha

often dropped in of an afternoon. I'd no idea how many visitors Bessie had in the course of a day. What with all the goings-on in the street, the girl never knew a dull moment. "Do you now?" The sudden question was sharp. "You've no cause to complain, have you, of being neglected?"

"I never said I had, Ma."

There were a number of dolls in various stages of undress on a stand, and a table beside the wheel chair was covered with bits of bright-coloured silk. The invalid was making a doll's dress, and it promised to be pretty. It was evident that she had a gift for this type of dressmaking, and she was very fond, she said, of her dolls. They were so much nicer than real people that she hated to part with them, but she had to do something to help with the expenses, so she sold them to a shop in Crabbe Major. The shop furnished the dolls, the neighbours gave her their old bits, and she did the work. She got as much as ten shillings a doll as a rule, more if it was a special order with some fine stitching.

"And it don't go far, I can tell you, my lady," her mother put in. "Not in the way of butter and cream and such things as the doctor orders."

"Who is your doctor now, Bessie?" I asked, hoping to lead the conversation to Martin. "Fothergill?"

"Oh, no, not him. I don't care for him. He's much too high and mighty to bother about people like me. We have a new man, just come to the village. He's moved into the Merriedews' old house, you know, where there's a teashop. He's got the flat above and is ever so nice."

Her mother sniffed. "He's young, you mean, and goodlooking."

"Now, Ma, it's you, and you know it, with an eye for the men. You know it was you who would have Dr. Martin."

"I don't deny it, do I? Never have done, never will — bad cess to him."

"Ma was daft on Martin," Bessie said, her eyes bright with spite. "Just because he gave her good morning and took her to town once in a way in his car. 'Guess where I've been,' she'd say, coming in. 'Joy riding, and with the handsomest chap in the West Country.' I never thought he was anything special for looks. Something funny about his eyes. I wasn't all that glad to see him when she brought him the first time. You remember, Ma; I told you it was no good, but you would have it. So I let him look at my legs and back, and then, believe it or not, he said there was nothing wrong with them! Sound as a trivet, he said. What do you make of that? There I'd been on my back ever since I was thirteen, and he told me there was nothing the matter. I was that angry. Wouldn't you be? I spoke up, I did. I said: 'What do you mean, nothing wrong with my legs? I can't feel them,' I said. 'They might be a couple of bales of cotton wool.' And he said, 'Yes. I know what they feel like, but do you want them put right?' And I said, 'Yes, but I don't want you messing them about,' or some words like that. So he just looked disappointed and went away, but I heard him tell Ma if I felt like that then he couldn't do anything."

Bessie drew breath, and began again. "I might have known better than to let him come back. But Ma cried, didn't you, Ma, something dreadful. So I said all right, let him try, anything for peace. And he began his tricks. I know now that they was tricks. The Vicar knew all the time. He warned me, and he warned Ma. 'It's unchristian,' he said, 'what the Doctor is doing. It's hypnotism,' he said, 'and it's evil, an evil and a dangerous thing. He'll get your daughter in his power.' But the Doctor was coming nearly every day and I was getting better, so Ma wouldn't listen. And I'd got to trust Martin by then. He'd say, 'You must believe in me, Bessie, or I can't do anything.' Always telling me to believe in him, and I did. It was like being bewitched. Of course he did all sorts of things.

Massage, that was lovely; electricity, light, heat — he'd send an ambulance to take me to hospital for that. Sometimes he would just put me to sleep, and when I woke up I would know I could get as far as the table by myself, and I did. Other days he'd be cruel to me. I don't mean he hit me or anything like that, but he would look terrible."

"Tell how it was when you fell down," her mother put in. "Tell what he did to you."

"You've got it all wrong, Ma. He didn't do anything when my legs went queer and I fell down; only when I couldn't try. When I was trying hard the sweat would pour down his face just as if he was the one with bad legs and was doing it all, and sometimes he'd be all funny afterwards like he was faint, or in a fit. I might have known he was queer, that there was something wrong. But he seemed to be fond of me. 'We're partners,' he'd say. 'We're in this together.' Then one day he took me out for a drive in his car. He'd been coming for the best part of a year, and I'd got so I could help a bit with the housework, but I didn't dare go out in the street. He took me out Oxshott way, and made me walk with him through the woods. He put my hand through his arm and said, 'Come, Bessie, show me how well you can walk,' so I did. I felt wonderful. I could have walked miles. It was April, but the sun was shining. There were violets in the woods. He picked a big bunch for me to take home to Ma, and he looked at me, he looked right through me. 'Don't forget today, Bessie,' he said, and there was such a look in his face, all shining it was, so happy I couldn't help laughing. We just stood there in the sun and laughed and laughed, like a couple of kids. And if anyone had told me that day he was bad, I'd have belted them. But it wasn't six months before that Larnigan woman got hold of him and he went away. I was riding my bicycle all over the place when I heard it."

"That didn't last long after he'd gone," Mary Holt said,

179

coming in with the tray. "After he'd gone, and under a cloud too, you gave up, and took to your bed again."

Mrs. Holt rattled the teacups. Bessie lay back on her pillows, all the animation gone from her face. Her forehead was wet, her exhaustion this time wasn't pretence. "I couldn't help it, Ma. You know I kept up as long as I could."

"I don't say you didn't. It's the Doctor I'm angry with, making you think all the world of him, then leaving you in the lurch."

"Wicked I call it," Martha Blundle said, bouncing in. "Downright wicked to raise the hopes in a girl, then strike her down. But I always knew he was up to no good with his hypnotizing and his fancy ways. Long before he took up with that Teresa I says to Mr. Blundle, 'Mark my word, Mr. Blundle,' I says, 'that Martin Marriedew is mad as a hatter; you can see it in his eyes. You watch,' I said, 'when he next comes in for a pint. Don't you be taken in by that smile of his, and his hand with the darts. You watch his eyes.' Plumb crazy, that's what he was from the beginning. Why else should he take up with all the riffraff in the place and those who come to my back door asking for leavings? Not Albert, mind you. There was no harm in Albert, and I'm not meaning him, poor thing. Spry as a cricket he was, and useful too, if only as big as a midget; but he set great store by the Doctor, poor little soul, for his undoing. Never a word could you say about the Doctor when Albert was by, but he'd square his fists and stick out his chin for all the world as if he thought hisself a giant instead of a miserable three-foot-two in his boots, and they size four for a child.

"There's some that were surprised at what Merriedew came to, not me. There's others who say he got off too easy. But I said to Mr. Blundle, it's only right, I said, by his family. The poor chap, I says, didn't know what he was doing, didn't even seem to know his own name when it was read out in court. You know, my lady, you was there. All gone he was by then, and out of his wits. None of the old Nick left in him by that time. 'Blundle,' I says, when I come home, 'I wouldn't have known him. When I think of him down here,' I says, 'turning all the girls' heads, and the old women's too, mark you. Miss Molly and Miss Sally, quite daft they were. And old Mrs. Graham at the Grange, not to mention Bessie here. In love with him, that's what happened to you, my dear. You fell in love with your precious doctor.' "

"Out of his wits, indeed!" Mary Holt handed me my cup of tea. "He knew well enough what he was doing when he came back to this village."

"What happened exactly?" I asked. "Miss Molly wouldn't tell me."

"Molly Tripp's a cat," said Bessie.

"Not tell you? Lord help us!" Martha scoffed. "If ever I knew a pair of nosy parkers, it's them two old maids."

"All the same," put in Mary Holt, "after it happened they never so much as came to enquire. And my girl, for all they knew, might have been lying here dead!"

A quick glance at Bessie reassured me. She was placidly eating cake; so I pressed on.

"You mean after the riot?"

"I do, and riot it was, believe me, and that Jeremy did nothing to help, nor your good man either, Martha Blundle, and Bessie lying there helpless in her bed on the steps of the Chariot."

"It wasn't her bed. It was only her mattress and pillows. And Blundle stood in front of her, didn't he, and kept the crowd off her? What more could a man do, I ask you, with stones flying and women screaming?"

"But what happened?" I asked once again.

"Shall I tell it?" Martha asked Mary Holt. "Or will you?"

"You tell it, I don't trust myself."

"Well, what happened," Martha said, "was a disgrace to

the place, and we all know it. But you see he'd got all the men's backs up. He sent that Jeremy on ahead, to put up notices of a meeting. He was going to speak on the green, it said, by the War Memorial, about Peace and Goodwill. But there was no goodwill going by then in this village for Martin Merriedew, not after the way he'd treated his mother, leaving her in the lurch while he goes hobnobbing with foreigners and heathens of all sorts. And then when he turns up, what does he do? Ask forgiveness from his own? Not he! He never goes near his own mother's door, but stays the night with Albert in his new house. Indecent, that's what it was. Whatever his brother Edward had said of him, even if it was lies, he'd no call to put his mother and sister to shame before the public. So they pulled down the notices and got ready to give him a warm reception. They left him alone for the night, and Blundle says that proves they didn't mean no great harm, only to make a fool of him, but it's my opinion it was on account of Albert. No one wanted to make any trouble for Albert, he having done so much good in the place. For Albert he'd come into a great heap o' money from an uncle who'd gone to America, and he'd bought himself that fine house up the road. You know the one — Heart's Ease it's called — half a mile from the village, and he'd fixed it up nice as could be, but Gawd it was enough to make the Pope laugh! You'd a thought it was a doll's house, with the chairs and tables, and all, just Albert's size, though there was big ones too for company, mind you, and there was plenty of that, I can tell you. Nothing high and mighty about Albert, which is more than can be said of most who've been potboys in publics. But Albert he was as friendly as if he'd been born to it. And the money that little chap gave away — why, Blundle says it was thousands! But mostly for children, a great one he was for children, him being the same size, I suppose that was it. Always giving children treats. Sick ones, you know, cripples and such. He'd bring 'em in charabancs and have a spread in his garden at the back. And it was the same the night Merriedew came. All the kids from the orphanage at Crabbe Major was brought in, and such goings-on, you could hear them laughin' and singin' away down the road. And some say there was a kiddie there who was hoppin' about on crutches with a twisted leg when she come to the party, and when she come out to get into the charabanc to go back she'd left her crutches behind. But you can't believe everything you hear, I says. Well, however that may be, they left him alone for the night, but were ready for him in the morning when he went to the green with Albert and that there Jeremy.

"The Larnigan boys were at the back of it all. The police was on to them like a knife afterwards, and they got six months, both of 'em, for disturbing the peace, even if it was proved they'd meant Albert no harm, and was only layin' for Merriedew. You see, they knew what he'd done to their sister. Leastways they thought they did. She was livin' with the Doctor by then up in Warrington, they knew that much. So they collected all the roughs in the place and some from outside, meaning to make sport of him, so Blundle says. And when he started to speak, out there by the War Memorial, they all began shouting and laughing at him and catcalling, and he just stood there, waiting for them to stop their noise. But Albert had come along and he climbed up on top of the Cross, and he was sitting there and he yelled at them. 'Give the man a hearing,' he yells. 'You know him, he belongs to this place.' And that got them excited, not laughin', ugly like, and they burst into this house and lifted Bessie here, mattress and all, out of her bed, and carried her shoulder high to the front steps of the Chariot and told her to walk. 'Pick up your bed, Bessie,' they shouted, 'and walk! Didn't he teach you to walk? Then walk, girl, walk!' But Bessie here could only cover her face with her hands. I was upstairs, looking out of the window, scared of my life I was; but Blundle had come running out from the taproom by

183

then, and was shouting to them to stand back or he'd send for the police. And Merriedew, he was standing white as a sheet up against the Memorial, not moving nor saying a word, with Albert on top of him, when someone threw a stone. Then another came flying and it hit Albert, who loses his balance and topples over, and Merriedew makes a lunge to pick him up and there's pandemonium, with stones flying and everyone pushing and shouting and screaming. And so it was they drove him out of the place."

"It was his Lordship," Mary Holt said, "who sent for the police."

"It was Blundle who carried Bessie here back to her bed, wasn't it, Mary Holt?"

"That's right."

"I know, 'cause I seen it all, from the front windows upstairs, and I saw his Lordship come running through the park gates. He was calling out 'Martin! Martin!' at the top of his voice. Seems they telephoned up to the house from the lodge, and he came running. But he was too late, Martin was gone and Green with him, though he came back after to settle down with his mother. There was only Albert. They found him lying on the grass by the side of the road in front of his house. He must ha' got trampled on in the scrimmage. Martin must ha' picked him up and carried him so far, then left him. He was lyin' quite peaceful on his side, with a hand under his cheek like a child, and no bigger than a child, though he was all of forty years, with a wizened-up face. When they picked him up he was dead; there was a bit of paper in his fist and it was written on the paper in the Doctor's hand, the same as he wrote his prescriptions: 'Let the dead of this place bury their dead.'"

Martha stopped. There was a silence. Then Bessie spoke. "I'd like another cup o' tea, Ma," she said.

Part Two

Chapter One

MAY it please your Lordship, members of the jury, this case — and I say it soberly — is the most shocking in which I have ever been called on to appear.

"The crime is high treason, than which there is none more heinous in this or any civilized country; and the accused is an Englishman born and bred in this country, a man of education, of gifted parts, who set himself up as a leader of men and inspired devotion in more than a few innocent loyal subjects of our king.

"The penalty for high treason is death, as in murder, for treason is a crime similar to murder but more awful, since the will to destroy life is aimed not at an individual but at a nation; in this case, at forty-five million men, women and children, all possessing the right to life, liberty and the pursuit of happiness under the protection of our sovereign and our laws; and all kin to the murderer. I call the man before you a murderer because he is one at heart. I shall prove it, even though I cannot tell you how many of his countrymen's lives were lost through his efforts, nor what the help he gave the enemy amounted to, nor what was the damage he caused to the courage of our own troops; for I do not know. It may all have come to very little — let us hope so. No one will ever know. There is no way of assessing such things in the vast chaos of the aftermath of a war. But I know this: those whom he helped were our enemies, those he willed to weaken and destroy were his own people. I am not thinking now of his blood kin,

187

though they too were included (his own younger brother was fighting in that area of war where he was at his ugly work). I am thinking now of the millions who are his kin by virtue of a common allegiance, a common home, and because they are members of what his late Majesty King George the Fifth once referred to as 'One Great Family.' This man acted against them with deadly purpose at a time when the very existence of that home and that family was threatened, and even the young children who belonged to it went in peril from the enemy outside.

"Murder is an ugly crime, members of the jury, but there are degrees of ugliness in murder; and I submit to you that treason is to be likened to the most cowardly of its forms. Treason is no crime of passion committed in the heat of the moment. Treason is cold. It is a secret plan prepared in a cold mind, in this case, as I shall show you, in a proud mind, and a mind of no mean intellectual attainment. A mind so brilliant indeed in some ways, so dark in others, that the question of the man's sanity was raised at one time by his own family, and because of this I must remind you of the great care taken by the authorities in our country to protect those who are incapable through mental disease of distinguishing right from wrong. A man may commit murder, he may even be proved a traitor; but if through sickness of his mind he does not understand the nature of his act, such a man is protected from suffering the extreme penalty for his evil deed. He is declared guilty but insane, and being insane is held to be innocent before the law.

"We need not bother about that here in this court. I only mention it to show you how careful we are in this land to protect the innocent even though they appear guilty. We needn't bother about it because the man before you does not plead insanity, members of the jury, he pleads Not Guilty. He will tell you that he did not do what he is accused of doing; but he will not say, and he cannot say, that he did these things not

188

knowing they were wrong, nor can my colleague who is here in his defence say it for him. There is no argument between us concerning the mental health of the prisoner. The question you have to answer is a plain question: did he or did he not commit high treason?

"Let us return, then, to what I was saying about degrees of ugliness in murder. There have been murderers inspired by passion, the passion of jealousy, of betrayed love, of rage, of fear. Some of these have received, if not sympathy, at least a partial forgiveness from the law and the public, and have been spared the death penalty. The prisoner does not belong in this company. His will to do deadly harm bears no mark of violent passion bursting suddenly into action; his crime was premeditated, it was kept on ice in that cold mind for a very long time; and when he was ready it was not translated into sudden violence. Here was no gun or knife levelled in fury at an enemy. This man acted slowly, carefully, as poisoners do who set about the death of people who trust them, by stealth and under the guise of friendship."

I knew Theodore Kennington, counsel for the Crown, by reputation, but I had never met him or heard him plead. Neither did I know Mr. Pringle, counsel for the defence, who was so much less impressive in appearance than his opposite number. But I knew Charles. That is to say, I had thought I knew Charles.

I have a copy of the proceedings before me: "The Assize Court. Greymouth, February 5, 1946. Judge, Mr. Justice Collit."

That was Charles on the bench almost within reach of my hand. My husband an hour ago, and he would be again when he slipped through the curtain behind him, lifted the wig from his head and let fall the scarlet robes that hid his aging, brittle bones; but not now. The stiff little wig changed more

189

than his long, sensitive, weary face. True, there was only pleasant Tim Beresford, the Judge's Marshal, between us, very spruce in his morning coat and white collar. If I leaned across him I could almost, if not quite, reach and get hold of Charles's left hand that was resting along the edge of the big book in front of him; and yet Charles wasn't there. Mr. Justice Collit had left him behind in our lodgings doing the *Times* crossword puzzle, and had taken his place. He too was not unfamiliar to me. I always went with him on circuit and except at murder trials sat on the bench at one remove from him. I had never before attended when a man was being tried for his life, and Mr. Justice Collit would have been better pleased had I stayed away this time, but as a rule he liked to have me there and would instruct me on the finer points of the evidence when the court rose and he came back to our lodgings to relax.

The Judge's lodgings in Greymouth I had always thought especially nice and the town itself quite the pleasantest on the Western Circuit. Warrington was a hateful place with its miles of grimy slums, and in my childhood we had always avoided it, but Greymouth I knew well. Its boisterous harbour and windswept docks had added largely in the old days to the fortune of the Patche family, and we had taken for granted as children, Francis and I, that it was in a sense our own town. Not that we visited it often. But Charlotte would take us every now and then to tea with the Bishop; we found the Cathedral Close that stood high behind the town, with a view from the Palace tower far out to sea, very romantic and there was a cake shop in the High Street that we much fancied.

The Judge's lodgings were down in the centre of the town but in an old secluded square and Fairchild, the Judge's butler, agreed with me about them. He said there was nothing like a good solid Georgian house for warming up in winter and keeping cool in summer, and the tenants who moved out when we came down were respectable people, who always left it in good order. "Hardly anything to do, your Ladyship, but a bit o' dustin' and airin' o' beds when we move in."

Fairchild was an institution. He had looked after more judges than any other butler in England and I doted on him. He was enormously fat with legs like an elephant's and he moved as softly as an elf. Sometimes I wondered about his private life and thought how wonderful it would be to have him as a permanency on our staff in London. But a small house in a London square wouldn't have suited Fairchild. He was a personage and a public servant. He would undoubtedly have felt that the administration of justice in the King's Bench Division would have failed to live up to its ancient traditions without him to poke fires in Judge's lodgings, put their Lordships themselves into their robes and decant the wines for the Lord Lieutenants and Sheriffs of England when they dined with us. Though I flattered myself that Charles and I were among his favourites, there were other justices who wanted him to look after them as much as we did and he was by no means always free to accompany us on our pilgrimages through the Assizes of the West Country. This time, however, we were lucky. Fairchild was with us and Mr. Justice Collit would be cossetted during the whole of this circuit. Tim Beresford and I would help, but it would be Fairchild who would see to it. It was more difficult to cosset Judge Collit than one might imagine because he never expressed a wish or found anyone at fault and would have lain awake half the night with ice-cold feet not noticing that I had forgotten to bring his bed socks. This had happened once, to Fairchild's horror, never a second time. Fairchild confessed that he always brought with him now in his own luggage a pair of bed socks for the Judge, just in case.

I knew that Mr. Justice Collit hated hot-water bottles, while he accepted bed socks as a necessity, and a number of his other small idiosyncrasies. I knew all the things about him, in fact, that he had in common with my Charles. I knew that he de-

191

tested jargon, had no patience with cranks, and assumed that most men would lie to save their own skins, as far as they dared, even under oath. But I didn't know what was going on in his mind while his calm dispassionate gaze rested on the prisoner's dreadful face and I was frightened. Judge Collit had sentenced more than one murderer to the gallows, but he did not approve of women as spectators at a murder trial and he had not expected me to want to sit through the trial for treason of Martin Merriedew.

He had not asked me to stay away. He had betrayed no feeling in the matter after his first faint look of displeased surprise when I had told him the night before that I meant to be there. He seemed to have assumed that I would sit at home alone in our lodgings or go to a movie while he weighed up the evidence for and against the man who had once been my brother's great friend. But he had been cool and courteous as always when he left with the Sheriff for the court, and I following with Tim Beresford had been nearly as cool until the prisoner was brought in and my frightened eyes were riveted to his face.

How close we all were to each other. The prisoner lifted up in the centre of the court, like an animal in a cage, was on a level with the bench, and there was a clear space in the air between so that the accused and his judge could look each other in the face across the heads of counsel. But how crowded the benches were. Counsel for the Crown, counsel for the defence and their juniors, clerks of the court, the press, how cosy they all were, and the twelve respectable citizens in the jury box, all so quiet, and the spectators in the galleries, so well behaved. One might be in church, listening to a sermon. Mr. Pringle, sprawling his ungainly length, appeared to be dozing with his sharp peevish nose pointing at the ceiling and the police walked on tiptoe, it seemed, so as not to disturb him. Mr. Kennington had no need to lift his voice. He'd better not if he wanted to impress the Judge. Mr. Justice Collit didn't like to be shouted at, nor care for grandiloquent periods and dramatic gesturings. But Mr. Kennington, I reminded myself, was not addressing the Judge, he was addressing the twelve men who would decide if or not Martin Merriedew would be hanged.

I cannot remember clearly my state of mind when I took my seat on that bench. One can recall one's actions during moments of stress, but not the emotions or reasons that prompted them. I know that I slept little the night before and ate no breakfast, that the old house seemed gloomy and chilly, that I imagined the imperturbable Fairchild disapproving, like everyone else, of my conduct, and that for an hysterical moment I wanted to justify myself in his small round eyes. I had, no doubt, my reasons but I cannot recall them now. I only know that I felt I must be there, that I did not expect to be more than normally harrowed, and that I discovered my mistake when it was too late to withdraw. I had found out, the moment Martin Merriedew was led into court, that this case was going to be intolerable and what kept me glued to my seat during the whole of the protracted proceedings was simply the fact that it was a little less unbearable to be present than to wait outside and wonder what was happening.

II

My principal worry before the trial had been Francis. I had told myself that he had forgotten Martin Merriedew, but I wanted to see him to make sure that this was so, and I had tried to find him, but had failed until the week before Charles and I left for Greymouth.

Francis had crashed in 1943. He had spent a year in hospital at some distance from London. I had been to see him as often as I could manage. Then he had gone home to Crabbe for a bit to convalesce, and at last to Roehampton to be fitted with a new leg. He had been difficult, distrait, and on the whole rather unfriendly, but he had not once mentioned Martin's name, not indeed since the outbreak of war, and he hadn't seen him for how long? Fifteen years? Thirteen? What difference did the number of years make? The war had blotted out the old world, it had split the living earth in two halves and opened a gulf down the centre of life. The Martin Francis had known belonged on the other side of the grave of the past, and was gone. I told myself that it must be with Francis as with me; but I wasn't sure, so I had tried to reach him. He wasn't at Crabbe when I telephoned; he was at Roehampton. When I got on to the hospital at Roehampton he had gone out. Yes, he would be back that evening, he was under treatment and his leg wasn't yet ready. Then when I rang again in the evening I was told that he had returned but couldn't come to the telephone.

It took me some days to realize that I couldn't reach him because he didn't want to see me. What did that mean? I refused to answer the question. I plunged into the business of remaking the house we'd once lived in into the semblance of our old home. I spent my time in a rabble of charwomen, plasterers, glaziers, and chimneysweeps, in wandering through the endless labyrinths of furniture depositories between mountains of chairs, tables, beds, basins, the litter of housekeeping. I must, I kept telling myself, get our furniture out of store and moved in before Charles and I left. I did get it moved in, and groaned at the sight of my favourite footstool and Charles's special armchair all eaten by mice and with the stuffing coming out. And every day or so I would ring Francis.

At last they told me at the hospital that he had gone, they didn't know where, but letters would be forwarded to Crabbe Minster; so I rang Charlotte and she said: "He's at Bingham's Hotel, up to his neck in this beastly Merriedew business. Haven't you seen him? Well, he is, and he's got Edward Merriedew with him."

I knew then that I was caught between Francis and Charles. Francis refused to see me because of Charles. He hadn't forgotten, he hadn't changed. He had tried repeatedly, I remembered now, to see Martin when he came back to England in '36, and had failed. Even at Crabbe that horrid day he had failed, he had arrived too late. And he had wanted — hadn't Charlotte said so? — to help Martin in his work, with money, had sent a biggish cheque; but the cheque had been returned. Now he was trying again. Martin needed money now for his defence. That was what Francis was doing, he was providing the money. And if Martin was found guilty?

What could I do? It was all but too late to do anything, there were only a few days left; and I could say nothing to Charles until I found out what Francis wanted. It was possible that Francis would prefer to have that cold fish Charles, as he called him, than someone else.

I went to Bingham's Hotel and pushed my way in to him. He was upstairs in his sitting room, with his stump on a cushion and a girl beside him taking down shorthand. He scowled when he saw me.

"Who let you in? I gave orders."

"I must talk to you, and alone."

"Why? What about?"

"The trial."

"What's it to you?"

"Charles will take the case unless we stop him. Shall I try? I've come to find out what you want me to do."

"Nothing. Charles won't listen to you. If he has made up his mind to take the case he'll take it, whatever you say or feel."

I sat down. The girl took herself off into the next room and closed the door.

"You think Charles as inhuman as that?"

"I do, where I am concerned."

"This isn't you, Francis; you aren't on trial."

195

"It's the same thing."

"Rubbish."

"Don't let's waste time. Edward will be back in a moment."

"Very well. Shall I tackle Charles?"

"No. If I had wanted you to I would have asked you. If I had thought you could pull it off I might have wanted you to try; but I knew you couldn't, and the reason is that you don't care. You think Martin's guilty."

"I don't."

"Well, you think it's quite possible, and that being so, I'd rather you didn't meddle."

"I'm meddling because of you."

"Exactly. If Martin Merriedew is found guilty and hanged by the neck till he's dead, I'll never speak to Mr. Justice Collit again, and you know it. That's what's eating you, nothing else. You'll lose your precious brother. You'll have to choose between him and your husband. Well, you'd better choose now, because whatever happens I don't see myself chewing it over afterwards with Charles."

"Would you be satisfied if he passed up the case?"

"No, not now. I've decided that we might do much worse."

"Thank you."

"Don't be petty, my dear. A man's life may depend on a word, a false move, a move taken now, the decision that I this moment have arrived at. Think that over. What you and I are saying today may decide the fate of a man who means more to me than anyone else on earth."

"You still feel like that?"

"Why should I have changed? Did you think that I would hate him because I let him down?"

"I don't know what you mean by that."

"Never mind what I mean. What did you think I'd been doing these twelve months?"

"What twelve months?"

"Martin was sent home from Italy over a year ago. He was arrested in Warrington a week later and has been locked up ever since. Didn't you know?"

"How could I? There was nothing in the papers."

"Oh, yes, there was. Nothing much, I grant you, in the London press, but the Greymouth *Mail* had it and the Warrington *Star*."

"I must have missed it."

"Charles knew, all right."

"I don't think he did, Francis. He was as surprised — "

"Rubbish, my dear, he knew and he kept it to himself. But that is of no consequence. Your life with Charles is of no interest to me — never has been."

"Have you seen Martin, consulted him about this?"

"No, he won't see me."

"And in spite of that — ?"

"What's that got to do with it? He's not interested, he has nothing to say to me; but I can still try to help. Now go, please, I'm busy."

I didn't see him again but I saw Charlotte. She told me that he had guaranteed the cost of the defence and that between the two of them they had prevailed on Pringle to accept the brief.

Charlotte already knew all she wanted to know about the case. Martin was guilty and Francis a fool; but she needn't tell him so, and if no one would help those wretched Merriedews she had decided that she would; so she had breezed up to London and started throwing her weight about. It was still considerable. Mr. Pringle, she had assured herself after a few well-placed enquiries, was the right man, and it appeared that he was a friend of a very old friend of my father's. More exactly, he had been a pupil in the chambers of a luminary at the bar twenty years ago when my father was in office, and my father had noticed him to his advantage. He had put something or other in his way, she didn't know just what; anyhow she had got at him and bullied him into taking the thing on. It hadn't been easy. Mr. Pringle, she said, was prim. He preferred to believe in his client's innocence when he accepted a brief, and wasn't much impressed by what Francis told him. And he had come away from his first interview with Martin very browned off. Martin took so little interest in his defence that it was being undertaken to all intents and purposes without him. Edward, on the other hand, took too much. He was driving the lot of them crazy. Martin was mad, according to Edward, always had been. Edward couldn't get it into his thick head that the defence couldn't plead insanity unless Martin said so. Edward kept on and on about it, and kept bringing up Martin's attacks on the Church as proof. He wanted Pringle to argue that Martin was unfit to plead because he had called the Dean and Chapter at Greymouth hypocrites, with fat ears and full bellies.

Edward, it seemed, had been following Martin round taking notes of his speeches. He had produced a great bundle of papers tied up with string and thrust it at Pringle. Pringle had looked through it and handed it over to Francis. Charlotte had seen it. Nothing to do with the case, all about blasphemy, and the Church rotting away. Money was the cause of the rot. The Church was nothing but Big Business. Martin preferred such concerns as Imperial Tobacco and Bearsteds; there was no humbug about their methods of publicity. But the Church pretended to stand for salvation, and while it talked about God it went into banking and moneylending, played the market, and invested in real estate. The Ecclesiastical Commissioners were good businessmen and good landlords. The blocks of houses they let out were all occupied, but the churches were empty. Then there was something about livings in the gift of ungodly families. Men called Divines were paid so much a year by the rich and the great to do their praying for them and get them tickets to Heaven. If they did their job properly they got on and ended up bishops. If Christ was to be saved for England, the Church that called itself Christian must be destroyed.

"Pretty hot," Charlotte said. Not that she cared; the Church could look after itself, and the stuff was of course no use at all to Pringle. Why bring in blasphemy? The charge was treason.

"And I've no doubt whatever," she said, "that Martin Merriedew palled up with the Germans. It's just what he would do. Pringle thinks so, unfortunately, and doesn't like it. He's an old maid, as fussy and precise as your Aunt Agatha. He wanted to throw up the brief at one moment, but I brought him round."

"How?"

She had the grace to blush. "Gave him a good dinner and tipped him off about Gideon Fish, the prize witness on the other side, and a bad egg if ever I saw one."

"I thought he was a friend of yours."

"Whatever made you think that? I took the man up for a time, and had him down to stay once because he amused me; I like sharpening my wits against people I disagree with; but I never liked him. Much too full of himself; one of those puritans who would string you up to a lamppost without winking once he was in power and he quite saw the moment coming. He was going to save the people, build a new world. He told me all about it, as cool as you please, in my own drawing room. 'You and your lot are going to disappear,' he said. 'Your time's up!' Then a big laugh. Quite the worst type we produce in England; nonconformist-tradesman, well-to-do middle-class; but hipped on religion, the old-fashioned kind, hell and damnation for everyone but themselves.

"I told Pringle, I said: 'I know that man. He's a fanatic, eaten up with ambition. He thinks God chose him, meant him to be a Hitler or something. That's why he joined up with Martin Merriedew. They were going to save the world together. Well, they didn't. The war interfered. Two of a feather, if you ask me. And both dangerous. I wouldn't give a penny piece between them for patriotism but it would be a score for you if you got Merriedew off.' Then that woman Teresa turned up, so he's happier now. He's got one witness for the defence anyhow, such as she is."

"Where did she come from?"

"From Warrington. She came up to see Francis."

"What's she like now? Did you see her?"

"No, but Pringle seemed pleased with her. He said she was tough and would make a good witness."

Charlotte had surpassed herself; she had even made Francis think she believed in Martin's innocence. But she didn't come to the trial. When she had tidied things up to her own satisfaction she took herself off to Crabbe. It was bad enough, she said, being obliged to sit through one of old Nightingale's sermons without interrupting; she didn't propose to listen to counsel droning on for hours, nor was she so far gone as to find entertainment in murder trials.

"You going, Barbara?"

"Yes, I'm going."

She stared, her hard blue eyes puzzled, then gave a shrug. "Please yourself," she said.

I asked Camilla at the last moment to come with me to Greymouth.

"Come and stand by me, Camilla."

"You mean sit through that beastly thing?"

"Yes."

"Not for the world, ducks."

"Please, Camilla. I'm in a jam between Francis and Charles. If Martin Merriedew is innocent he'll be acquitted. You can trust Charles for that. I'd rather come up before Charles than anyone if I were wrongly accused. All the same it is going to be pretty ghastly. Please, Camilla."

"No, sweet, I'm sorry, I couldn't possibly, and if I were you I wouldn't either, just in case it goes wrong."

"What do you mean by wrong? If Merriedew is guilty he's got to hang. There is such a thing as justice, isn't there?"

"Of course, ducks, but there are other things too in this world. There's friendship, for one. And the wretch doesn't seem to have much of that to count on, does he?"

"How do you know?"

"Oh, I've asked round. I was staying near Greymouth not long ago for a Hunt Ball. You'd be surprised at the amount of talk there is going on in that town. Quite nasty most of it. You'd think some of his old patients would stand up for him, wouldn't you? Too scared, I suppose. I called on several people, a poor little parson for one, whom I used to know in the East End. According to him, your Merriedew was a saint, too good for this world, too single-minded, he called it, and too Christ-like. Oh, much too Christlike to be acceptable to this genera-tion. But the Dean told another story. According to the Dean, he led a riotous life, drank like a fish and consorted with the scum of the earth, crooks, tarts, roaring pansies. Whatever he did, you see, was wrong. He was that kind of man, the perfect target to shoot at. You know how it is, surrounded by crowds of adorers in the old days, and now there's no one to say a good word for him."

"That's not true; there's Francis, for one."

"Is he giving evidence for the defence?"

"No, he wanted to, but Pringle says Charles couldn't take the case with his brother-in-law as a witness."

"I should hope not. That would be — "

"Well, he's not going to, he's only putting up the money."

"Who else have they got?"

"Martin's two brothers."

"My poor child, he hasn't spoken to any of his family for years, they all think he's mad. What good can they do him now?"

"I don't know."

"What about the lot that worked with him in that field hospital?"

"I don't know, I tell you."

"Well, I do. They've all run out on him."

"Are you surprised?"

"Yes, I am."

"You said yourself, Camilla, that he would smell."

"I know, but he wasn't my friend; I didn't love him; I only saw him once in my life. But suppose it was you. If you sold out your country, duckie, and were going to hang for it, what would you expect me to do? Swear I'd never known you?"

"No, of course not."

"Well, then?"

"Are you trying to make out that he's a friend of mine?"

"He was once, wasn't he?"

"Yes, when we were kids."

"And you can go and watch the chap you liked as a kid tried for his life?"

"Yes."

"Pretty hard-boiled, aren't you?"

"Maybe I am. If I am I can't help it. I've got to go. I've got a thing about it."

Camilla's stare was very uncomfortable, then she, like Charlotte, gave a shrug. "If you must, then you must. But suppose he is innocent?"

"Then he'll be acquitted."

"Yes, presumably, and discharged and treated for the rest of his life like a leper."

"I don't see why."

"After all the mud slinging? Be your age, my dear. Warrington and Greymouth will kick him out, so will England."

"Then you won't come?"

"No; I simply couldn't take it."

So here I was alone. And I remembered what Camilla had said as my eyes searched the gallery for Martin Merriedew's friends. The three high bleak windows behind the public gallery let in enough light from the grey winter day to confuse and blur the many faces, but I recognized Martha Blundle, red as a peony, in the front row with Molly Tripp beside her, and that surely was Mrs. Holt on the other side. Bessie must have given her mother a day off to come to the show, and the three were getting their money's worth. Mary Holt offered a paper bag and Miss Molly popped a chocolate into her rabbity mouth as I looked. Martha was savagely chewing gum.

Francis was in the Sheriff's gallery. He appeared to be alone. He spoke to no one, and never took his eyes from the prisoner's face. Who else is there? Camilla had asked. There must be some up there in the packed gallery who owed a debt to the man in the dock and had come out of gratitude. He had cured so many humble folk in the town, it couldn't be true that he had only one friend here today. Even William Joyce, whose trial had been holding the public's attention just lately, had had two friends who stood by him. "Germany calling. This is Germany calling." I seemed to hear the voice sounding beyond the confines of the court, and if I heard it, why not the others? The fame of the traitor William Joyce would obscure Martin Merriedew, but it would not help him.

III

"Martin Merriedew on the 10th day of March 1943 and on divers days thereafter, being then to wit a person owing allegiance to our lord the King and whilst on the said several days

203

an open and public war was being prosecuted and carried on by the German and the Italian realms and their subjects against our lord the King and his subjects, then and on the said several days traitorously contriving and intending to aid and assist the said enemies of our lord the King and his subjects did traitorously adhere to and aid and comfort the said enemies in parts beyond the seas without the realm of England, to wit, in the territories of North Africa called Libya, Tripolitania and Tunisia and in Italy where our armies were engaged in war against Germany and Italy.

"Members of the jury, the prisoner at the bar, Martin Merriedew, is charged in an indictment containing three counts."

Bill Cummins, the Clerk of the court, a cheery comfortable man, had read out the indictment. The jury had then been impanelled and sworn. No women, only men. What kind of men? Worthy men, respectable citizens, loyal subjects all of our lord the King? Did I know any of them by sight? Yes. The handsome grey one with the whiskers was the manager of the best drapers in Greymouth and the pink plump one owned our favourite cake shop. His son had been killed at Salerno. I had sent my condolences. How many of the others had lost sons or brothers at the war, or wives, perhaps, and children in the bombing? Greymouth had had more than its share of bombs. There were areas down by the docks with scarce a house standing. The inner harbour was still choked with rubble, and here was a man accused of bringing aid and comfort to the enemy that had done this to Greymouth. A man, moreover, who had made no end of trouble before, who had broken up families, led young men astray. The members of the jury were no worse and no better than most men, but they had stood by their country when it was in danger, they had paid their part of the account of the war, in blood and tears and courage, and none were traitors. That was the thing. Here was a man accused of treachery to every one of them. He was about to be charged with it. Once again we had all had to listen to the almost identical words.

"Members of the jury, the prisoner at the bar, Martin Merriedew, is charged in an indictment containing three counts. Each of those charges is a charge of high treason." Again the identical words were repeated. "To this indictment he has pleaded Not Guilty, and it is your charge to say, having heard the evidence, whether he is guilty or not."

Then Theodore Kennington had got to his large easy polished feet and opened the case for the Crown.

Mr. Kennington was well known for his elegant appearance. It was said that his wife laundered his snowy linen with her own dainty hands and even curled his wig, but that obviously couldn't be true. The wig never came home and he often did, though not every night, if the gossips were to be believed. Who would expect it of a man so large, so ruddy, so full of ardour and eloquence? Mr. Pringle was a shrimp compared to him; not short, he was tall, but limp and thin, with a stoop and a sharp, peevish face. No one had ever gossiped about Mr. Pringle's infidelities. He had buried his wife years ago, and lived alone in morose seclusion. A bitter man, it was said, with a grievance, the usual grievance of ability that has failed to receive the recognition it considers its due. For he was undoubtedly an able man. Not eloquent like Kennington, but cunning and dangerous, especially when it came to dealing with a hostile witness.

Counsel for the Crown was talking about Crabbe. "What of the prisoner's background, members of the jury? Was he lucky or unlucky in his beginnings? I myself would say that he was one of the very lucky ones. Here you have a God-fearing English family of the best type, living in a charming country village. He is the eldest son of a doctor, a general practitioner beloved in the village and country round. His mother is the daughter of a parson. It is a happy family in a happy home. Three sons and a daughter, all of them gifted, and all destined, apparently, for distinguished careers of public service. The eldest son, who stands before you, follows in his father's footsteps; the second son takes Holy Orders; the sister becomes a hospital nurse; and the youngest of the family receives a commission in a famous regiment. This, the youngest of the four children went with his regiment overseas in 1940, he fought in the areas of war mentioned in the indictment, was three times seriously wounded, survived to attain the rank of colonel, and is now on leave from Germany, having come to attend the trial of his elder brother.

"That brother, gentlemen of the jury, became the mainstay of his family when the father died. He had won scholarship after scholarship at his grammar school, had gone up as a student of distinction to the London School of Medicine, had received his degree just before his father's death, and then went back to his village to take over the father's practice. I could call witnesses to tell you how he carried on that practice. There were criticisms, there were quarrels with colleagues, there were even some scandals; he began to show himself almost at once as a quarrelsome man, with little respect for the opinions of others; but I don't know that they are relevant, my lord, to our enquiry. The point I would wish to make is simply this: his was a devoted family, and it depended on him. His mother and sister depended on him for the roof over their heads. His brothers depended on him to see them through their several periods of training. Suddenly he left them, without provision for their needs and without warning, to go off on some mysterious errand that he will or will not tell you about. I cannot, for I wasn't with him. No one has been found who was with him. No one can tell us what he did, except himself if he so chooses, during those years. For he stayed away three years, members of the jury, and when he returned he was a stranger to his family. They had managed without him. The mother baked cakes and sold them, the sister taught in school. Friends came to the rescue and made it possible for the brothers to finish their training. Was the prisoner grateful? Was he glad to find, when he at last came home, that they had pulled through without him? He didn't go home, members of the jury. He didn't go near them. He came to the city of Warrington instead (it is not fifty miles from this court), and set up as a quack doctor, a sort of faith healer. You will hear more of that. There may be no harm in it, I don't know. All I know is that the medical men of the town didn't like his methods, any more than the churchmen did, or the police. For he combined his hypnotism, autosuggestion, divine healing, whatever you choose to call it, with a campaign of social reform so extreme that the civil authorities were obliged to take action. He attacked the Church and the Government, not one political party in the State but all parties. Tory, Liberal, Socialist, they were all one to him, and all bad, as were the Church of England, Wesleyan Methodist and Roman Catholic churches. He had become a dangerous social agitator, and there was harm in that, whatever you may think of his methods of healing the sick."

Charles leaned forward. "You expressed a doubt just now as to the relevance of his medical methods in this trial. It would seem to apply equally to his religious opinions."

"Quite so, my lord. I would not mention them if I believed them to be merely opinions, or indeed opinions in any real sense. If you will allow me, I am proposing to show that this man had no principles and no genuine opinions of any kind concerning the welfare of our country. I am proposing to show that he cared for nothing about that, but was a charlatan and an anarchist, whose one aim was self-glorification. By anarchist I mean a man with no respect for the law, a man who set himself up as above the law; and when I call him a charlatan I mean that he pretended to do things he did not do, and

207

to be what he was not. In other words, he was a humbug."

"A humbug is not necessarily a traitor. I at least should be sorry to entertain such an idea."

"I too, my lord. But hypocrisy is an indication of the will to deceive, to sail under false colours; and when it is combined with cynical defiance of the law, it is not inconsistent with disloyalty as a citizen. I am describing the man's dangerous and ill-fated character, my lord."

"I quite understand what you are doing." Charles's tone was dry. "I only wonder if you are not being a little tedious. Still, if the defence raises no objection?" Mr. Pringle contented himself with a sideways movement of the head. "Very well then, but be brief, if you please."

"I thank you, my lord. As I was saying, the police of this town were obliged to intervene on more than one occasion at the prisoner's meetings; for he held meetings that drew very large crowds. I could produce a hundred witnesses to tell you about these affairs. I shall call only two, both men who had faith in him, one who left him before the war, the other a man who stuck to him through everything and went with him overseas, and worked beside him in the field hospital that is mentioned in the indictment, and there began to doubt him, until finally in Italy, in one of those canteens and rest camps you have been told about, he heard him on Christmas Eve 1944 endeavouring to persuade our men to lay down their arms; and so at last, horrified, disillusioned, heartbroken — for he had loved the prisoner — he denounced him to the military authorities.

"You may ask, my lord and members of the jury, why the accused was allowed to go on for so long with his sly, underhand scheming against the safety of our troops? You may wonder how it was that he could carry on his traffic in the lives of his fellow countrymen with the enemy undisturbed and unsuspected, for so many months? To understand how it was you must picture to yourselves the conditions in a field hospital in a desert in wartime. The prisoner, my lord, was an orderly in that hospital. A very humble occupation, you may say, for a man with a brilliant degree from the London School of Medicine. You may think that he should have been drafted into the Army Medical Corps, and he would have been except for the fact that he had been debarred by the British Medical Association from the practice of medicine in 1938. That is why this brilliant man was employed in the comparatively humble capacity of an orderly. As a doctor he had been disgraced, but as an orderly, and what I believe is termed a dresser, he was trusted.

"Put in plain language, he was there to nurse the wounded, make their beds, tend to their needs, and dress their wounds. I understand that in such mobile hospitals there are, as a rule, no women nurses. Field hospitals are considered too near the front, the life too rough, and the danger too great for women, though I daresay the women themselves disagree. In any case there were none in the unit we are speaking of, so the work of mercy and comfort otherwise expected of nursing sisters even in times of battle fell to the orderlies. It was the prisoner and his companions who listened to the last words of the dying, closed their eyes and gathered together their small possessions, or wrote letters home for those who lived yet could not write, sometimes because they were blind or had no hands. It is not my purpose to harrow your feelings, members of the jury; but I would remind you that the man before you on trial for treason was wearing a uniform. Though not a combatant, being a declared conscientious objector, he still was in khaki, and he wore a badge recognized by all the civilized world as carrying with it an authority that is sacrosanct, the badge of the Red Cross. And it provided protection for those who wore it. I do not say that in all cases the enemy treated this badge as sacred, but of this I can assure you: because of it the prisoner would not have been shot as a spy had he been captured. The Geneva Convention protected him and his fellow workers. For he was not alone. He was a member of an organization recognized by the military staffs and War Offices of both sides, and he had with him a group of young men, a dozen or so, conscientious objectors like himself, who had been his helpers before the war and had gone with him overseas under the sign of the Red Cross.

"They had been sent out, please note, by the War Office. They had not found their own way through the perilous channels of war; they had sailed with our troops in a military convoy, protected by our destroyers. And while discharging their hospital duties when they arrived, they were not only enjoying such amenities as are possible in a camp in a desert, but were protected again by his Majesty's armed forces. Not fully protected, but more protected than many of the women and children at home in England. In wartime the people of this land do not expect full protection. They think themselves lucky if they survive. But this man was more lucky than many. He was not called on to go into battle. He was enjoying the full, indeed an extra measure of the protection which it is possible to extend in time of war to an unarmed subject of the Crown; and it was not only the sign of the Red Cross, it was the tanks and guns and bayonets of our forces that were protecting him. Our air, land, and naval forces stood between him and the enemy. Without them he could not have remained in those regions for one day or one hour. They were, in a word, holding the line, while the prisoner, masquerading in the clothing of mercy, made friends with the enemy.

"He had exceptional opportunity for this, members of the jury, because the line of battle was fluid. As you all know, the fighting in North Africa swung back and forth. It was a war of movement, of rapid advances and withdrawals. When the enemy advanced, they overran our lines, engulfed such units as field hospitals and took over our wounded who had been left in them. The same thing would happen the other way round. The enemy in full retreat would abandon their field hospitals, leaving their wounded in our hands. This happened at least once to the formation of which the prisoner was a member. Then there was the usual toll of wounded prisoners brought in by the ambulances. All in all, hundreds — indeed thousands — of wounded Germans must have been received in our hospitals during the war. I haven't the figures, but it is common knowledge. What is of more special interest to us is that in the field hospital to which the man in the dock belonged, it was the custom to put him in charge of the prisoners at his own request for a plain, and what seemed a sufficient, reason: he spoke German. That was his opportunity, my lord, to betray his country and his comrades; and I shall prove to you that he made good use of it.

"But before I go on, I would pause for a moment on a word, and ask you to let its meaning sink into your minds and hearts. The word is 'allegiance.' It was twice read out to you today. It is the key word of the indictment against the prisoner, and it has been used quite recently in another court. It was the Attorney-General who used it, and I can do no better than quote what he said: 'The very basis of allegiance is this' — and I am using now the language of Blackstone, our old Master of English law — 'that so long as the Prince offers protection to his subjects, so long that subject owes a debt of allegiance to the Prince.' Protection by the Prince, by the Crown, by the State. Protection, on the one hand, and allegiance, on the other, are, in the submission of the Crown, reciprocal things, correlative things, the two go together. Allegiance, members of the jury, is the duty of loyalty and faithfulness owed to a sovereign by a person within his protection. I shall leave it to you to decide whether the man on trial before you owed allegiance to our king, our country, and you, his fellow countrymen.

"I will not weary you now with the dismal story of his treachery in that hospital. You will hear the evidence. It may seem to you strange that none of his followers, that no single member of that group of young men who worked with him, should stand up to defend him today. That fact alone may seem to you to condemn him; but I do not want you to allow it to influence you. The evidence against him will not be the evidence of absence, nor that alone of his Commanding Officers and the one companion who worked with him most closely. There is a letter in his own hand. You will be asked to study it, and will decide whether or not you agree with me that it proves without shadow of doubt that the prisoner not only meant to send, but was in the habit of sending, information to the enemy.

"This letter will be handed to you presently. Come with me now to Italy, and to a scene so typically British that one could laugh with a warm heart if it were not so tragic. The war has moved north through the mountains, it is winter in Tuscany; it is Christmas Eve. Our troops are fighting in the black night, in a blizzard. But somewhere, never mind where, it is well within the sound and range of heavy enemy artillery, there is a shelter. It is flimsy enough, its walls shake in the icy wind; but inside it is warm and bright. There is a red-hot stove, there are lights — lights on a Christmas tree! Yes, there is one, and it shines through air thick with tobacco smoke, and there is a sound of singing, of music, for the place is crowded with men and they are singing at the top of their lungs: songs about shepherds, watching their flocks by night; songs about a jolly old boy, King Wenceslas; a song that begins 'Silent night, holy night' — you all know it. Which of us doesn't know it? We learned it as children. Christmas carols, that's what our men were singing, with the black night outside and the guns pounding. And the prisoner was there, gentlemen of the jury. Perhaps he joined in the singing, I don't know; but I do know that he was whispering, he was asking the men what good they thought they were doing, what good could come out of the war, even if they won it? He was asking them why they put up with it? He was telling them to chuck it, telling them the enemy were men like themselves who wanted to go home as much as they did, telling them their officers had no right to send them out into the night to kill and be killed. Finally he shouted at them. This was devil's business, he said, and they were doing it. Let them rebel before it was too late. They could stop it even now if they rose up all together.

"You will hear what he told them from two men who heard it, the man who had suspected him in North Africa, who had protested privately but kept quiet because of his long friendship with this traitor, but at last denounced him to the military authorities, and another.

"That is my case, gentlemen of the jury. If, having heard the evidence and, under the direction of my lord, having taken cognizance of the law, you are convinced that this man failed in his duty of allegiance to our king and country, you will declare him guilty and he will be hanged. If there is a doubt in your minds you will acquit him. It must be one or the other. I shall now, with the help of my learned friends, call the evidence."

Chapter Two

I

COUNSEL for the prosecution called half a dozen witnesses before he put Gideon Fish into the box. Of these there were four whose evidence seemed to me of special interest. Two officers of the R.A.M.C. who had been in command at different periods of Martin's field ambulance, one in the desert, the other in Italy; a security man; and a N.A.A.F.I. servant, bartender in the canteen on the Christmas Eve that Mr. Kennington had dramatized so effectively in his opening speech.

The first, Martin's C.O. in Libya, was a pleasant youngish colonel, a member of the Royal College of Surgeons with a practice in London, called up on the outbreak of war to serve with the forces. He gave the accused a good character for his work as a hospital orderly. It had seemed to him a pity that a fully qualified medical man should waste his time on the humble tasks of scrubbing out bedpans, but Merriedew had seemed to prefer such manual jobs to the more interesting work of surgical dressings, blood transfusions, and so on, which he could have done had he chosen. Yes, he had been put in charge of the wounded prisoners at his own request. There had been some complaints of his overfriendly attitude towards these Germans but he had assumed this to be due to his religion and he himself had been too busy to enquire into the ethical principles of his hospital orderlies as long as they did their work properly. The prisoner's group were all conscientious objectors and had been very efficient. They were voluntary workers and received no pay, but were under military discipline, otherwise they would not have been there. Yes, they were civilians, but with the status of N.C.O.'s as far as their rations went, sleeping accommodation, and so on. No, they wore khaki but were not in military uniform. Yes, a somewhat peculiar arrangement, but prevalent in the Army. There were many such groups attached to military hospitals in North Africa, and other war areas. You had had occasion to caution the prisoners. He didn't know what he would have done had one of these voluntary workers been guilty of a grave misdemeanour — sent him home, probably. Their status was rather like that of nursing sisters; you would hardly put a nursing sister in irons, however outrageous her behaviour. Yes, the prisoner's treatment of the Germans had upset his group, but he himself had had only one fault to find with him. He drove himself too hard, and as a result was at times overwrought; but he wasn't the only one. They were all overworked and overwrought at moments. Life was no picnic in such units in the forward areas of the desert. They lived under canvas and were often on the move as the tide of battle flowed back and forth. Yes, they had been overrun in '42 by the enemy. One of Rommel's sorties in force had engulfed them. He and his staff had remained with their wounded. Yes, they had been of necessity in contact with some of the enemy formations. He didn't know if the accused had made friends with any of them; he might have done. As he spoke German he had been useful as an interpreter. The Germans they had had to do with had been very correct. They had thought they were winning the war, and were in a good humour. No, he had not received a visit from General Rommel, he was glad to say; but the German officers who had inspected his unit had been very civil. Yes, when the tide turned and Rommel's forces withdrew, his lot had found themselves once again without their own lines. Yes, they had been under fire for a bit and had had a few casualties. No, the accused had not lost his head or seemed overwrought at such moments. On the contrary, he was particularly cool when the bombs dropped; not reckless exactly, but unconcerned. Yes, he would describe him as indifferent to danger.

Mr. Kennington did not seem put out by the answers of his witness. He remarked that he was interested to hear that the accused had shown himself cool and collected under fire. But how did that fit in with his overwrought nervous state at other times? The witness didn't know how to explain it. He had never understood the man in the dock, had always felt there was something strange about him. A moody man, reserved, given to periods of intense depression, especially when nothing much was going on. But, as he had already said, efficient and never spared himself.

Yes, he had known of cases when German wounded had escaped, or been said to have escaped, during the fighting in the desert. It would not have been impossible. His own opinion was that many more Germans could have escaped had they wanted to especially after El Alamein. Large convoys of enemy prisoners coming back from the area of that battle were often in charge of a single British N.C.O. He had watched them from his tent as they passed down the track towards Mersa Matruh and Alexandria. His impression was that the Germans had no wish to find their way back to their own lines; they knew supper was waiting for them inside British barbed wire and didn't want to miss it.

The court was delighted to hear this, even some of the jury smiled. But Mr. Justice Collit's fingers twitched with irritation. Counsel for the Crown and the pleasant young Colonel continued their duet.

Did the witness recall any incident in regard to prisoners supposed to have escaped from his unit?

Yes, an incident had been reported to him. It had occurred during a rush. There had been a battle up the line, and the wounded were pouring in. It had been necessary to make room in the tents. Yes, the wounded were evacuated by ambulance, as far as railhead, and at night as a rule; it was safer at night. No, there was no road, properly speaking. There was only the one road along the coast; but there were tracks, and the track to railhead was marked. Even so, it wasn't difficult to get lost in that area. Anyone who had driven a truck or ambulance in Libya would know that. If you wanted to get lost, then of course it was easy. All you had to do was go west instead of east. There was nothing much to stop you. The desert was open, all the way.

All the way where?

To the enemy lines, their holes in the ground.

Had the incident he referred to been connected in any way with the prisoner at the bar?

Yes, it had been reported to him that the accused had volunteered to drive an ambulance-load of German wounded to railhead, but had never delivered them at their destination.

"Did you question him about this?"

"Yes, and accepted his explanation of what had occurred."

"And what did you decide had occurred?"

"The facts as reported to me were these: it was the accused's night off; he was on night duty; he would do six nights on duty, then sleep one night. This was his night to sleep, but in the rush he had stayed up, had volunteered to drive, as we were short of ambulance personnel, and had set out for railhead with four Germans all lightly wounded. They never turned up at railhead. The prisoner walked into my camp at sunrise, apparently suffering from concussion, and stated, when I questioned him later that day, that he didn't know what had happened. I accepted his story. The ambulance was found in a wadi a couple of days later minus a wheel. The German wounded were not found. Though the wadi in question was not on the way to railhead, but lay in the opposite direction between us and the Germans, it didn't occur to me to suspect

217

my orderly of connivance with the enemy. I was transferred two weeks later to another unit and forgot the incident."

Mr. Pringle, when he rose to cross-examine the witness, contented himself with asking him about the regulations in such
field ambulances as his own, regarding the treatment of
wounded prisoners of war.

They were based, the Colonel said, on the precepts laid
down in the Geneva Convention.

What were they?

The witness didn't know them by heart.

"But you know the gist of them, I take it, since you applied
them?"

"Certainly; they were the principles of common humanity."

"I would like you to be a little more precise." Mr. Pringle
blinked and pursed his lips. "Let me get at it this way: did you
starve your war prisoners?"

"Certainly not."

"Did you operate on them?"

"Obviously, when it was necessary."

"Under an anaesthetic?"

"Of course."

"You didn't cut off the legs of German wounded without
chloroform or some such merciful drug?"

"Such a thing was unheard of."

"You let them suffer, in other words, no more than was
inevitable?"

"That is so."

"You didn't neglect them?"

"They were treated, medically and surgically, precisely as
we treated our own men."

"And in other respects, did they receive the same treatment
as our wounded?"

"I don't understand the question."

218

"Perhaps you will understand this one: what were the German wounded given to eat?"

"The usual rations."

"Equal rations with our men, with the orderlies, for instance?"

"Yes, if their physical condition permitted."

"It was bully beef, I presume, mostly?"

"Yes, and tea and bread and jam."

"Jam as well, to go with the bread?"

"Yes."

"Suppose one of the German wounded had a large appetite and wanted an extra hunk of bread, would he get it?"

"They had all the bread they wanted."

"Or a second slice of bully beef? He could have that too?"

"Yes, I think so. Yes, certainly, if the M.O. allowed him a full diet."

"What about jam? Suppose he had a sweet tooth and, though a German, had a great liking for the excellent plum jam that was talked about, as I recall, in the House of Commons? Suppose this wounded enemy called for more jam?"

"I don't know about jam."

"Ah, you draw the line at jam. That is what I wanted to know. You drew the line somewhere, presumably, between the treatment accorded to our men and the German wounded, though I didn't know just where; but I know now. You drew it at jam. Our men could have extra jam, the enemy only the strict ration. But tell me this, would you have suspected one of your hospital orderlies of treachery if you had seen him give a war prisoner more than his exact portion of jam?"

"No, of course not."

"I thank you."

Mr. Pringle folded up, and the witness stood down. The prisoner in the dock had shown no sign of interest in these proceedings.

An N.C.O. of the R.A.S.C. followed. He had been in charge of transport in the field ambulance at the time of the incident of the wrecked ambulance, and Counsel for the defence reduced the value of his evidence to nil in my opinion. The witness stated that the accused had taken out the ambulance without his authority and he had been pretty well fed up over the whole business. Cross-examined by Pringle, he admitted that at such moments, with wounded arriving in a steady stream during the night, it was impossible to keep track of all his vehicles and not unusual for one or more of the Red Cross workers to help with the evacuations. But Kennington confined his questions for the most part to ascertaining the exact spot where the wrecked ambulance was found, and this he did with the help of a military map. The witness pointed out that the wadi in question was a good fifteen miles to the southwest of their own camp and on no track that could lead to railhead. It had been a clear night with a three-quarter moon, on the wane. Merriedew knew the area quite well and could not have taken the direction he did take in error. Asked by Pringle what he thought had actually happened, he said that his own explanation was what it had been at the time. Merriedew must have chosen to drive these Germans towards their own lines. At a given point in the desert he had let them out, then deliberately wrecked his ambulance and walked back to his own unit. Fifteen miles? Yes.

And how far were the German lines? He couldn't say. There were no lines, properly speaking — the area was fluid, the nearest German post might be another ten miles on, but the enemy patrols were active — one of them could easily have picked up the four men — Wouldn't they, in that case, have picked up their English driver as well, and taken him prisoner? Not if he was more useful to them in his own unit.

"I see, your theory is that the man on trial in this court was in league with the enemy, that he handed the four wounded prisoners over to a German patrol, was allowed to go free, turned round in his tracks, wrecked his ambulance in a convenient wadi and walked home, pretending to be suffering from concussion. Is that your theory?"

"Yes, it must have been something like that."

"Why do you think he chose this particular wadi?"

"It was as good a place as another. Deep sand, no one about."

"But was it so convenient? Why, if he did all this deliberately, didn't he drive himself back after he had handed over his prisoners, get onto the track that led to railhead and then wreck his ambulance nearer home?"

"Maybe there wasn't a nice deep wadi handy — or perhaps he didn't think of it."

"If he was as cunning as you make out, it seems to me that he would most certainly think of it. I put it to you that your theory doesn't hold water for one minute, that the only possible explanation of what occurred is that the wounded Germans knocked Martin Merriedew out, dropped him in the desert and made off toward the German lines, wrecking the ambulance themselves when they encountered one of their own patrols. What's wrong with that theory, can you tell me?"

"Nothing wrong with it except the prisoner himself."

"You refer to the man in the dock?"

"Yes."

"And you mean, just what, by this insinuation?"

"I mean that I didn't trust him."

"I see. You have worked out this theory of yours to fit in with your view of his character?"

"Well, it did fit in."

"How well did you know him?"

"Well enough."

"You had a lot to do with him?"

"Not a lot maybe."

"Did he often drive the wounded to railhead?"

"He did when I asked him."

"In his off time?"

"Yes."

"But it wasn't his job, was it?"

"No."

"He wasn't in any sense under your orders, was he?"

"No."

"He did it as a favour?"

"To help me out — yes."

"But you didn't trust him?"

"No."

II

Major Trumble, the Security Officer, was a stolid man and he gave his somewhat sensational evidence in a matter-of-fact manner. He informed the court that there had been a German agent masquerading as a British officer of the Royal Army Service Corps on the staff of Divisional Headquarters, the division to which the field ambulance in question was attached. He had been with the division for some months before he was suspected but he had been caught out eventually, tried by court-martial, and shot. No, not in the desert, in Italy. The war and the division had moved on by now. The period he spoke of was the winter of '44–'45. The German spy had passed under the name of John Banks. He held a temporary commission with the rank of captain and had been in charge of medical stores among other things. He had his own pick-up, and it was a part of his duties to visit such field units as the one to which the accused belonged every once in a way. How often would depend on the conditions prevailing. the numbers of wounded, the stores required, and so forth; or more probably, as it turned out, on the calls of his own private business. No, his movements were not supervised. He was his own driver.

He had to give in a work ticket, naturally, when he applied for petrol, but no one bothered much about checking mileage in that area, and the field hospital wasn't far from Divisional Headquarters, a matter of five miles or so. This man who called himself Banks had been perfectly free to come and go as he wished. Had he been questioned about his frequent visits to the field ambulance he could have proved that he went each time on a legitimate errand. A clever chap; said he was a Cockney; spoke English with no accent, Cockney or otherwise, well educated, excellent bookkeeper. But in the end Military Security, that is to say, the witness, had caught him out. The court would not expect details. The chap had proved to be a spy, and been shot. Yes, they had found a transmission set in his pick-up, and he had confessed to being a German by birth, and a secret enemy agent. He had seemed indeed to be proud of it.

"What had this to do with the prisoner at the bar?"

A book had been found among the spy's belongings, with an inscription on the fly-leaf, in the prisoner's hand, and his signature.

"What book was it?"

A small book called *Areopagitica, and other Prose Works, by John Milton.*

"Was this the book?" Counsel handed a slim volume to the witness, who opened it.

"Yes."

How did he recognize it?

By the writing inside.

Perhaps he would be good enough to read what was written to the court?

"There's a date: March 21, '44. Then the words: 'To my friend, John Banks, from Martin Merriedew,' and the number of his unit."

"You recognized the signature?"

"No, I'd never seen it before, but I knew where to find the unit."

"What did you do with this little book?"

"Took it with me to the hospital and showed it to the C.O."

"And did he identify the handwriting on the fly-leaf?"

"No, the accused identified it himself."

"In your presence?"

"Yes. He has sent for, and he admitted having given the book to the man who called himself Banks."

Mr. Kennington waved a large white hand at Mr. Pringle, murmured, "Your witness," and sat down.

Mr. Pringle seemed to hesitate, he fumbled at his dangling eyeglasses, his manner, when he spoke, was mild.

"What did my client say when you told him this sensational story about a man who was presumably a friend of his being shot as a spy?"

"I didn't tell him."

"You didn't tell him that his friend was discovered to be a spy?"

"No."

"Or how you happened to be in possession of the book? Didn't he ask about that?"

"Yes. But there was no need to tell him the truth. On the contrary, it was inadvisable at that stage to say anything about the affair."

"At what stage?"

"At that stage in the proceedings."

"What proceedings?"

"The proceedings we proposed to take."

"Against my client?"

"No, against his friend Banks. A court-martial was pending, we might have wanted to call the accused to give evidence."

"What kind of evidence? Did you hope to get evidence of

224

complicity? Did you suppress the truth wanting to catch him out too? Was that it?"

"No. He might have been wanted as a witness, that was all, to begin with anyhow."

"But he wasn't called, was he, as a 'witness'?"

"No."

"Why not?"

"He was already gone before the court-martial took place."

"Gone where?"

"Home, to England."

"I see. Let's go back a bit. What did you tell him, in place of the truth, when you showed him this book? How did you explain the possession of it?"

"I told him his friend Banks was reported missing, and that I had found the book among his effects."

"Is that all you told him?"

"Yes."

"How did he take the news?"

"He was upset."

"Did he ask any questions?"

"He asked me to let him know if his friend turned up."

"And what did you say to that?"

"I said he'd hear, like as not, in due course."

"He didn't ask any more questions?"

"No."

"He seemed satisfied with your statement?"

"Yes."

"But upset you say — Just how upset was he?"

"I don't know how to answer the question."

"I'll put it differently. Was he frightened when you showed him the book and told him his friend Captain Banks was missing?"

"I don't know if he was frightened or not."

"If he knew all along that Banks was a spy and if he himself was in league with him, wouldn't he have been alarmed to hear that he was missing?"

"I suppose so."

"He would have guessed, wouldn't he, if he was the man's accomplice, that there was more in this visit of yours than you disclosed?"

"I've no doubt he did."

"In that case, wouldn't he have betrayed at least some sign of curiosity and anxiety in regard to your statement?"

"I daresay."

"But he didn't?"

"He was upset, as I said."

"But he didn't ask you any further questions?"

"No."

"He merely acknowledged that he had given the volume to his friend Banks?"

"Yes."

"He did acknowledge quite openly and naturally that Banks was his friend?"

"Yes. He couldn't very well do otherwise, seeing what was written in the book."

"But he showed no sign of being frightened, betrayed, in fact, nothing more than the normal emotion any man would feel at being told that a friend of his was reported missing in a forward area of the war zone? Am I putting it fairly? Would you agree to that?"

"Yes."

"Just one more question. Was there anything about this book other than the inscription on the fly-leaf that made you suspicious?"

"No."

"You consider it a harmless book in itself?"

"I suppose so."

"Did you read any of it?"

226

"No."

"You didn't look at it while you had it in your possession?"

"No, only at the fly-leaf. I may have turned a few pages."

"But it didn't strike you as doubtful or dangerous, or indeed in any way interesting as a piece of writing?"

"No."

"In fact you have no idea what it is about?"

"No."

"I thank you."

Mr. Pringle sat down, but Mr. Kennington had a further question to ask.

"You have said that the accused was upset when you showed him the book and told him his friend was missing, but that he asked you no questions as to how you had come by the volume. Is that right?"

"Yes."

"What impression did the accused make on you at the time? Can you be a little more definite about that? Was he flustered?"

"No, I thought him a pretty cool customer."

"No more questions."

The witness was now allowed to stand down, and was followed by a grizzled little man with a red face and fierce eyebrows. A major this time. He had succeeded the pleasant Colonel whom we had already heard, as C.O. of Martin's field hospital in Italy. He didn't give the accused a good character. Too erratic. Too nervy. One of those religious chaps; held prayer meetings in his tent, or some such nonsense, but didn't know how to look after himself. Always overdoing it. The witness wasn't a bit surprised when he went off the rails.

Counsel for the Crown asked what he meant.

Talking pacifism, running down the war to the men.

What men?

The men in hospital and outside. The witness had discovered after the dust-up that he'd been at it for a long time.

"What dust-up?"

"The dust-up in the N.A.A.F.I. canteen on Christmas Eve, when he was reported to me for inciting the men to mutiny."

"Who reported this?"

"The man in charge of the bar in the canteen was the first. Then one of his own group came along, a Red Cross chap called Gideon Fish."

"What did you do?"

"I had the man up."

"Which man?"

"The man in the dock, Martin Merriedew, and questioned him. He'd been manhandled and didn't look pretty, so I made other enquiries. They'd beaten him up and chucked him out of the canteen, and quite right too, in my opinion. So I handed him over to the Military Police."

"Just a minute. Had you had any trouble with the Military Police in regard to the accused before this?"

"Not with the police, but a security officer had been to see me."

"Do you see this officer in court?"

"Yes."

"You identify him as the same who came to see you?"

"Yes."

"What did he come about?"

"He wanted to question the accused concerning a book."

"Did you see the book?"

"Yes."

"Is this it?"

The Milton was identified again, and the gist of what the security man had told us was repeated. Mr. Kennington then asked when this interview had taken place.

"Some days, as I remember, before the dust-up I'm talking about."

"How many days?"

"Two or three."

"The prisoner was still carrying on with his duties in your hospital?"

"Yes."

"No accusation had been made against him?"

"No."

"The Security Officer went off with the little book, and you heard no more about it?"

"Not at the time."

"Had you known this so-called Captain Banks?"

"I'd seen him about."

"He used to come to the hospital?"

"Yes."

"Did you know he was a friend of the accused?"

"No, but I had seen them together."

"Let us consider now the affair in the canteen. You questioned the prisoner at the bar, and then handed him over to the Military Police. Why?"

"The N.A.A.F.I. man and his own chap Fish had both reported to me that he had been inciting the troops to mutiny; and he admitted the truth of the accusation when I questioned him."

"The man at the bar confessed to having incited the troops in this canteen to mutiny?"

"As good as."

"I am afraid that that is not quite good enough for the court. What did he say? Give us his own words as exactly as possible."

"I don't remember his exact words. They sounded like nonsense to me. To tell the truth, I thought he'd gone off his head."

"You can't recall anything that he said?"

"I remember one thing."

"What was it?"

"It was a piece of pure insolence."

"Please repeat it."

"He asked me who I was, and what authority I had over him."

"You can't give me his exact words?"

"As near as I can remember, they were: 'I told them the truth. What right have you to question me?'"

"Did you see him again after that?"

"Haven't laid eyes on him since, till today."

"How was that?"

"He was sent home."

"And you had no more to do with him?"

"I made my report to the Advocate-General at G.H.Q. and had one interview with him on the case."

"With the Advocate-General?"

"Yes. He asked my opinion. I gave it. I said I considered the man a religious crank and a lunatic. Anyhow he was a civilian. The best thing the Army could do with him was to wash their hands of him, and send him home; and that's what they did."

Counsel then asked if, in his opinion, it would have been possible for a member of his hospital unit to have forwarded information to the enemy, and the witness said yes, in his opinion it would have been perfectly possible. They were in Italy, after all, quartered on a population that seemed friendly enough once the British marched up the road, but for all anyone knew the whole area was in cahoots with the enemy. These people had been on the other side less than a month before. What was to prevent any one of the I-ti peasants meeting a spy in our forces over a bottle of wine in a café, and going off up the road with his cart full of turnips and a message tucked inside his boot? Impossible to keep tab on the local inhabitants in those mountains.

The Major, when he stepped down, left an impression in court of a nation disrupted by distress, defeat and confusion under cover of which Martin Merriedew might have talked any day in the week to any number of enemy agents. I knew that part of Italy; I had been there with Camilla, but we had been young then and at peace. When Martin was there it was winter, the roads running up the spine of Italy had been choked with guns, the villages along them disembowelled, the farmsteads broken under their mantles of snow. I pictured him going about his work under straining canvas among the dead and the dying, while the mountains shuddered and echoed to the roar of the guns. Did he slip out at night to visit the enemy in some squalid café that showed a little light amid the rubble and filth? The thing was grotesque.

The next witness was a very different type from any we had seen. He was graceful and timid. He had a mop of carroty curls and a girlish voice. He was so nervous that he started to giggle after he had taken the oath; and I swear he was on the point of saying, "Yes, dear," more than once to counsel for the Crown.

Yes, he had been in charge of the bar in the N.A.A.F.I. canteen in question on Christmas Eve of '44. It had been frightful, quite frightful.

What had been frightful?

The weather, to begin with — a regular blizzard, and then the row. And they'd made the hut so nice, too, with holly and streamers and a Christmas tree. It had really looked a treat.

"We can imagine it; but I must ask you to confine your remarks to answering my questions."

"So sorry!" The witness wriggled.

"Did you see the prisoner that night?"

"What prisoner? Oh, yes, of course. I forgot who — Yes, he came in just after the pantomime, with his friend."

"What friend?"

"The chap who was always with him, a Red Cross chap, called Fish."

"Did they often come to the canteen?"

"Yes, they'd come in for a bottle of beer once or twice a week."

"Had they made trouble in your canteen before?"

"Not real trouble."

"Well, what happened on Christmas Eve? Just tell us in your own words, but in as few of them as possible."

"Nothing happened for a bit, not to notice. They each had a beer. There was an awful squash, as you can imagine, but the boys were quieter than usual. No ragging, just singing. They were homesick, you see, it being Christmas, and a snowstorm outside shaking the hut something dreadful. Then I did notice that the prisoner wasn't joining in the singing, he was standing up against the wall near the bar, holding his beer, with a face as white as a sheet and his eyes staring — really, he looked quite mad, quite raving, you know. I thought, 'That chap's going to give trouble,' and I looked round for his friend, but I couldn't see the other one, and I was wondering what I had better do when the boys round the stove started up that song, 'Quiet night, silent night,' and the prisoner flung down his bottle of beer, and dived into the middle of the crowd round the stove, shouting, 'Stop! That's not your song, and you've no right to sing it. It belongs to the men you call your enemies. They're singing it now over there on the other side. They've a better right to it than you, haven't they, if one of their people wrote it? But here's an idea. Why don't we go over there and sing all together?'

"The boys were so surprised that they'd stopped when he shouted, but then one of them laughed, and he turned on him like a tiger — really he looked quite terrible. 'It's no joke,' he yelled. 'Or if it is, the joke is on you, and it's being played by the devil. What do you think you're doing here? Who sent you out here with orders to kill those chaps and be killed? You think you are fighting for God, for your king and your country. It's a lie. You're being fooled. Why do you do it? Why go on with it? Those men up the road aren't your enemies, they're your fellow men and as helpless as you. Come, and I'll show you. Come, follow me!'

"They'd all been like paralysed up to then, but suddenly they went for him. There was pandemonium. That's all I know."

III

Martin Merriedew had shown no flicker of interest while these witnesses gave their evidence; and he showed none when Gideon Fish stepped briskly into the box. He was quiet as a dead man.

I had got used to his dreadful, lost, unchanging face. My eyes, continually dragged back, were familiar now with his inscrutable head. I could see that the skull wasn't bald. It was merely shaved, and its dome bone-white like the skin of his face and hands. I could even detect, as if it were an all but obliterated drawing under the transparent livid bones, the shape of a face I remembered, but I was watching to see if there would be any change in his expression when his old friend took the stand; and there was none. The gouged eyes didn't turn towards the witness box. They weren't blind, a dark light seemed to shine out from under the jutting brows, but the steady gaze was fixed on a point at a great distance, and the whole long motionless figure, perhaps because his clothes were the same grey colour as the shadows on his face, appeared far away.

Gideon Fish, on the contrary, came so close when he took the stand that the effect was of a powerful impact. I could see that his eyes were bloodshot and could hear him breathe. His hold on the rail in front of him was so tight that the knuckles of his large hands were white. A handsome man, hideously handsome, swarthy, with a smooth dark narrow head and a heavy passionate mouth.

"I swear by Almighty God that the evidence I shall give shall be the truth . . ."

233

He had a fine resounding voice, the trained voice of a public speaker and parliamentarian. Why not? He had been a Member of Parliament for thirteen years before he met the prisoner. He had represented the Central Division of this very city of Greymouth in the House of Commons, having won the seat for Labour in 1924, and had held it until '37, when he resigned his parliamentary duties. He gave us these facts about himself in a rapid, biting tone, explaining with no sign of regret or confusion that he had resigned his seat and made over the income from his family business to his brothers, in order to throw in his lot with the man at the bar, and keep the rules of his group. Yes, one of the rules was to give up one's property. The members of the Merriedew group were attempting to put into practice the principles of true communism. He had been interested in the experiment. It had never, so far as he knew, been tried in the modern world, no, not even in Russia. No, he had never been a member of the Communist Party. He had been attracted to the prisoner's brand of communism because it was nonpolitical. No, the group, as far as he knew, had had no political affiliations. Its leader had professed no interest in politics, so he himself had given them up.

What more had he given up for the sake of the prisoner at the bar? Well, one might say his public. He had been a leader himself in the left wing of his political party; and he had taken second place to the prisoner on joining his band. Yes, he supposed he had been what one would call a revolutionary.

What it all came to was that he had given up his revolution for the sake of the accused, as well as his independence, his life in fact; he had changed his mode of life. No, he had not found the austerity intolerable. There had been a certain excitement in not knowing where your next meal was coming from; that is to say, it had been exciting for a time. The prisoner created excitement wherever he was. He had been an inspiring leader. What the witness had found galling was the idea of

234

begging, of being a beggar. It was one of the prisoner's fixed ideas. Humiliation was a part of his prescribed discipline. He had gone one better than the Communists. He always went to extremes in everything, but he had the gift of inspiring devotion. Unfortunately, the idea had proved impracticable. The witness had been obliged to recognize the fact even if the prisoner hadn't. The accused in his opinion was a visionary and a dreamer — or so he had believed — with no sense of reality, but with great gifts; the gift above all others of making men believe in the impossible, in an unrealizable world. He had called it the Kingdom of Heaven on Earth. Yes, the witness had believed in him. But now, though counsel didn't allow him to say so, he wanted him to hang, and was there to see to it that he did.

Mr. Kennington's junior was a chubby man, rosy, pleasant, and comfortable; but he seemed to be nervous of his witness. He handled the elastic individual with the biting voice and alert eyes as if he were afraid that the saturnine head might snarl at him or even tear him with its teeth. They were strong, long, and gleaming white.

"What was it that first attracted you to the prisoner? How did you come to join him?"

"I heard him speak for the first time in the early summer of 1937. I liked what he said and the way he said it. He was a powerful speaker, with a shining presence. He used a different terminology from mine, but I believed we had the same ideas. I wanted a social upheaval that would do away with class privilege and poverty. He was going all out for the Kingdom of Heaven. His appeal was to the heart, not the mind, but it came to the same thing, or so it seemed to me, so I threw in my lot with him. Then I grew to love him." The witness held out apologetic hands. "He was a very beautiful man. He had, as I have said, a shining presence." The dark eyes flashed towards the silent figure in the dock.

Someone sniggered. Charles rapped on his desk. His sceptical gaze hadn't taken the direction indicated, it scanned the court with a faint look of disgust, then came back to the witness.

Counsel cleared his throat. "Was it necessary to resign your seat in the House of Commons?"

"To be precise it was not necessary, but he demanded it. He said that I was wasting my time in the House. I agreed with him. You were obliged to agree with him, or clear out. He was very persuasive, very convincing, very urgent; and always quite certain that he was right."

"Did that annoy you?"

"No. I saw that it was necessary for the others. A leader must lead. None of the others questioned his authority. He exacted obedience and got it. My position was somewhat different; he gave me a certain degree of responsibility; when the others quarrelled among themselves he would leave me to settle their disputes."

"And did you?"

"Yes."

"Although you didn't always see eye to eye with him, you supported him?"

"Yes."

"But you didn't always approve of his methods or agree with him?"

"No."

"On what did you disagree?"

Witness hesitated. He opened his hands, looked at them, then clenched them again. Then, as if compelled to speak in spite of himself, he flung up his head and said: "We used to argue at first about ways and means. I wanted action. He had power. I wanted him to exert that power. He could have moved thousands. He could have done great things. He wouldn't. And after a time I gave in. I obeyed his slightest wish and hung on his words as they all did."

"You had doubts about him at this period?"

"No. That is to say — no, I can't call them doubts."

"What would you call them?"

"I will call them reservations. I didn't doubt his integrity, but I began again to have doubts of his wisdom and his emotional stability."

"What gave rise to these doubts?"

"His moods; his dislike of his own profession."

"You mean medicine?"

"Yes. He had quite definitely the gift of healing. People flocked to his clinic. He closed it down, gave it up, said he didn't want to be known as a healer. His dislike of publicity became an obsession."

Charles was fidgeting; I could tell by the way his fingers twitched; but he didn't intervene, and Mr. Pringle made no objection, so counsel continued.

"Well, go on. You had doubts of the prisoner's common sense and stability?"

"Yes. It was the same with his public speaking as with his medicine. He declared it was useless. He said he was becoming just another loud-speaker, blaring words into ears deafened by noise. He had periods of black depression, would shut himself up for days, and speak to no one, go without food; then suddenly emerge, call for wine, and we would sit down to feast from an empty larder."

"How did you manage that?"

"I managed. But it was all very difficult. He had become known locally as a saint and healer. We turned scores of the sick away. Then came Munich, and he was galvanized by his hatred of war into action. He began an anti-war campaign. He stumped the country. By the spring of '39 he was so obsessed by his idea of stopping the war that I feared for his sanity."

"But you were a conscientious objector yourself, weren't you?"

237

"Yes, but I didn't seriously believe that we could stop the war."

"And he did?"

"Yes. That is to say, he knew it was practically impossible, but said it was only the impossible that was worth doing. Then in August they asked him to leave the city."

"Who asked him?"

"The Mayor and Town Council of Warrington."

"Was he living there?"

"Yes, at the time."

"And did he go?"

"Yes, we left together, but not at once. We were packing up when war was declared. We left some weeks later."

"You volunteered as a group to go overseas?"

"Yes."

"And were sent out as Red Cross hospital orderlies, and posted eventually to a field hospital in the Western Desert? Is that correct?"

"Yes."

"You were under his orders in the field ambulance?"

"Yes, he was the head of our group with the courtesy rank of a lieutenant but messed with us. I was his second-in-command."

"You ran your unit between you?"

"Yes."

"You were still intimate at this time?"

"Yes. We shared a small hut. He did night duty usually. The arrangement suited us both."

"Was he, in your opinion, a good head of this unit?"

"In some ways yes, but not altogether."

"What was wrong with him?"

"He was too emotional — too much affected by the horror. We got used to it, he didn't. We dealt usually with the worst cases and had a fifty per cent mortality, until we took over the wounded prisoners. — A dozen deaths in a night in our ward was the usual thing, but he seemed to feel that each one was his special responsibility and his personal loss. I was afraid that he would break down under the strain and was glad at first when the C.O. put us in charge of the German wounded. I thought he wouldn't take it so hard when they popped off. I was mistaken. I began to suspect there was something seriously wrong with him."

"Just what do you mean by that? Did you think he was mad?"
"No, disloyal."
"Disloyal to whom — to yourself and your unit?"
"No, to the Army, to our own men."
"When did you first suspect your leader, as you called him, of disloyalty?"

"I didn't suspect him for a long time; but I began to distrust his attitude immediately the first batch of German wounded arrived."

"Didn't he look after them properly?"
"Oh, yes, much too well."
"Can you amplify that?"
"I can. His kindness to them was altogether excessive. They despised him for it, and made a fool of him. They would shout at him to fetch things, then when he brought the bedpan, or whatever it was, they would say they didn't want it and laugh at him. But he never ticked them off or reported them. The worse they behaved the nicer he was to them. Then sometimes they would be ashamed of themselves and make friends with him."

"How did you know this, if he took over at night when you went off day duty?"

"I used to stay on to help him for a part of the night if there was a rush of work, and sometimes he would talk to me."

"What about?"

"About the horror he felt of the whole thing, how he hated the war and loved his patients."

"I thought you said his patients were the enemy wounded?"

"They were."

"And he told you he loved them?"

"Yes And it was true, he did. He showed it in the way he treated them, especially of course the bad cases. Several died in his arms. Tears would stream down his face when this happened."

"You didn't like that?"

"No, I thought it dangerous and silly."

"Did you tell him so?"

"I told him I thought it was dangerous."

"What did he say?"

"He said it was more dangerous to hate your enemies than to love them."

"Did you ask him to explain what he meant by that?"

"Yes, but he told me to think it out for myself, and if I couldn't, then to mind my own business."

"You were not getting on too well by this time?"

"No."

"You quarrelled?"

"No, we didn't quarrel. I told myself that he was soft and left it at that; but we had a serious disagreement over a young German officer."

"How was that?"

"It was during the battle of El Alamein. The hospital was a shambles, everything in confusion, all of us run off our legs, our men mixed up with wounded Germans, officers, other ranks, all pell-mell. We'd been giving blood transfusions all day and had run out of plasma, when the German came through from the operating tent with a chit pinned to his blanket ordering a transfusion. He was a lieutenant in the Hussars, and quite young. I could see he was very bad, grey in the face, pinched nostrils, ice-cold flesh. I knew the signs, but I couldn't carry out my orders. We had no blood left to give him except our own. We were all donors of course, but we couldn't give ours very well without going off duty for a bit. It meant being laid up for at least half a day if you gave a couple of pints of blood. And mine wasn't much good. I'm B group on the blood count; Merriedew is A, and it was his turn; but he was already booked for one of our own officers who was on the operating table having his leg off. So I told the stretcher-bearers to put the German down behind the screen at the end of the tent, where we always put them to die in peace. But Merriedew said no, we could save his life. I said we couldn't, we had run out of plasma. He said he knew that, he would give the blood, he was ready, and to get on with it, there was no time to lose. I then said what about our own chap in the operating room, he was an officer in a crack regiment, a captain; and Martin — I mean the prisoner — said that would be all right, our chap wouldn't need it, and if he did he'd do both. I told him he couldn't; he was below par already, he'd never be able to give two lots of blood, four pints was too much for anyone. 'The Captain,' I said, 'is one of our own people. This boy is an enemy, though you seem to forget it.' 'He isn't my enemy,' Martin said. 'Do what I tell you and be quick about it.' "

"And you did?"

"Yes."

"And did the German survive?"

"Yes, he was evacuated."

"What about the other, the British Captain?"

"He never came through to the ward. He must have died on the operating table."

The court had listened spellbound to this story. Now Charles leaned forward.

"So the prisoner was not required to give two lots of blood in one day?"

"No, my lord."

"Tell me, as an expert in these harrowing matters, could he have done such a thing or was it a vain boast?"

"I could not say, my lord."

"But what is your opinion? For what it is worth, I would like to have it. This is a strange case, and because it is a strange case I have shown great leniency to counsel. Pray grant me the same courtesy."

Gideon Fish hesitated for the first time, and for the first time seemed uncomfortable.

"Martin Merriedew," he said at last, "was a man of splendid physique. He could have done it, but it might have cost him his life."

"I thank you." Charles leaned back, he looked at the prisoner. Did he murmur the words, or did I imagine that he said to himself: "He couldn't do it now."

Chapter Three

I

CHARLES adjourned the court at this point, it was four-thirty by the big round clock in the yellow oak balustrade opposite the bench and I fled to avoid meeting Francis. Edward and Michael Merriedew were waiting outside, to be called as witnesses for the defence, but my brother could only listen, and watch. From his high place in the front row of the Sheriff's gallery, leaning far out with his head hanging down, his concentrated effort of attention had twisted his face into something inhuman. He had looked like a hawk, ready to swoop, and I knew that his helplessness gave the last exquisite touch of agony to his suspense.

But what could he have said on behalf of the man whom he had not laid eyes on since '36 that would be relevant to the charge of treason? He could have sworn that during all the years of their youth, when he and the prisoner had been friends, it was Martin Merriedew who had insisted on their obligation to their own people. He could have told how it was Merriedew who had stipulated, when they signed their pact to dedicate their joint lives to the service of their fellow men, that their first duty was to England. But that had been twenty years ago. A pact entered into by a couple of schoolboys could hardly be admitted as evidence when the pact itself had come to nothing. The fact that the Earl of Greymouth had been a great friend of the accused and still believed in him might just possibly have told in favour of the prisoner with the jury, though I doubt it, had they remained friends; but the truth would have come out that they had not met once since 1936, and had held views dur-

243

ing the war diametrically opposed. Of what use would it have been for Greymouth, the ex-pilot of the R.A.F., to have declared under oath that he believed the prisoner to have been throughout the war a loyal subject of the King? The words on the grave of the Unknown Soldier in Westminster Abbey gave the lie to him. Every War Memorial in every village in England shouted him down. What could Francis or Michael hope to do for Martin if he was already judged and condemned by our glorious dead? But was he? And if he was not, if they in their graves were ready to rise up in his defence, how could Pringle make the living understand or believe this? The dead were glorious because they had given their lives. What more can a man do than lay down his life for his friend? But they were mute, and the law of the land was the law of the living. Suppose the sons, husbands, and brothers of the people who crowded the court were to come running out of their graves to storm the place, and demand that a stop be put to the worship of death? The truth would be unbearable. Perhaps all truth was unbearable. In the meantime I was afraid to speak to my brother, and this in itself would have given the hue and feel of a bad dream to the slowly advancing, revolving drama that had kept turning as it inched forward, turning and turning round the solitary man in the dock, opening and shutting out flashes of truth as if the intermittent beam of a lighthouse was playing on his closed face.

But there had been other factors that created a sense of unreality, while contributing to my bewilderment and distress. The collision of two kinds of light, the strong warm dizzying light from the great heavy hanging electric fittings, pushing away but not blotting out the cold false daylight beyond the high blank windows behind the gallery; the easy way of Counsel with each other, and their rustling papers; the apparent but very deceptive lack of formality about the decorous proceedings, the intimacy and quiet of the whole thing, the total absence of excitement that made the court into a family gathering in a drawing room, of bewigged gentlemen blandly ignoring the intrusion of strangers who stared and eavesdropped. Even the jury were paid only a perfunctory attention now and then. And with all the slow mild talk being concerned with a discussion of the prisoner's misdeeds, his presence, more than any, was ignored for decency. One couldn't really call a man names while he was there, it simply wasn't done; so they had all agreed, it seemed, to pretend that he wasn't present. And he had helped them in this by seeming to be more like a ghost than a breathing human being. With it all, the sense of the slowly revolving wheels of the law had acted like a drug, so that one's stupefied brain forgot that under the cosy appearances of orderly well-being a naked pointing finger was swinging like a metronome between life and death.

A police inspector, an old acquaintance, taking me under his wing in the narrow dark corridor behind the bench, said there was a bit of a crowd outside, hostile on the whole to the prisoner; they were keeping these at a distance, of course; but he had thought it best to send my car round to the back. Unfortunate, he said, showing me the way, that the accused had been so well known in the town. I might have heard of him in the old days before the war. Yes, I said, I had heard of him; I had in fact known him many years ago. "Fancy that!" The Inspector's face had denied all curiosity as he put me into the car. "Good day, your Ladyship. We'll have the pleasure of seeing you in the morning, no doubt?"

I gave tea to the Mayoress and a number of local ladies in the sedate anonymous drawing room of the Judge's lodgings, as I was expected to do. I had done it all so many times before that there was no need to keep one's mind on the business of courtesy. Habit and the exquisite efficiency of Mr. Fairchild saw me smoothly through.

Charles came in for his usual glass of sherry when the ladies

245

had gone, and gave me a leisured opportunity, as he sipped, to remark on the day's proceedings did I wish to. I refrained. We were eight at dinner: the Sheriff and wife, the Lord Lieutenant and wife, Tim Beresford and Bill Cummins; two tables of bridge, and I didn't mean to linger long in the dim old room after our guests had left. It had dignity. It was rich in old panelling, and decent as to brownish velvet hangings and shaded light. Thackeray would have given an air to it. Charles Lamb might have made it convivial. Dickens could have used it as a suitable background for his sinister Mr. Tulkingborn but to me it was suffocating, and Charles and I seemed to be imprisoned in it together.

I was beginning to realize how much had happened to me in court and how far I had travelled, but I didn't feel that I could tell Charles about that. Instinct warned me not to inflict on him any part of the turmoil in my own mind; for I had been travelling back a long way into the past, and what had been happening to me was the re-emergence of a swarm of details long since forgotten, thick as a cloud of locusts, of the boy and the youth who had been welded and beaten by the years into the strange iron man in the dock. On the other hand, it would, I felt, be awkward, if not positively dangerous, to say nothing. Silence would be taken by Charles to mean doubt, fear, the hint of a passionate partisanship, the old, eternal feminine emotional response to a problem that he despised in general in women, and dreaded in me. So I waited just long enough to reassure him, as I believed, lighting a last cigarette, and said in what I flattered myself was a casual tone that it was a bore about the jury.

"Oh? What's wrong with them?" Charles was lying back in an easy chair, his thin legs crossed, his knees rather higher than his head, an idle elegant foot dangling.

"Only that they may not come to this with open minds, since they belong to the place."

"Merriedew never, as far as I know, lived here. He is more intimately associated with Warrington. This town was the hunting ground of the chief witness for the Crown."

"I know, but they both came quite often, and together."

"Then the partisans of the one should offset the other, presumably." Charles passed a weary hand over his face; but I went on.

"There was the beginning of a legend. Merriedew performed so-called miracles and made trouble. I remember seeing letters in the Greymouth *Mail* from hysterical women he had cured. Then there was a scandal, a case of a child who died. He was blamed for not sending the child to hospital; there was, I believe, an enquiry. It was the occasion of his being debarred by the B.M.A."

"I have seen the reports, my dear." Charles's tone was mild but dry. "The police didn't blame him for criminal negligence; the medicos did. But he wasn't crossed off the register — he merely stopped practicing professionally."

"Oh, then you know all about his past history in this town?"

"I know, I believe, what I need to know. Enough anyhow to discount the exaggeration of the hysterical women you refer to. There are none, as you know, on the jury."

"Exactly."

"You would have preferred it had there been?"

"Oh, no. But I seem to have heard that he broke up more than one family."

"How? By running off with the wife? That sort of thing doesn't appear in the police reports."

"No, nothing of that sort. They left their husbands and children and the kitchen sink to lead, as I understand, the good life, and the husbands didn't like it."

"I don't quite see, my child, why you bring this up now. If it is in the interests of pure justice, I can assure you that the accused has not messed about the womenfolk of the citizens

247

on the jury. The court is not careless about such things."

I felt myself flushing. "He never, I'm certain of it, messed women about."

Charles eyed me a moment in silence. His gaze was speculative; then he sighed. "If you wish to imply that the Merriedew case is being unfairly handled, I would remind you that he had the right and the opportunity to refuse any or all of the men on the jury."

"But he wouldn't be aware of any animosity. If he had ever noticed it, he would have forgotten."

Charles took this in for a moment in a new silence, and the room seemed to tighten round us.

"Do you feel, then," he asked presently, "that you know him?"

"No. But I feel as if I had got to know something about him today."

I waited for him to speak again and question me if he wished to. It was my turn now to be courteous. It was only fair to give him his opportunity to upbraid or snub me; but he did neither, so I said good night and went up to my room. How careful we were of each other!

I didn't sleep much. The swarm of memories tormented me. I kept wondering about Francis. Where was he? Had he gone back to Crabbe for the night or was he staying with Edward and Michael in a hotel? Wherever he was, he too would be lying awake. I could lift the receiver, there was a telephone by my bed; but what could I say to him? And Charles would hear me. Charles had not asked the question I dreaded. Had he done so, I would have been bound to tell him that a slowly rising surge of emotion was overwhelming my reason. And if I had been obliged to admit this, then for sheer decency I would be equally obliged to leave Greymouth and go home. But he had let me off. We could still pretend that I too was interested only in justice.

He kept his light on for some time. He was probably fiddling with one of his bits of Greek translation. But Mr. Kennington was undoubtedly snoring under a comfortable near-by roof. And Mr. Pringle? I found that I could entertain for a brief moment the shadow of a reassuring suspicion that Mr. Pringle too might be sharing my troubled vigil; but the shadow vanished as I remembered the neat wigs under the bright warm light, heard again the rustle of papers, and saw Theodore Kennington lay a large complacent hand on Mr. Pringle's narrow irritable shoulder before they took their seats. This case for them was no matter of life and death, it wasn't even a question of pure justice. It was a contest and a game, and one of the two, perhaps even both, would be crowned with laurels at the end of it.

II

Mr. Kennington took over from his junior next morning, putting Gideon Fish back on the stand and going over with him the story we had heard of the escaped ambulance-load of prisoners. All the witness had to add to the pleasant Colonel's evidence was his own impression that the accused man had been exceedingly friendly with the four Germans, and that he had thought it very odd on the part of his colleague to offer to drive an ambulance that night to railhead when he would have been so much better employed at lending a hand in the ward. Counsel for the Crown didn't appear to think much of the story. He said it all sounded, at this distance and in this place, rather far-fetched and flimsy. Indeed he suggested to the bench that if his Lordship found there was no case on this point to go to the jury he wouldn't take it to heart. The scene in the N.A.A.F.I. canteen on Christmas Eve was another thing altogether. There we had a serious and strongly substantiated accusation of an attempt to spread disaffection among the troops and incite them to mutiny in the midst of a desperate battle.

Could the witness tell them anything about what had happened that night?

Yes. The prisoner had begun to spread disaffection among the men at first on the quiet. He had got a number of them in turn into corners, and had been telling them they were fools to go on fighting. Who would father their children if they got themselves killed? They thought they were fighting for their country and for victory; but there would be no country left worth fighting for in the end, and no victory. There was no such thing as victory in modern warfare. There was nothing ahead of them but defeat, misery, regret, and a great weariness. Let them put a stop to it while there was still something left to love and enjoy.

"You heard him say these things?"

"Yes."

"Why didn't you stop him?"

"I tried to. He wouldn't listen. He shouldered me aside and told me, as he did so often during those days, to mind my own business. He was in an excitable state. I thought it best to avoid a row."

"But there was a row?"

"Yes. He suddenly shouted at the crowd round the stove to stop singing Christmas hymns, and they went for him."

"Do you remember what he said to anger them?"

"It sounded like a rigmarole to me. Something about following him, laying down their arms, and going with him up to the German lines."

"And they threw him out?"

"Yes."

"And you with him?"

"I went with him, yes. I tried to protect him."

"And did you?"

"To some extent, but he was knocked about."

"Then what happened?"

250

"The C.O. sent for him next morning."

"Were you present at the interview?"

"No."

"Did you see him again?"

"No. I was in the ward on duty when he came back to our tent to collect his things."

"Did he collect all his things?"

"No."

"You found that he had gone, but left some of his belongings behind in the tent that you shared with him?"

"Yes, he had left some books, extra clothing, things of that sort."

"Any letters?"

"Only one."

"A letter addressed to him?"

"No, a letter he had written."

"Was that the letter you sent to the Home Office?"

"Yes."

"There were no others?"

"No, no papers of any kind."

"How did you know that he had written the letter you found?"

"It was in his handwriting."

The letter was then put in evidence. Bill Cummins handed it up to Charles. I could have snatched it before it was passed on to the witness.

"Is this the letter?"

"Yes."

"You recognize it as the one you found among the prisoner's effects?"

"Yes."

"Where did you find it?"

"Inside one of his books."

"Open?"

"Yes."

"There was no envelope?"

"No."

"You read it?"

"Yes."

"Why did you keep it?"

"It shook me. It was an incriminating letter."

"Incriminating to whom?"

"To the prisoner."

"What made you think so?"

"It was unmistakably the letter of an enemy agent giving away information."

"Why didn't you hand it over to your commanding officer at once, if that was what you thought of it?"

"I couldn't bear to."

"You didn't want to denounce your friend as a spy?"

"No. I'd been told he'd been sent under guard to Corps Headquarters. I believed he would be court-martialled for the business in the canteen, and I thought that was enough."

"So you suppressed it?"

"Yes."

"But kept it by you?"

"Yes."

"Didn't you realize that you were committing a grave offence by so doing?"

"Yes. That is why in the end, when I heard that the Army had washed their hands of him and packed him off home, I sent it in."

"To the Home Office?"

"Yes."

"When did you send it to the Home Office?"

"About a month later."

This letter was Exhibit 2. Exhibit 1 was the book, the pocket edition of Milton's *Areopagitica*. The jury were given photo-

252

static copies of the letter. So was I. As anyone could see, it is not a complete letter, or even a complete page of a letter. The right edge is ragged, at least one word is missing at the end of each line, and the bottom right-hand corner of the sheet isn't there, it was torn off. There is no date, no heading, and no signature; but it is in Martin Merriedew's small neat hand, and was written apparently with a fountain pen in ink of a purple shade on a page of cheap paper with faint blue lines, the sort of paper one might tear out of a schoolboy's copybook. It is soiled and smudged. Probably eight, maybe more, words are missing besides those which may have been at the bottom of the page; but only two of the missing words are important. These are key words, and could prove, if one had them, together with the address, the innocence or guilt of the writer. Counsel wrangled over this. Each fitted in the two blanks to suit his thesis, and each offered his completed version as the only one possible that made sense. So there were three versions of Exhibit 2, the original fragment; the same, completed by the counsel for the Crown, became the communication of a spy to the enemy; the third, similarly processed by the defence, became an innocent if foolish private letter to a friend; and Mr. Pringle asked that it might be read in conjunction with a second letter (Exhibit 3) written by Martin Merriedew to Teresa Larnigan and received by her on the 15th of November 1944.

Here are the two letters.

Exhibit 2

1 I regret that you did not receive my
2 I cannot get you the information you
3 I have no transport and no excuse to
4 the unit in question. I believe the 2nd
5 has moved back to the village I mentioned
6 Ill equipped, and inexperienced they were
7 I could enquire, but their casualty lists are
8 And I would probably learn nothing of

9 I am suspect now in that
10 Very isolated but determined to
11 Do not count on me for
12 But continue to trust
13 I send this as always by

Exhibit 3

Do not plague me, Teresa, with small questions. I regret that you did not receive my last letter, but it contained nothing that you wanted to know. I may have forgotten to post it. I cannot remember. I move heavily, like a sleep-walker in a fearful dream, with brass trumpets blaring in my ears and my feet clogged by bleeding mud. Or it may be that some gaping idiot robot with brass buttons for eyes stopped it. There are thousands employed in this hurricane of death at such things. They sit in flimsy sheds under iron hail, reading and reading millions of just such foolish letters as mine to you. Do not send me on silly errands, Teresa. What is the anguish of a mother whose son is reported missing? If he fell in battle or was blown to the winds in fragments that left no trace of him, what difference can it make? There is no glory to be won in this butchery. He is only one of ten thousand. I soil my boots in his blood every day. All spilt blood is the same. None is precious. It is cheaper by the pint than the beer we buy in our canteen.

I could not send you the information you ask for could I get it. Doing the little kindness to your desolate friend would be a crime. My communication might fall into the enemy's hands and help him; and we must neither help nor love our enemy now, Teresa, we must only hate and kill him and be very careful of what we say and do about him in the interests of security, the security of the men who are sent out to be slaughtered next day.

The word enemy is a big word. It bundles together eighty million men, women and children. But we do not kill the children, it seems, by design, only by accident.

I am suspect here because I do not pay the word the compliment of behaving as if it had any meaning. Even my own group doubt me. They believe now in death and hate and the enemy, they are frightened by the sight of the pale horse with Hell following after. But I believe and will always believe in Life, Teresa, and Love. Life that is everlasting and love that is of God.

Do not fail me. I am alone here because I believe in the Spirit

254

of Life during the Reign of the Dead. It will end. It is not forever. I believe with all my soul in the Kingdom of Heaven and life that is everlasting. Have you thought of what that last means now, Teresa? If life is eternal, if the dead do not die, then what of the agony and the hate that is boiling up around me now? Is it doused, is it wiped out as if it had never been? The Scriptures tell us that God will wipe away all tears from their eyes, there shall be no more death, sorrow, crying, nor pain; but how will God wipe out this horror? It will take Man a thousand years of peace to begin to make the Earth ready for the Kingdom of Heaven.

Do not fail me, Teresa. I am sick and alone.

Martin Merriedew.

The lines on Exhibit 2 were numbered for the benefit of the jury so that they could follow the arguments of Counsel. The key words are missing from the ends of the fourth and sixth lines. The last bit of each line is missing; the other missing words were, however, of no importance, the context was clear; but if the reference at the end of line 4 is to the 2nd Field Ambulance, as the defence maintained; and if the missing word at the end of 6 is "overworked," and the whole was written in answer to a letter from Teresa, then it was innocent. But if the blank at the end of line 4 refers to the 2nd Battalion of a fighting unit actually engaged in that area at that time, and the truncated word is not "overworked" but "overrun," then the document would read inevitably as a betrayal of military information to the enemy, a proof that the writer had been doing this regularly over an extended period, and that he intended to do even more in future.

Exhibit 2, in other words, might prove great foolishness on the part of the writer or protracted and systematic treachery. Counsel for the defence admitted that his version was no more convincing in itself than his colleague's. He did not insist on the overriding logic of his reading. The rightness of his deduction depended on the jury's opinion of the prisoner's whole life, not of his war service only; and that was the very thing they were discussing. What he did insist on was that the incriminating fragment should be read together with Exhibit 3. It was the prisoner's letter to Teresa Larnigan, he declared, that explained the soiled bit of paper with a ragged edge, cutting off the end of each line so conveniently for his colleague's thesis. Wasn't it odd that it was the right-hand edge that was ragged? If the sheet were a leaf, as it appeared to be, from a notebook, and if it had been carelessly torn out of the book, one would expect the inside edge, where the leaf was attached to the binding, to be torn, wouldn't one? Didn't this odd circumstance suggest that the sheet had been tampered with after it was found, and, if so, cunningly and with malicious intent? Mr. Pringle put these questions to the jury, when he put Teresa's letter in evidence. It was possible, he admitted, that both he and counsel for the Crown had failed in their search for the right words to fill in the gaps in the first document. They had been obliged to use their imaginations, and their imaginings had been differently coloured, one by a predisposition to believe in the writer's guilt, his own by his conviction of the man's innocence. He did not therefore ask the jury to accept as unassailable the work of his own honest reasoning, but he did ask them to agree that the dirty piece of paper as completed by him was a letter that might well have been written by the same man who had written the letter marked Exhibit 3 to his friend Teresa Larnigan. But, and he hoped the jury would follow his reasoning, the letter to Teresa Larnigan was not the letter of a man in league with the enemy. He suggested that unless the prisoner were suffering from a disease called schizophrenia, or split personality, he could not have written the letter as completed by counsel for the Crown intending to forward it to an enemy agent. He would go further. He put it to the jury that Exhibit 3, the letter to Miss Larnigan, which she had received on November 15 of the year in question, might very well contain a reference to the fragment Exhibit 2. He couldn't prove it, but he believed that this was so; and if it was, then the evidence of the witness as to when he had found the piece of paper was false. He hadn't found it after the trouble in the canteen on Christmas Eve. He had found it at least six weeks before, and had kept it for his own evil and mysterious ends. Counsel offered this to the jury as a suggestion well worth their consideration.

Charles asked Mr. Pringle, when the letters had been circulated, what had become of the other members of the group to whom the writer referred.

"The group was scattered, my lord."

"You have been in touch with them?"

"Yes, my lord. There has been some correspondence."

"But you are not calling any of them as witnesses on behalf of your client?"

"No, my lord."

"Why not?"

"None volunteered to come forward, my lord."

"You are telling me that none of these friends of the prisoner's were willing to say a good word for him?"

"None, my lord."

III

Mr. Pringle was not an attractive figure. He had a high chirping voice, and reminded me of a grasshopper or a daddy-long-legs. He was prim, precious, pernickety, peevish, and ungainly. He had a habit of jerking one of his long legs, then the other, as if his trousers irritated him, and his eyeglasses were forever bouncing off his sharp nose. When this happened he would catch them on their ribbon and wave them back and forth on a long finger. He had the air at such moments of a petulant, rather foolish pedagogue. He had it when he began to cross-question Gideon Fish.

But he surprised me. I couldn't think where he had got the information that enabled him to pounce on the witness as he did, until I thought of Teresa. Even then I couldn't make out for a long time what he was driving at. I know now, he has told me; but I only began to have a glimmer of his purpose toward the end of the cross-examination.

He was very close in his questions concerning Exhibit 2. He wanted precise information, first as to the kind of paper the letter was written on.

"Would you call this ordinary letter paper?"

"No."

"What would you call it?"

"It looks like a page out of a copybook."

"Did the accused have such a copybook in his possession?"

"Yes. You could get one for sixpence in the canteen."

"You saw him with such a book?"

"Yes."

"Didn't he have any proper letter paper?"

"I don't know."

"Did you have any?"

"Yes."

"Would you have lent him some had he asked for it?"

"Certainly."

"What about the paper on which he wrote the letter Exhibit 3 to Miss Larnigan? It's better paper, isn't it?"

"Yes."

"Did you give him this paper?"

"No."

"So he bought this lot apparently."

"Yes, or had it with him."

"Did he write many letters to your knowledge?"

"No, I don't think he did, but he may have done. We weren't together much during the day."

"But you remember seeing him write in such copybooks?"

"Yes."

"What did he use them for?"

"Anything and everything: notes to some of us about our work, hours off, change of duties, things like that."

"He would tear out a page and give it to one of you?"

"Yes."

"So you were familiar with his notebooks?"

"Yes."

"Did he leave one or more behind when he was taken away?"

"I don't think so. I don't remember seeing any in the tent."

"But he left other books?"

"Yes."

"What sort of books were they?"

"Pocket editions of his favourite books, essays, poems, a New Testament I remember, and the poems of John Donne."

"But no notebook?"

"No."

"He left his New Testament and the poems of John Donne, but took with him a cheap notebook from which he was in the habit of tearing out pages to give to the members of his group?"

"Yes; he must have done."

"Doesn't that strike you as odd?"

"No, unless — " The witness hesitated.

"Well, unless?"

"Unless there were things written in it that he didn't want me to know about."

"Writings of an incriminating character? Is that what you mean to suggest?"

"Perhaps. Or bits of information he'd collected and meant to use."

"Intended for the enemy?"

"Yes."

"He would be careful in that case to take the notebook with him?"

"Yes, or destroy it."

"But you have told the court that you found this loose sheet

259

of paper inside a book he had left behind. What book was it, by the way?"

"I think it was *The Wasteland.*"

"What's that?"

"A poem by T. S. Eliot."

"Are you sure that's where the paper was?"

"Yes."

"Very well. You tell us that the accused left this scrap of paper, intended to convey information to the enemy, inside the pages of a book of verse, a book that you might very well open and look through, that you did in fact open. Wouldn't you call that very careless of him?"

"He must have forgotten that he had left it there."

"Was he a careless and forgetful person?"

"Yes. And he can't have had much time that morning. He must have been flustered."

"What morning?"

"The morning that they took him away."

"What would he be flustered about?"

"If he had a guilty conscience — "

"Exactly. If he had had a guilty conscience and had written a letter intended for some German secret agent, wouldn't it be the one thing he would remember when he got into trouble and want to destroy before it damned him?"

"One would think so."

"What were your relations with him at the time?"

"Quite friendly."

"On both sides?"

"Yes."

"You were still very intimate?"

"Yes."

"And had complete confidence in each other?"

"Yes. That is to say — "

"Well? What were you going to say?"

"I was going to say that the war had made a difference."

"Had you forgotten that fact for the moment?"

"No."

"You remember now that you told the court you had disagreed with him before this about his attitude towards the German wounded?"

"I hadn't forgotten it."

"You had quarrelled about it, hadn't you?"

"No, we didn't quarrel. We agreed to disagree."

"But he didn't count on you, did he, to aid and abet him in any treacherous dealings with enemy agents and spies?"

"Certainly not."

"Or confess to you that he was one himself?"

"No."

"So he wouldn't have wanted you to catch him out, would he, if he were in communication with the enemy?"

"No."

"He would have known, if he was a spy, that you would denounce him if you discovered it?"

"Yes, he must have known."

"So he wouldn't normally have left incriminating evidence lying about for you to pick up?"

"No."

"But you did pick up this sheet of paper, didn't you?"

"Yes."

"And denounced him on the strength of it?"

"He had already been sent to G.H.Q."

"But had not, as far as you knew, been accused of being a spy?"

"No."

"So you felt that it was up to you to see to that?"

"Yes; if you must put it so."

"How else am I to put it? He wouldn't be on trial now for his life, would he, if you hadn't denounced him?"

261

"I don't know. How can I know? He might have gone on — until — "

"Until he was caught in this devil's business by someone else. Is that what you mean?"

"Yes. Anyone might have discovered it."

"But the Army had washed their hands of him, hadn't they, as a harmless lunatic, religious fanatic, some sort of crank?"

"I don't know what the Army thought of him."

"No, I don't suppose you do; but you do know what you yourself thought, and I want you to tell me. Why were you immediately convinced on reading this letter that he was guilty of treason?"

"I wasn't convinced. I didn't at first believe the evidence of my own eyes. That's why I kept the letter back."

"That reminds me: when did you find it?"

"The day they took him away."

"That was Christmas Day 1944, wasn't it?"

"Yes."

"What did you do with it when you found it?"

"Put it in my wallet."

"And kept it there for how long?"

"Until I heard that he had been sent home."

"How long after was that?"

"About a fortnight, maybe a month later."

"Wasn't it more like three months?"

"It may have been."

"Didn't you know that they kept him hanging about in a camp in the Delta for nearly three months?"

"No. I didn't know what had become of him until I heard that he had been sent home."

"Why didn't you hand the thing over to the Commanding Officer of your hospital when you found it?"

"I didn't want any more scandal in the unit."

262

"But you thought it was your duty at the end of three months to forward it to the Home Office?"

"Yes."

"You agree that it was after three months?"

"Yes."

"You posted it then in the ordinary way, through the Military Post?"

"No. I took it with me when I went home on leave."

"You delivered it yourself at the Home Office?"

"Yes."

"Why didn't you post it in the ordinary way?"

"Our letters were censored."

"I see. You wanted to be quite sure that it reached its destination?"

"Yes."

Mr. Pringle allowed this admission to sink in, then picked up his copy of Exhibit 2, adjusted his eyeglasses and peered at it.

"Now I would like you to look with me carefully at this letter we've been talking about. How would you say it got torn in this peculiar fashion?"

"The accused was always tearing pages out of his notebook."

"But this ragged edge is on the outside, isn't it?"

"Yes."

Mr. Pringle turned to the bench. "I have endeavoured, my lord, to obtain an effect similar to this document by scribbling in a copybook of the same type, then tearing out the page, and I found that I could do it if I wrote on a left-hand page of the book, writing inwards, so to speak; but it did not seem to me that it would be natural to do so if I were writing a memo of importance, for this court, for instance. And I could not fail to notice when I tore out the page, rather carelessly I admit, that I had destroyed the sense of my document. Indeed, had I intended such a memorandum for your Lordship, I would not have been satisfied with it, oh, not at all. I would have discarded it and rewritten the thing. If your Lordship will allow me — "

Mr. Pringle's long awkward arm tendered a sheet of cheap paper to the Clerk of the court, but Charles waved it aside. "I quite get your point, Mr. Pringle, and that may very probably be just what the accused did. He probably discarded the spoiled sheet and wrote another."

Mr. Pringle blinked. "I thank you, my lord." His coup had misfired, but he turned, as peckish as ever, to the witness. "Is that," he asked, "what you think happened?"

"Yes, it must have been that."

"This bit of paper is, then, you take it, a spoiled draft of a communication he had meant to send to the enemy, but discarded?"

"Yes."

"But we cannot be certain, can we, for whom it was intended since there is no address, no beginning, and no end. In fact we cannot be certain, can we, my lord, that it was ever intended for anyone, since it was never finished, nor forwarded, but was left instead lying about within the pages of a volume of verse where anyone could pick it up?"

"I am not in the box, Mr. Pringle, if your question is addressed to me."

"My apologies, my lord." Counsel turned back to the witness. "What I find difficult to understand is how you should have had such a low opinion of your leader as to jump to the conclusion that this letter with no address, no beginning, no end, and a dozen words missing, was the letter of a spy."

"I didn't jump to the conclusion. As I said, it was a great shock to me."

"Why?"

"Can't you understand? We had been friends and colleagues. I had loved the man."

"Yes, so you told my colleague." Mr. Pringle was silent for

264

a moment, his tone was honey-sweet when he spoke. "And now, please tell me just when you began to hate him?"

If counsel had intended a hit, the effect was greater than he could have hoped for. The swarthy face of the witness grew black with blood. It took him quite some seconds to answer. When he did, it was with a snarl that showed his teeth. "I never hated him."

"Not even when you believed you had discovered him to be a traitor?"

"No, not even then."

"You don't hate him now?"

"No."

"But you want him to hang, don't you?"

"I object, my lord!" Kennington was on his feet. "Counsel is bullying the witness."

"Objection sustained. I confess I am surprised, Mr. Pringle." Charles was more than a little annoyed.

"I am sorry, my lord, to have offended you. I fear that I was carried away by my feelings."

"Precisely. The very thing that surprised me."

But Pringle too could use irony. "I will leave the question of the letter for the moment, my lord, while I cool down."

"I think you would be wise to do so."

Counsel turned to the witness. "Let us go back, if you please, to the English West Country town of Warrington. You have told us that the accused gave you a certain authority in his group of workers. What sort of authority did you have?"

"You might say I was his second-in-command, or his chief of staff."

"He delegated you to carry out his orders?"

"You could put it that way."

"And what were they?"

"I don't understand."

"The question seems to me simple enough, but let me put

265

it this way. What were the rules he imposed in your community? Were there many?"

"No. Only two. Poverty was one; we must own nothing. Peace was another; we must all take our stand against war."

"Did you hold to these yourself?"

"To the second absolutely — I was a conscientious objector."

"What about the other? How did you manage to run the community without money?"

"I couldn't; it was impossible; I had to make other arrangements."

"What arrangements did you make?"

"I rented an old building and turned it into a hostel. We called it the Community House."

"How did you reconcile this with the rule of poverty?"

"I didn't attempt to. When I found that his ideal didn't work in practice, I raised enough money to keep us."

"Did he agree about this?"

"No."

"You did this without his knowledge?"

"Yes, he never asked where the money came from. Practical details didn't interest him. He expected the impossible and believed in it. More than once when there was a great crowd at the Community House, he told me suddenly to hand round refreshments."

"And did you?"

"Yes. I went out and scrounged for beer and sandwiches."

"Why didn't you tell him there was nothing to give these people?"

"I don't know why, but I couldn't tell him."

"Who paid for the beer and sandwiches?"

"I did."

"But you have told us that you gave up all your property when you joined him."

"So I did, in a manner of speaking. I had made my own fortune over in trust to my brother on the understanding that I could draw what I liked when I needed it. So I drew for the group's expenses."

"I see. You fooled him."

"For his own sake and the sake of his work."

"What work was that?"

"His work among the sick, for one thing, and his crusade for peace."

"But you told counsel that he gave up his work among the sick, didn't you?"

"Yes, he did in the end."

"You used the words 'he had power, he could have done almost anything but he refused to exercise his power.' Do you wish to correct that?"

"No, it was true."

"What sort of power were you thinking of? His gift as a healer?"

"Yes."

"Was that the only thing about him that appealed to you?"

"No."

"You mentioned at one moment his power as a speaker."

"Yes."

"Wasn't it his power as a leader of men that attracted you in the beginning?"

"Yes, it was."

"You have called yourself a revolutionary; didn't you expect him to head a great uprising of the people?"

"I may have done."

"And weren't you bitterly disappointed when he refused to do anything of the sort?"

"I was disappointed, yes."

"But you stuck to him in spite of your disappointment?"

"Yes."

267

"Still hoping to use him for your own purposes of revolution?"

"I wasn't hoping to use him. He used me."

"But you were fooling him all the while, weren't you? Up to the outbreak of war?"

"I was doing what I thought best in his own interests."

"Well, let's leave it at that and consider one other point. You have stated that the Mayor and Town Council of Warrington asked your leader to leave the city shortly before the war. Why was that?"

"They accused him of inciting the munitions workers to strike as a protest against our war preparations."

"Was it true?"

"Yes. He used to stand outside the factory gates at the dinner hour or in the evening when the men came out and address them."

"Did he go alone?"

"No, I went with him."

"What of the other members of the group?"

"They came too, sometimes."

"How many were you at the time?"

"A dozen, all told."

"You were all asked to leave the place?"

"No, only he and I."

"How was that? Weren't you all pacifists?"

"Yes, but he and I were the ones who made trouble."

"I think you said that you didn't leave just at once."

"No. We were packing up when war was declared, then I lost him."

"What do you mean, lost him?"

"He had been in a very strange state, very depressed. We were listening in that Sunday morning, and when we heard the Prime Minister's voice saying 'We are at war with Germany!' he gave a sobbing shout and rushed out of the house. I ran after him, but he was nowhere to be seen. It's a poor quarter: ware-houses, factories, some pubs. He must have turned into some yard or alley. I didn't find him. We all searched, no one had seen him, he had clean disappeared, so I informed the police. He turned up ten days later in London at Scotland Yard. They kept him while they telephoned to me and I went and took him away."

"Where did you take him?"

"To a little place in the Lake District, to rest."

"He was ill?"

"Yes. I was afraid that he was going out of his mind."

"It was after this that you and he volunteered to go over-seas?"

"Yes."

"He had recovered and was passed as fit?"

"Yes."

"And the others joined you?"

"Yes."

"And you went out as a group?"

"Yes."

"Well, we have found our way back to your field hospital; so let us consider again, and this time calmly, this mutilated piece of paper called a letter, and let us assume for a moment that it was intended for the enemy. What would you say that the accused meant to do with it when he wrote it? Put it in the post?"

"No, he would hand it on to some enemy agent."

"Did you ever come across one?"

"There was a man called Captain Banks."

"There was indeed. We've been told about him. Did you know him?"

"Yes, he used to come to the hospital."

"And did you suspect him for what he was?"

"No."

"When was it that you last saw him?"

"I don't remember."

"Did you hear at some time or other that he had been discovered to be a German agent?"

"Yes."

"When did you hear this?"

"I don't remember."

"Wasn't it shortly before Christmas?"

"As I say, I don't remember."

"Don't you remember any of these dates? Didn't you know that the accused had been questioned about a book he had lent this man Banks?"

"Yes, he told me."

"Ah, at last you remember something. And what did he tell you?"

"He told me that Banks was missing, and that a security officer had found a book of his among Banks's belongings."

"That is all he told you?"

"Yes."

"Did he seem worried?"

"He was upset."

"He thought Banks was dead?"

"He thought he might be."

"And what did you think?"

"I thought the same."

"Didn't this occur just before Christmas?"

"Yes."

"In that case, if Banks was already missing, how is it that you suspected your friend of intending to hand on to him this treacherous document?"

"I didn't. I never said so. I only mentioned him as a proof that there were German agents about, disguised as British officers."

"Let us make an end of this nonsense. I put it to you that

you did not find this letter among the effects of the accused the day that he was taken away by the Military Police, but at least six weeks before. I put it to you that he didn't take it away with him or destroy it or hide it because it was a harmless letter to a friend, and he had forgotten all about it. I put it to you that it was a letter he had written to Miss Teresa Larnigan early in November; that you knew it was an innocent letter when you found it, and that you mutilated it yourself so as to make it appear an incriminating document, written with treacherous intent. I suggest further that, having cunningly truncated the document to suit your purpose, you then took it to the Home Office in order to ruin the prisoner and get him hanged for treason, knowing that he was not guilty of treason. Do you deny this?"

"Yes."

"You have told us that he disappointed you long before the war; do you wish to correct that statement?"

"No."

"You have admitted that you deceived him in regard to the fundamental principles of his community; do you wish to change that?"

"No."

"You have stated that you feared for his sanity on the outbreak of war. Is that so? Were you afraid that he was going out of his mind?"

"Yes, but he recovered."

"Exactly. He recovered, if, as you say, he was mentally ill. He recovered sufficiently to work for three years in a field ambulance under a strain that might well have broken an ordinary man. Other witnesses have declared that he never spared himself. I needn't dwell on it. But he didn't break down, he carried on. And I put it to you, finally, that you now accuse him of treachery because you wanted to be rid of him when the war ended, because you wanted to be free to live your own life

271

and get on with your own plans when the world was once more at peace.

"I put it to you that the letter you have proffered as evidence of treachery is a private letter to a friend. I shall call on that friend to prove it. We will scrutinize the letter again and it will be for the jury to judge of its meaning. They may think both the letters produced in this court very foolish. I didn't like them myself. I find them strange and painful to read. They are the letters of a man, one might say, with a one-track mind, an unbalanced mind, but they are not, I submit, the letters of a traitor and I put it to you that you recognize this fact as I do; just as you know that there was nothing in the conduct of the accused in this field hospital that had any semblance to the conduct of a traitor, but was the conduct of a man moved by charity, mercy, and pity. Finally, I put it to you that you made up your mind to ruin the man you said you once loved because you were disappointed in him long ago; because you couldn't use him as you had hoped, but were tied to him, and couldn't be free of him as long as he lived, and so came to hate him."

Chapter Four

"GIVE me the liberty to know, to utter, and to argue freely according to conscience above all liberties."

Mr. Pringle, opening for the defence, read from the slim volume and held it up for the jury to look at.

"Here in this little book, my lord, members of the jury, lies the key to our mystery. For this is a strange case and a mysterious case, members of the jury, and to arrive at the truth of it we must penetrate the depths of a man's mind, or, if I may put it so, the secrets of his soul. You may think that an odd form of speech to use in a court of law, my lord, but here is a man, accused of treachery, who is incapable of treachery, a man of outstanding integrity, whose whole nature and whole life prove him to be the exact opposite of a traitor.

"For what is a traitor, what kind of man is he who will betray his king and his country? My learned friend has compared a traitor to a murderer who acts by stealth as poisoners do. Let us ask ourselves what the motives can be of such a criminal? Money is one possibility; he might betray his country for money. Fear, that is to say, cowardice, is another: he might believe that the enemy was going to win the war and want to be on the winning side. Or an overwhelming vanity: the enemy might get at such a man and seduce him from his allegiance by flattery and with promises of a glorious future. Finally, there is hate: a traitor might be compelled by hatred of his own people and his own homeland to betray in order to destroy them.

"The man on trial for his life in this court is none of these things, members of the jury. He is not a stealthy man. He did nothing secret, either during the war or before it. His conduct from his early manhood has been open as the day. Nor is he a man hungry for money. He has no money and never had any worth mentioning. He exercised his profession of medicine for a period in his home village, but I don't suppose he made much money out of that, and what he did make went to the support of his widowed mother, his sister, and his two younger brothers. Then he gave up even this source of income.

"There are religious orders — you must have heard of them — whose members vow themselves to poverty. The prisoner at the bar took such a vow and imposed it on his followers; for he was a leader of men. You have heard it from a witness for the prosecution, I needn't dwell on the fact. What I want to make clear to you is that from 1936, when he returned after an absence of three years to his own country, he gave himself to the service of his fellow men and got no money for it.

"He came home, as I say, to this country, his own country, and gave his life serving his own people; but most especially to the poor among them, the sick, the aged, and the children; in other words, to those who needed help. He was a giver; I was going to say — and why should I not? — a giver of life. He spent himself and his life for others. There are children running about the streets of this city today who owe their health to him. I shall call witnesses to tell of it. And he lived, while he gave himself to his work, a life of extreme austerity. It was a selfless life, a life so austere that only a very few of those who loved him, for he was beloved, could live up to it. There was no hate in him for his fellow men, he loved them. Nor any vanity. He shunned all publicity. The last witness called by my learned friend told it. But he was a man who would not compromise, who tolerated no half-measures, who hated humbug of all and every sort. He was bound to get into trouble with the authorities, and he did get into trouble: with the medical authorities, with the Church, with the civil authorities. But there was no secrecy about it. He was a troublemaker, I don't deny it, nor wish to deny it. But there was nothing underhand about his conduct. He plunged into conflict, inspired and impelled by convictions which you may disagree with, but which he flung down in the open, as the champions in the old days would fling their gauntlets into the arena.

"Please look with me now at this little book. The essay from which I have quoted, the *Areopagitica*, was first published in the year 1644; but the volume I have in my hand was printed and published in 1927 by J. M. Dent and Sons of London. It is a collection of prose writings by the great English poet, John Milton, and it is a classic. The prisoner at the bar gave a copy of it to a man who turned out to be an enemy agent. The fact is not disputed. What I dispute is the inference drawn from the fact by the Security Officer who witnessed for the Crown. That witness was not familiar with the contents of the book. He didn't look beyond the fly-leaf, which bore the prisoner's signature; and he seems to have assumed that Martin Merrie-dew was in league with this spy because he gave him the book and called him his friend. It is an unjustified inference to draw, members of the jury, and there is not a shred of proof of it. The accused will take the stand and give his own evidence as to that. He will state on oath that he was totally unaware that the man who passed as John Banks, a captain in the R.A.S.C., was a German agent, but believed him in all innocence to be a friend, and one with whom he had a common bond, the love of good books.

"The accused gave the man Banks the book, members of the jury, as a friend, and because he believed him to have had a mind like his own, a serious mind, a mind occupied with serious things like truth, liberty, conscience, and the rights of human beings to think for themselves.

275

"I will ask your indulgence and read to you again from the introduction to this little book. We needn't go beyond the introduction; had the witness who talked of it troubled to look into it he would have found these words on the second page.

" 'No man can be sure that he has found the truth until he has compared all forms of error. No man can be sure that his will is firmly set towards the goal until he has gone forth into the battle and proved his armour against all possible forms of evil. It is the same in conduct as it is in speculation. In both, the individual soul is responsible, in neither can it shuffle off its responsibility upon the infallibility or the authority of others. It is the individual reason, the individual will that alone counts; and the essence of both is individual choice and individual decision. Destroy these and we have destroyed the one thing that gives value to the trust of life we have received from God; we have struck at that which makes the very being of the soul; we have killed will and reason.'

"My lord and members of the jury, I would have you notice one thing. It is a small thing but not without interest. This book was one of the favourite books of the prisoner at the bar. He took it with him, together with the New Testament of the English Bible and the poems of another English poet, John Donne, when he went overseas; and he gave it to a friend. It has been put in evidence by my learned colleague as tending to bolster up the Crown's case for treachery; and I have tried your patience by reading from it; but I have not chosen the two passages I have read to you, at random. If you will look, my lord, at the second page of the volume, you will notice that the words I have read are underlined; and that's why I chose them. Someone underlined them, and it wasn't I, my lord, nor the Security Officer who didn't look into the book; nor could it have been done by the police who have had charge of the book. The underlining was done by one of two men, either by the man on trial in this court for his life, or by the enemy agent called Banks to whom he gave the book. If inferences are to be drawn, my lord, during these proceedings, I think I am justified in drawing this one: that it was Martin Merriedew who underlined the words I have read you, and that he did so because he found them especially interesting, since they expressed what he himself felt and believed. '. . . individual choice and individual decision, destroy them and we have destroyed the one thing that gives value to the trust of life we have received from God; we have struck at that which makes the very being of the soul.'

"The prisoner at the bar is an individual, members of the jury. He is a man who has always thought for himself and fought for the truth as he saw it. He did not go into battle in defence of his country, he is a pacifist, no one denies it, and a conscientious objector, like his former colleague who has given evidence meant to hang him; but he has been engaged all his adult life in a battle for liberty of conscience, for the individual responsibility of the human soul, that gives value to the trust of life we have received, as that great poet, John Milton, put it, from God.

"And his battle landed him in trouble, my lord and members of the jury, as I have already said, with the authorities, both in peace and in war. He is a fighter for the truth as he sees it; and he was forever fighting. My learned colleague has described treason as a secret and deadly plan, kept on ice in a cold mind. Nothing could be less like the prisoner. Nothing has come out in the evidence brought against him that suggests anything of the kind. The mind that emerges from the evidence is no cold secret mind. On the contrary, the witnesses who have witnessed against him have painted for us the picture of a fiery mind, a passionate mind, a courageous, obstreperous mind that refused to accept an authority in conflict with his conscience, and insisted on individual liberty when the mass of our men and our women had been asked, had been ordered, to surrender their liberties for the good, yes, for the salvation of our nation.

"A man of peace at loggerheads with the rule of war. I do not pretend that he was docile, that he accepted all the precepts and regulations of wartime. He refused to kill, he refused to hate, even the enemies of his country; but he was not a traitor, he was not disloyal to our king or his fellow citizens, and the Crown has not proved that he was. The onus of proof lies with my learned friend, members of the jury. He must prove beyond reasonable doubt that the prisoner at the bar is guilty of treachery. He has undertaken to prove that he is guilty on three counts, and he has proved none of them. The story of helping an ambulance-load of German wounded to escape is a pure hypothesis, supported by not a single witness. My learned colleague himself has admitted the circumstantial evidence in this charge to be flimsy. As to the far more serious matter of communicating with the enemy, there is this business of the enemy agent called John Banks, and a letter in the prisoner's hand. You have seen the letter, you have scrutinized it, and another. I shall call the witness to whom, I believe, both letters were written. I have no doubt about this. Both these letters were innocent letters written to Teresa Larnigan. There is to my mind no room for doubt in regard to the innocence of the fragment of a letter that my learned colleague declares to be a criminal communication to the enemy and a proof of treachery.

"You may not like either of these letters, members of the jury, you may think them foolish, rash, dangerous letters to write to anyone in wartime. You may find fault with them as tending to sow seeds of despondency and despair in those who read them. You may find them lacking in the burning flame of patriotism that carried our armies to victory, and you may decide that they prove the man who wrote them to be a man who hated war with such passion that he forgot the cause for which we were fighting, namely, the survival of our nation. I myself do not like these letters. They shock me. They strike me

278

as the letters of a man so overwrought by the horrors of suffering he had to deal with that he was driven half out of his mind; but they are not, members of the jury, the letters of a traitor.

"I come to the third count against him, that he endeavoured to incite our troops to mutiny in a N.A.A.F.I. canteen on Christmas Eve of 1944.

"Something unpleasant happened in that canteen on that evening, there is no argument about that. The prisoner said something, did something that caused a row, and the men went for him. But I am not at all sure of what he did say, and I do not believe that he was trying to incite the troops to mutiny. He wasn't as mad as all that, members of the jury. Imagine for a moment the scene, so picturesquely imagined for you by my learned friend in his opening speech. The man at the bar had gone to the canteen with a friend, the same friend who has witnessed against him. They were civilians, they wore khaki but not military uniform. They were hospital orderlies with the badge of the Red Cross on their sleeves, and they were known, at least to the bartender of the canteen, as conscientious objectors, both of them. What sort of prestige would that give them, do you think, in the eyes of fighting men who knew they might well be for it, as they would put it, next day or next week? How could the man on trial hope, if he had any such intention as is imputed to him, that the men round that stove would listen to him if he told them to throw away their guns and their ammunition, strip their military badges from their shoulders, and refuse to fight?

"Does it make sense to you? It doesn't to me. The witness from the N.A.A.F.I. canteen was very glib, members of the jury. He had a speech by heart, and he recited it, but I don't know that he heard Martin Merriedew say it, or anything like it. There was a crowd in that hut. There was a lot of noise going on, a lot of singing and shouting, and a lot of drinking. The bartender probably doesn't know how many pints of beer he had served out that night, but it amounted to a good deal; and the wind was howling outside, the guns were pounding. Martin Merriedew did shout something, members of the jury. He may tell you what it was, I shall ask him to tell you; and it angered the men, and they went for him. But whatever it was, I am convinced that to call it the crime of inciting to mutiny is ridiculous. And the other accusation that has been tacked on to it, the accusation brought by his friend and companion, that he had been quietly and secretly persuading to the same thing in corners, I throw out of court as a malicious invention. No, members of the jury, all that I am prepared to believe in this story is the statement of the N.A.A.F.I. servant that the accused appeared ill and overwrought, and that he suddenly shouted at the crowd to stop singing hymns, and that they went for him. I am prepared to believe this because it is in character. My whole case, you may say, is based on evidence of Martin Merriedew's character; and if you do, I answer, why not? Everything that has come out in the evidence of the witnesses for the prosecution is evidence of the same character; a character so open, so individual, so actuated by motives at variance with those of his associates that even the members of his own group quarrelled with him. For how did it all begin? Who started this trouble and set in train their suspicions? The accused man himself, members of the jury, started it all. And how? And why? I will tell you. He became an object of suspicion because he was kind to the wounded German prisoners in his charge, because he quite openly treated them as human beings, because he unashamedly held them in his arms when they were dying. What would you have done in his place? What would I? I don't know. I wasn't put the problem. If I had been in charge of an enemy who was dying on a stretcher at my feet, I might have hated the uniform so much that I would have turned my back on him. I don't know. The man at the bar didn't do that. I don't know what went on in his mind. But I do know what he did, and I put it to you that if he had been acting as a secret enemy agent, and if he had been engaged in sending information to the enemy, he would not have acted as he did, but would have made a cunning pretence of hating the Germans with whom he was in league. I put it to you that his conduct in that field hospital was conduct motivated by mercy, and love for his fellow men. It was never at any moment the conduct of a traitor."

II

Francis had had, I know, great difficulty in finding witnesses for the defence. He had failed with the members of Martin's group and with Jeremy Green. At one moment he had thought that he had succeeded with Jeremy, but in the end the poor creature had been too frightened. It was the same with almost all of the people in Greymouth and Warrington who had adored Martin Merriedew in the old days. Fear of being involved with the police, fear of the Church and the Town Council who had been down on him, fear of their neighbours — it was asking too much, even of those who still remembered what he had done for them. But Pringle did manage to call half a dozen witnesses before he put Teresa on the stand. After Edward and Michael, he called Fothergill, a pleasant young woman named Sally Hopper, a rugged old one, by name Mrs. Mildred Moggridge, and Camilla's parson friend, the Reverend Nathaniel Smith-Carey, the last three from Warrington.

Edward was an impressive figure in the witness box. Tall, thin, haggard, and angular in rather shabby black with haunted eyes and a dog collar not too clean, he had the appearance of a prophet.

He was vicar, he told the court, of a parish in the East End of London and he owed a deep debt of gratitude to his elder brother, who had made it possible for him to take Holy Orders. Although they had disagreed ever since he could remember on

281

questions of church doctrine, he believed him to be an upright man of high moral principle, a deeply religious nature, a loyal subject of his Majesty the King, and a man incapable of treachery. They had been in their youth a very united family and when their father had died, Martin had taken his place at the head of it, supporting them all for three years by his medical practice. Yes, they had been left in straitened circumstances when the accused went away. He had remained away for three years. Witness didn't know why he had gone, and he had seen little of him since. To be precise he had only seen him once to speak to until he visited him in the County Jail at the end of the war. Yes, he had gone to see him at Greymouth in 1936 but had had no conversation with him on that occasion. Pressed by counsel, he admitted that his mother and brother had been with him and that the accused had refused to see them.

"Why was that?" Pringle was sharp.

"He gave no reason."

"Can you think of none?"

Poor Edward. He had been prepared for this and fully drilled. Though I was at a loss to understand what Pringle was after, he himself knew quite well, but it went hard with him to say it. He gulped before he brought it out. "The truth is I was convinced that he was out of his mind, I was determined to put a stop to his activities and I believe that he knew this."

"You suggest that that was his reason for refusing to see you?"

"Yes."

"What made you think he was out of his mind?"

"His attacks on the Church, his claims to divine inspiration and to miraculous powers."

"You had followed his activities closely?"

"Yes, I went repeatedly to hear him speak."

"Did you ever hear him say anything in any of his speeches

282

that was in any way seditious or disloyal to your king and your country?"

"No."

"Your quarrel with him, if I may call it a quarrel, was on religious grounds only?"

"Yes. I thought his pretensions blasphemous and hoped that he was mad."

Cross-questioned, Edward admitted that Martin spoke German, read German, and might have spent some part of his three years abroad in Germany between 1933 and 1936, but he didn't know if it was so. Questioned again on this point by Pringle, Edward said yes, his brother Martin was of a studious type, had always been a great reader, and had a gift for languages. He had a schoolboy's knowledge of Greek and Latin, and read French as well as German. No, he hadn't specialized in modern languages, he had studied medicine, he had been in correspondence, he believed, with French and German medical men, especially those specialists who dealt with nervous disorders, but he was not aware of his having formed any close friendships in Germany. He had been, as a boy and a student, rather insular in his outlook. When a school friend had invited him to accompany him one summer to Europe he had said that England was good enough for him and the two had gone to the Lake Country instead.

Michael added something rather touching to this. He looked very handsome, very fierce and rather stupid, but he managed to convey to the court that he would take on anyone who dared call his brother a traitor, and he confessed that all during the war he had been trying to understand what to him was incomprehensible — namely, pacifism — simply because there must be something to be said for anything his brother believed in.

He said that the accused had been his hero as a small boy, and that when they grew up though they thought the opposite about most things, especially about fighting in defence of one's country, he still thought the world of him. He didn't pretend to understand him, but knew that he wasn't a coward or a sneak. He repeated that he had thought a lot about this business of pacifism lately and had come to the conclusion that there was more than one kind of courage. It wasn't his kind, but he remembered an incident in his childhood when his brother had refused to fight and, taken all in all, he believed the accused to be the bravest man he'd ever known.

Fothergill followed. He was consultant now on nervous diseases for the county but he could only give Martin Merriedew the character of a very earnest, unselfish, brilliant, but unorthodox physician. Cross-questioned, he admitted that he argued with the British Medical Association: Merriedew was not a charlatan but his methods were dangerous. He could have continued his practice had he been willing to compromise — he wasn't.

The young woman Sally Hopper did better. She told the court and the sceptical Judge Charles Collit that she owed the sight of her eyes to the prisoner. She had been blind and now she could see.

Mr. Justice Collit leaned forward at this and scrutinized the fresh young face. The bright eyes returned his gaze. Charles's voice was gentle but had an edge to it when he spoke to her.

"That is a very strange thing to say, my child. Perhaps you will be good enough to explain how this miracle came about?"

"I was two when I had a blow on the right eye."

"And how old are you now?"

"Twenty-two, my lord."

"Well, what happened?"

"I come of working people. My parents were poor, my father drank a lot. It was he who did it, poor Daddy, when he was drunk, with a stick, I think, I don't know. But I know they were both ashamed afterwards to take me to the doctor, because my mother told me."

284

"Never mind what your mother told you. Just tell me what you know of your own experience. It is for your mother to tell us, if necessary, what she felt at the time."

"But she's dead, your Lordship. They're both dead."

"I see. Well, go on. What do you remember?"

"All I remember is that I had my eye bandaged for ever so long, months and months it was, as much as two years, they told me, only I mustn't say that. And then when at last they took off the bandage, I couldn't see out of that eye at all."

"Which eye was it?"

"This one." Sally Hopper pointed to her bright right eye with a rough finger.

"But the other worked all right, I take it?"

"Yes, all the time I was at elementary school. It did the work for both was what Dr. Martin said. Then when I was thirteen that began to go too. So I told Dr. Martin, and he put them both right again. Right as rain they are now, my lord."

"And how did he do that?"

"With talking to me, and showing me how to do exercises and such."

"Talking to you?"

"Yes, my lord, and telling me to talk to myself. Autosuggestion, he called it. He said my right eye, the one that was hurt, wasn't damaged; it had just forgotten how to see during all the time it was covered up with the bandage. And he said he and I could teach it to see again, and we did."

"And how long did this take?"

"It was the best part of a year, your Lordship, before I could see to read a book; but I kept on with the exercises long after that. I do even now if I remember, or my eyes get tired at work."

"What work do you do?"

"I work at the children's hospital at Warrington, my lord. I've been a V.A.D. there through the war. Now I'm qualifying as a nurse."

285

"And what are your feelings now toward the prisoner?"

"The prisoner?" Sally Hopper looked round. "Oh, you mean Dr. Martin?"

"Yes, I mean Martin Merriedew."

"I love him, my lord, with all my heart."

Charles sat back. He handed Sally Hopper over to counsel; but counsel had no questions to ask, and she stepped down, to be followed by Mrs. Mildred Moggridge, a mournful old body done up in shawls and a bonnet.

Mrs. Moggridge was seventy and alone in the world. She had had a daughter who had come to no good, and her daughter had had a child born out of wedlock and deaf and dumb. The daughter hadn't cared for the child, but Mrs. Moggridge had loved it, the helpless critter, and so had Dr. Martin. Mrs. Moggridge went on to say that the Doctor had taken no end of trouble with Andy, that was the child's name; and so she had been to all the Doctor's meetings. She was a regular attendant, front row of the pit; and if anyone said a word against the Doctor for his opinions on politics and such, she'd go for him, whoever he was. Yes, in course she'd been there at the gates of the factory when he talked to the men. Yes, he'd talked down the war, but it hadn't begun then, not that she knew of. He was for peace, was the Doctor. Who wasn't, including Mr. Chamberlain, hadn't he said so more than once on the wireless?

Judge Collit was bored by Mrs. Moggridge and cut her short. He was even more so by the Reverend Nathaniel Smith-Carey. Mr. Smith-Carey was obviously of the class Mrs. Moggridge would call gentry. He was as obviously half-starved, and he brought something rare and exquisite into court, but the Judge didn't get it. It was like a faint fresh perfume, like a breath of pure ozone such as one breathes in Switzerland in spring, when the slopes are covered with wild flowers. And with it he brought something else, an element that had been lurking, all but unnoticed, under the decent comfortable surface of things, the element of terror. But Mr. Smith-Carey, very small and frail in his shabby black coat and dog collar that was too big for his skinny little neck, wasn't of a type to impress a judge who mistrusted the sacred cloth at any time, and squirmed with fastidious irritation at the sound of what he called religious jargon, even when the words sounded hardly above a whisper from a throat constricted by an agony of earnestness.

For the Reverend Mr. Smith-Carey was like a child. His head was fringed with down as soft as a baby chick's, and he spoke in a high trembling piping child's voice; but what was frightening him, what was reflected in his pale eyes as horror, was a thing everyone else seemed able to ignore; the image of death, the fact that the man in the dock might be hanged by the neck until he was dead; and that what he himself said, however little it might be, might weigh just enough to tip the balance and save the other's life.

But what could he say — I seemed to read the desperate, modest search for words in his quivering face — except the truth that the prisoner was a good man, a lovable man, a man who loved God and his neighbour with all his heart?

There was nothing else that he could say, so that is what he said. And in his innocence he expected them to believe him, he didn't suspect them of cruelty. He told the Judge, the jury, and the assembled barristers that the prisoner had been his friend, that he had clothed him when he was naked, and nursed him when he was sick, and held him up when he was faint with weariness. He had given him courage and faith and love, he had given him life; and he ended, the poor little trusting creature, by telling the court that the prisoner at the bar was the most Christlike man he had ever known. And the court laughed at him. Not the Judge: Charles didn't laugh, he winced. Nor counsel for the Crown: he only smiled, like the reporters. But titters scampered like rollicking mice through the gallery, and at the sound Mr. Smith-Carey's Adam's apple jumped above

287

his collar, he lifted a thin shabby arm as if to ward off a blow or hide his crimsoning face, and before the angry bench could impose silence and bid him stand down, his eyes had filled and spilled over with tears.

It was too much for Charles. He told counsel for the defence that his patience had been severely tried for too long. He failed to see how the evidence of his witnesses could have any but the most remote bearing on the case before the court. The charge was treason, not cruelty to children nor general moral turpitude. He presumed that even a traitor could be kind to his friends; and the treachery, if there was treachery, had taken place not before but during the war, and in those areas where our troops were fighting for their lives. Counsel for the defence had not as yet produced any witnesses who had been the prisoner's co-workers and companions during the war. Didn't he have any? No. Counsel referred to was sorry to say he had none. But with his Lordship's permission he would call one more witness, the witness to whom the letter Exhibit 3 and, as he himself believed, the mutilated letter Exhibit 2 had been addressed. Miss Teresa Larnigan had not followed the prisoner to the war zone, but she had followed him in her mind and kept in touch with him. She had written to him, and he had answered her, at a time when he was supposed to be in communication with the enemy. With his Lordship's permission, Miss Larnigan would now take the stand. His Lordship signified his assent and leaned back with a sigh.

Chapter Five

I WOULD not have known Teresa Larnigan had I passed her in the street. Very decent in a grey coat and skirt, she might have been any sturdy woman of the middle or comfortable working class; but it was not difficult, when I looked close, to recognize the younger Teresa whom I had met thirteen years before at the Doctor's gate in the strong figure who strode into court. She moved with the ease of abounding vitality. She had filled out and was bigger than I remembered, a tall woman with broad shoulders and a magnificent physique; the other had been a slight creature. Her face was lined, the once fair skin was darker, but the lines round her eyes and mouth were good-humoured, her chin was firm, her hair, under the brim of her grey felt, gave off its old silvery sheen; perhaps it was white now, one couldn't tell, and her eyes were still intensely, vividly blue.

She was forty-one, the same age as myself. After the life she had led she should have been bloated or shrivelled, but her deep chest didn't sag, her throat was full and round, only her mouth had withered. It had been voluptuous, I remembered, with full, sulky, sensual lips. They were puckered now, but she had about her a sparkle, a look as if laughter might bubble out of her in a moment, an incredible air of youth, and her voice was as young and fresh as that of the girl who had told us that, though she had been blind, now she could see.

She squared her shoulders, looked Charles straight in the eye, and lifted the book.

"I swear by Almighty God that the evidence I shall give shall be the truth and nothing but the truth."

No mumbling about that. She glared at Charles as she spoke the words. She wasn't frightened, she was angry. It would take more than a crowded court and a skinny old judge in a red dressing gown to frighten Teresa. She'd been had up herself, more than once, in police courts. She'd been nearly fourteen the first time, and had been sent to a reform school. The second time she'd got two years, and she had deserved it. But they couldn't do anything to Martin Merriedew. He was different. No one on earth could do anything against him. The thought that he might be condemned and hanged didn't occur to her as a serious possibility. "Don't make me laugh!" She might as well have said the words aloud. Then why bring him here and put him through it like this, sticking him up there for all to stare at as if he were a crook of some sort? It was all lies, and they knew it, or if they didn't they were fools. "What sort of fool are you?" she seemed to be saying to Charles as she handed the book back to the officer of the court.

Then she turned and looked across at the prisoner, and a smile of great sweetness transfigured her face, and I saw him look up; his sombre gaze met hers that was confident and protective; he had at last recognized someone.

Pringle was on his feet.

"What is your name?"

"Teresa Larnigan."

"Where do you live?"

"In Warrington, in the lodge at the almshouse."

"You work there?"

"Yes, I am housekeeper at the Almshouse Infirmary."

"That is a county appointment?"

"Yes."

"How long have you held this appointment?"

"Three months."

"What did you do before?"

"I was in the Fire Brigade."

"And what sort of job was that?"

"It was a war job. We went out during the air raids to fight the fires and rescue people."

"You have known the prisoner for some time?"

"Pretty well all my life. We grew up in the same village; but I didn't really get to know him until he came back there as a doctor."

"How was that? It's quite a small place, isn't it?"

"We were a rough lot, we Larnigans, we didn't mix much. I went away when I was thirteen, and afterwards he went up to London."

"So you only got to know Martin Merriedew when he came home to take over his father's practice in Crabbe village?"

"Yes."

"That was in 1930?"

"Yes."

"You had come home by that time to live in Crabbe village?"

"No. I was living in Bristol, but I went home sometimes to see my family."

"What were you doing in Bristol?"

"I was on the streets."

"Do you mean that you were making your living as a prostitute?"

"Yes."

The gallery gasped. As one man, it opened its mouth and gasped with delighted horror.

"Silence!"

Charles was angry. When order had been restored he leaned forward.

"Is this necessary, Mr. Pringle?"

"I think it is, my lord."

"I find it most unpleasant myself. The woman is evidently

a reformed character, she holds a responsible position in a neighbouring town. You can surely not intend to damage her in the eyes of her employers?"

But Teresa had her own ideas about that. "You needn't worry about me, my lord, or him either. He knows that I'd be on the streets still if it wasn't for Martin."

Charles was taken aback. "Do you know where you are, my good woman?"

"I do, my lord."

"Then speak when you are spoken to, otherwise hold your tongue. You are here to answer the questions addressed to you, nothing more. Do you understand me?"

"Yes, my lord."

"Very well. Now, Mr. Pringle, as I was about to say, this woman, however obstreperous, is not, after all, a hostile witness, and I fail to see just what you hope to prove by raking up her unsavoury past. She has volunteered the information that she has no objection. I have. If it were the counsel for the prosecution who chose to do this, I might understand."

"If your Lordship will allow me — " Mr. Pringle sniffed. He was, as he confessed to me later, very nervous, but he didn't show it. "If I may be treated with a modicum of patience, I think my purpose will become clear."

"Oh, if you want to do Mr. Kennington's work for him!"

"That is not my purpose, my lord, oh, not at all."

"Well, it seems to be."

"If I might be allowed, my lord, to be my own judge of that." Mr. Pringle turned back to his witness but took his time about it. He blew his nose on a large, rather soiled handkerchief, adjusted his eyeglasses, and looked down from his exaggerated ungainly height at the collection of wigs surrounding him, sniffing again audibly as he did so.

"Now, Miss Larnigan: you were making your living on the

streets in Bristol, and you met the prisoner on one of your visits home to the village of Crabbe Minor; is that correct?"

"Yes, I was sick, I went to his surgery."

"You consulted him as a doctor?"

"Yes."

"And then?"

"Then we became friends."

"You gave up your evil life in Bristol and stayed at home after this visit?"

"No. It wasn't quite like that."

"You didn't give up your old life?"

"I did and I didn't. I got a job in a pantomime for a bit, in Plymouth, and they took me on in the bar at the Feathers in Crabbe Major. But that didn't last long. I always found myself back again where I'd been."

"But you remained friends with the prisoner?"

"He didn't throw me over, if that's what you mean. He should have. It went against him being seen with me, I know that now, but he didn't care. He kept on trying."

"Trying what?"

"To get me out of it, off the men and the drink. Then he went away."

"That was in 1933?"

"Yes."

"And what became of you after that?"

"I got a job on the railway in Warrington."

"You gave up your old life after he had gone?"

"Yes. He'd told me he was going and unless I gave it up I would never see him again, so I did. I knew it was the only way to get him back."

"And did he come back?"

"Yes, to Warrington, on a Friday by the eleven-forty-five, the slow train from London. He stepped off it and I was there."

"Where?"

"On the platform."

"You had gone to meet him?"

"Oh, no. I didn't know he was coming. My job was charring in the carriages, so I was there with my pail and mop waiting for the train."

"And he stepped off the train?"

"Yes, halfway down the platform."

"What did you do when you saw him?"

"I dropped everything and ran down the platform to where he was."

"You were glad to see him?"

"Glad isn't the word. I was that excited I was laughing and crying. I was all over myself. But all he said was: 'So there you are, Teresa!' just as if he knew I'd be there. And I said, 'Yes,' and he said, 'Come along then,' so I did. But I tipped the wink to the guard, so as he'd know I'd be back. It was a Friday, my week's pay was due, and I kept my wits about me for all I was so excited. So I asked him — I mean the prisoner — when we got out of the station, where did he want to go, to a hotel? And he said no, he'd only got two-and-ninepence, so I took him to a house I knew. They were good people and they took him in, then I went back to my job."

"You kept on your job?"

"Yes, I had to. I told him that night. 'What do we do for money,' I said, 'if I give up my job?' And he said that was all right with him, for me, he meant. 'And what about you?' I said. But he said I was not to start worrying him about money, the money would look after itself, and he didn't want any. I thought it was daft, but it worked out all right."

"How did it work out? Did you set up house together?"

"Oh, no. I stayed on at the Railway Hostel until he started his Community House; but I looked after him from the beginning."

"What do you mean by that?"

"I'd see to his clothes, do his bit of washing, things like that. He was very bad at looking after himself."

"And what did you do at the Community House?"

"Cooking mostly, and housework."

"You gave up your work on the railway?"

"I'll say I did. It was a full-time job cooking in that house."

"Were you paid for it?"

"No. That was one of his things — no money."

"And were you happy there?"

"Of course, he was there, wasn't he? It was his place; as much, I mean, as any place was."

"And you stayed there in the Community House until the war?"

"Yes."

"And then joined the Fire Brigade?"

"Yes, after he had gone."

"Now, Miss Larnigan, I want you to look at this document." Pringle handed her the letter marked Exhibit 3. "Do you recognize it?"

"Yes."

"You know the handwriting?"

"Yes, of course."

"Is it the prisoner's hand?"

"Yes."

"How did you get hold of it?"

"It is a letter he wrote me. It came by post in the ordinary way."

"When did you receive it?"

"On the 15th of November 1944. The date is marked in blue pencil."

"Who marked it?"

"I did, the day it came. I always did the same with all his letters."

"But the postmark, as I make out, is the 14th?"

"I didn't get it until the 15th."

"Why did you note the date on the envelope?"

"So as to keep all his letters in proper order."

"You kept all his letters? Carefully noting the dates?"

"Yes, in a tin box where they would be safe. As safe, I mean, as I could make them in the bombing."

"The raids on Warrington?"

"Yes."

"You were a member of the Fire Brigade in Warrington in November '44, when you got this letter?"

"Yes."

"You had heard from him before this?"

"Yes."

"He wrote you regularly?"

"Not regularly; I only had twelve letters in four years."

"The eleven letters in the bundle you handed over to the police, and this one that is marked Exhibit 3?"

"Yes."

"You have no other letters from the prisoner in your possession?"

"No."

"And you never had any?"

"No."

Counsel turned to the judge. "I have thought it right to refer to this bundle of letters, my lord, as evidence of the goodwill of the witness. They were private letters; she gave them up of her own accord; you have seen them, so has my learned friend. Any one or all of them could have been produced in this court had it been so desired. We agreed between us that they contained no additional information relevant to this case, so we have put them aside. May I take it that this somewhat unusual proceeding meets with your approval, my lord?"

"As to not troubling the court with all this correspondence, yes, I approve. As to dragging the bundle into the case in order to throw it out again, I can't see what you gain by it."

"The letters make a series, my lord."

"As to that, we've only her word for it that she didn't receive a number of others, some of a more questionable character."

"That is true, my lord."

"Well, never mind; let's get on with the evidence."

"I thank you, my lord. Miss Larnigan, please be so good as to look at the beginning of the letter you hold in your hand. The writer says he cannot send you the information you ask for. Do you remember anything about that?"

"Yes, of course I do."

"You had asked him for some information?"

"Yes. There was a woman, she had been bombed out of her house, her son had been reported as missing. Someone had told her his battalion was in Italy. I asked Martin to try to find out about him."

"And did he find out?"

"No, he couldn't be bothered."

"How do you know?"

"It's here in the letter. He ticks me off properly, doesn't he? 'Don't plague me, Teresa!' and I got no answer at all the first time. He says he answered so he must have, but I hadn't got it, so I wrote again."

"When did you write the first time, asking about the woman's son?"

"Some time in October."

"October '44?"

"Yes. You can see for yourself. He says in this letter he must have forgotten to post the other."

"You think he was referring to this same request of yours for information about the boy?"

"Who else could he be talking about? I hadn't asked about

anyone else, and I didn't go on badgering him, believe me, not after getting this telling off!"

"Were you surprised when you got this 'telling off,' as you call it?"

"No. He was always ticking me off in the old days: sometimes for being too gay or talking too much; then again it would be for worrying, when there was next to nothing in the larder."

"I'm not asking you about the old days, but about this letter. What did you think when you got it?"

"Well, I did think it was a bit hard. I couldn't very well read out to the poor creature what he'd said about her not mattering, could I? But I knew what he meant. He didn't mean he wasn't sorry for her. Some people thought he was a hard man, but he wasn't, just the opposite. He'd go white as a sheet, sometimes, when he saw all those cripples and loonies waiting for him at the clinic."

"We are at cross-purposes, Miss Larnigan. What I want to know is this: did you expect him to get you the information you asked for about this boy's battalion?"

"I thought he might. There was no harm in trying."

"Didn't you know that it was against military regulations to pass on such information, or even ask for it?"

"I may have known. If I did I never thought about it. I didn't think it mattered."

"Please think so now, and think back carefully. Did the accused at any time send you any information of any kind about the movement of troops, the disposition of our forces, or the presence of certain military formations in his area?"

"You ought to know. You've seen all the letters, and you've talked to him, haven't you?"

"Miss Larnigan!" That was Charles.

"Sorry, my lord. But anyone ought to know Martin had no use for all that military stuff."

"On the contrary. That is just what we don't know, and are

trying to find out." Charles was stern. "And I will tell you this: you are doing the prisoner's case no good by your frivolous attitude."

"You mean, my lord — ?" Teresa caught her breath and was silent. For the first time, she was frightened.

"I see that you understand quite well what I mean. Mr. Pringle?"

Pringle repeated the question. "Did the prisoner at any time send you any information about any military units in North Africa or Italy?"

"No, never, unless you count hospitals."

"He wrote you about hospitals?"

"Yes, don't you remember? In one letter there was a lot about that new drug penicillin. He said the Americans had all they wanted, but the British hadn't. He was trying to scrounge some for his lot from the 2nd American Field Hospital."

"Thank you for reminding me. I shall ask you to look at another piece of paper in just a moment. But before you do that I want to ask you something more about this letter. What do you think Martin Merriedew meant when he wrote: 'Do not fail me, Teresa'?"

"I know quite well what he meant. He meant that I mustn't lose faith in him. He knew I wouldn't, but he wanted me to say so. It was only human, wasn't it, when he was so lonely?"

"But why should he be lonely? He had his own group with him, hadn't he?"

"Yes, but he knew they were going back on him."

"He didn't trust them?"

"It was the other way round; he knew that they didn't trust him. He always knew what you were thinking. It was the war, you see, that made the difference between him and the others."

"But they were all pacifists and conscientious objectors, weren't they?"

"Yes, but it didn't mean the same to them. Or if it did, they

299

forgot what they believed once they got out there. They changed, he didn't, so they despised him. They didn't understand."

"He counted on you to understand?"

"Yes."

"And did you?"

Teresa hesitated, then she said: "No, but I knew he was right."

"Now I want you to look at this other piece of paper."

Teresa was given Exhibit 2; as she looked at it, she turned white. When she lifted her eyes to Charles, I thought I caught a look of appeal, and it seemed strange to me that she should look to Charles for help.

But Pringle called her back to him.

"What do you make of this piece of paper, Miss Larnigan?"

"It's a part of a letter from Martin."

"Please read it."

"There are some words missing."

"Can you fill them in?"

"I don't know, but I think so. Oh, yes — I see!" She looked up and smiled her relief.

"What do you see?"

"It's about that hospital, the bit that's torn off. It's the letter he didn't send on."

"You think that's what it is?"

"Yes, yes, it must be, the 2nd Field Hospital, that was the American place where they had all the penicillin." Her face was radiant.

"I thank you, and I think so too." Mr. Pringle sat down.

And Mr. Kennington got up.

II

"Have you ever been in jail, Miss Larnigan?"

"Yes."

300

"How many times?"

"Twice."

"For shoplifting?"

"Yes."

"Were you sent to a reform school when you were thirteen and a half?"

"I was just on fourteen."

"And did you run away from this school?"

"Yes."

"But you were caught stealing and brought back?"

"Yes."

"How long did they keep you, all told, in this school?"

"Until I was eighteen."

"And what did you do when you came out?"

"I went into service in a family."

"Did the prisoner's father, Dr. Jasper Merriedew, get you this position?"

"Yes."

"And how long did you keep it?"

"Three months."

"Were you dismissed or did you leave it of your own accord?"

"I left of my own accord."

"Are you sure of that?"

"Yes."

"Wasn't there some trouble with the son of the house?"

"Yes. He wouldn't leave me alone. I hated him."

"Are you sure your employer didn't dismiss you because you seduced this young man?"

"I hated him. I've said so once."

"How old was he at this time?"

"I don't know."

"Wasn't he two years younger than you?"

"He may have been."

"You knew he was younger than you, didn't you?"

"Yes. That made it worse."

"I see. Well, you left the family, and then what did you do?"

"I went home for a bit."

"To Crabbe village?"

"Yes."

"Where the prisoner lived?"

"He wasn't there then, he was in London."

"You didn't see him on this visit home?"

"No, only the old doctor, Martin's father."

"And did the prisoner's father get you another job?"

"Yes, in a hotel in Bristol, as a scullery maid."

"But that didn't last long, did it?"

"No."

"And then you went on the streets?"

"Yes."

"How old were you when you first went to jail?"

"Nineteen."

"And the second time?"

"Twenty-one."

"You did two years the second time?"

"Yes."

"You managed to keep out of prison after that?"

"Yes."

"But not, I think, out of the police court. You were picked up drunk by the police more than once, weren't you, between the years 1930 and 1933?"

"Yes."

"How many times?"

"I don't know."

"Too often to count?"

"Quite often."

"When was the last time?"

Mr. Kennington waited, then when Teresa kept silent he said: "Come, you remember, surely, the last time you were picked up by the police, don't you?"

"Yes, I remember."

"When was it?"

"The day before Martin went away."

"In 1933?"

"Yes."

"You went to a public house called the Three Feathers with the prisoner, and got drunk?"

"No, I didn't get drunk when I was with him."

"Do you deny that the prisoner went with you on that day to this public house?"

"No, I don't deny that. He did come with me. We had lunch together at the Three Feathers."

"And got drunk together?"

"No, I tell you. It was after he'd gone. He'd told me at lunch-time that he was going away and that I wouldn't see him again for a long time. I got drunk that night."

"You told the court just now that he told you you would never see him again unless you gave up your old life."

"Yes, that's right."

"So you went and got drunk that very night."

"Yes."

"And you were picked up by the police?"

"Yes."

"You didn't see the accused again for three years?"

"That's right."

"But you were a reformed character when he got back?"

"I'd given up men and drink, if that's what you mean."

"And after he got back, did you live with him?"

"No, I stayed on at the Railway Hostel."

"And where did the prisoner stay?"

"With friends, for a bit."

303

"Your friends?"

"Yes, they were good people."

"He made his home with them for how long?"

"I don't remember."

"He was their guest?"

"You mean, did he pay for his board and lodging?"

"Yes, that is what I mean."

"No, he didn't, he hadn't got any money."

"Did you pay for him?"

"No."

"But you had money, hadn't you? What did you get for charring in railway carriages?"

"Two-pound-ten a week."

"And you looked after the prisoner's clothes and so on?"

"Yes."

"But gave him no part of your wages?"

"No."

"You were in love with him, weren't you?"

Teresa hesitated. She looked again at Charles and this time her eyes implored him, but he gave her no sign of encouragement, so she turned back to her tormentor, who repeated his question.

"Were you or were you not in love with the prisoner? Please answer me."

"You could call it that in the beginning before he went away." She spoke slowly and distinctly, as if carefully considering her words. "But he never had any use for me in that way. He wanted to help me, not use me. And after he came back everything was different."

"What do you mean by different?"

"He was a different man, and I felt different."

"In what sense?"

"It is so difficult — I haven't the words." Her face was troubled.

"You didn't feel the same about him but he was in love with you now — is that what you are trying to tell me?"

"Oh, no — just the opposite. I loved him more, but he was quite separate, it broke my heart."

"Because he wouldn't have anything to do with you?"

"No, because he was so lonely."

"With all those people around him?"

"Yes. He loved them, he looked after us all, but they didn't understand him."

"And you did?"

"Yes, a little."

"So you consoled him in his loneliness?"

"I would have done anything, I would have given my life for him — but all I could do was darn his socks and see to the cooking."

"Would you lie for him?"

"Yes, if it would help."

"You would lie under oath to save him from the gallows?"

"Yes, of course."

"And you would have me believe that you never lived with the prisoner?"

"You mean as man and woman?"

"Yes, that is exactly what I mean."

"No. It wasn't like that! It was never like that!" Teresa's face was crimson.

"You had been a professional prostitute, hadn't you?"

"Yes."

"And a drunkard?"

"I used to drink too much sometimes."

"And you had been convicted for stealing, hadn't you?"

"Yes."

"And now you tell me that you wouldn't hesitate to commit perjury to save this man on trial for his life in this court."

"Yes."

305

"Then tell me this. Why should I believe one word of the evidence you have given?"

"Because of him. I could lie and I would lie, but he will not. He is the truth."

III

Had I seen Pringle, or Tim Beresford, or Bill Cummins during the lunch hour on that second day, I would have been less cheerful; any one of those three might have corrected my confidence. Even Charles. Charles would not have talked to me, but he would have noticed my brighter mood, and might have handed me, by way of warning, a copy of the Treachery Act. But Charles didn't come back to lunch. He had asked for sandwiches to be sent in, and Tim stayed with him; Bill was off somewhere hurriedly lunching with friends, and Pringle had gone down to see Martin in his cell; so I lunched alone under Fairchild's soothing but enigmatic eye, and told myself that things were going very well.

Kennington had been clever, but he had, I felt, overdone it. He hadn't known when to stop baiting Teresa; and Teresa had proved herself tough, tougher no doubt than he had expected, tougher than any woman could have been who was not speaking the truth. Wasn't it just a case of the truth being indestructible? Kennington hadn't broken her down because her relations with Martin Merriedew were innocent and their innocence must have been evident to the court. She herself was the proof. She had been like a lighted candle, steadily burning, in an atmosphere so thick with suspicion of evil that a flame of less absolute purity would have spluttered and been put out.

Charles had seen it, he had believed her, I was sure of it. I could tell from the way he addressed her, and she had known this. Something had passed between them that had made for confidence. He had said himself that she was a reformed char-

306

acter. Very well, if this were so, I argued to myself, picking vaguely at the wing of cold chicken Fairchild put in front of me, then the new Teresa who had taken the place of the drunken tart and jailbird, was surely, in her own big healthy body, a proof of Martin's power for good, and his spiritual integrity.

And Pringle had brought this out. He was handling the case, it seemed to me, surprisingly well. My mother must have been mistaken in thinking he did not believe in his client's innocence. But perhaps he had changed, as I had done, during the course of the trial. The startling thought occurred to me as I stirred my coffee: I too had been prepared, only two days ago, to believe Martin Merriedew guilty of treason. Now I was not only convinced of his innocence, I believed that his case was already all but won.

I was a fool. Subconsciously I knew it. I was aware of such a bound, such a leap of relief that I forced myself, even then, to go back in my mind to the moments during the proceedings when I had been frightened. There had been something about the way Gideon Fish gave his evidence. What was it? I knew what it was: it was the fact that every now and then he had blurted out something favourable to the accused, as if driven by some inner compulsion to tell the truth in spite of himself. In the matter of the young German officer, the British captain, and the blood transfusion, when he admitted that Martin might have given his blood to both: hadn't he conveyed to the court an impression of Martin's heroism, of a man prepared to give his life if it was required of him? Why, if Gideon Fish was lying and was doing this out of hate, had he admitted the truth that the British Captain had died on the operating table? Why hadn't he lied with more effect, and held Martin responsible for this Britisher's death? It came to me suddenly that just possibly Gideon Fish had not been deliberately lying at any point; that, on the contrary, he had believed he was throughout telling the truth; in other words, that he believed Martin Merriedew to have done what he accused him of doing, that he believed him in fact to have been a traitor.

A disturbing idea but it explained the sense of conviction carried by his evidence. It explained the man himself. He was passionate, vain, and ambitious. Pringle had brought out a good deal of this in his cross-examination. He had had great schemes, great hopes, great plans all centred in Martin and they had all come to nothing. Martin had refused to lend himself to his schemes. But the two men had still had one thing of importance in common; they were both militant conscientious objectors. Teresa had suggested that the impact of the war itself had changed the other members of Martin's group. Suppose this were true of Gideon Fish as well? Suppose he too had been converted during the war from his pacifism to a belief in the duty of a man to fight, and die fighting to defend his country? Wouldn't that be an explanation of the hatred he came to feel for Martin? Here he was tied to a man whom he had once believed in as the glorious leader of a revolution, but whom he saw now as a milksop, a spineless creature who turned the other cheek toward his enemies and prayed for those who despised him, the kind of Christian in fact that he, Gideon, loathed. And, loathing him, he had begun to suspect him, and in the end had come to believe in his own suspicions.

I don't know to this day if this was true; on that second day of the trial I was only groping, only dimly aware of some such explanation. But if it were true, I ask myself now as I did at that time, then what of all that business of the undelivered letter? What became of Pringle's admirable efforts to prove that Gideon Fish had doctored it? That it was in fact a fragment of a letter to Teresa seems to me to admit of no argument. Even Charles agrees with that. But could Gideon Fish have found it as it was when produced in court, and have truly believed it to be the communication of a spy? Or did he, because he already believed Martin was a spy, deliberately mutilate the innocent letter in order to bring the man who filled him with horror to what he believed was justice? I don't know. I shall never know. The unhappy man's mind remains for me a closed book. At the time it was only mysterious enough and dark enough to disturb my optimism and frighten me a little.

But I wasn't as frightened as I should have been because I had forgotten that Martin was being tried under the Treachery Act. I told myself that the only charge against him which could possibly be proved was the charge on the third count of inciting to mutiny; and that he wouldn't be hanged for that. Had I looked at the opening words of the Act before going back into court, I would have known better.

Here are the words:

An Act to make further provision for the Trial and punishment of Treachery. (23rd May 1940).

Be it enacted by the King's most Excellent Majesty, by and with the advice and consent of the Lords Spiritual and Temporal and Commons, in this present Parliament assembled, and by the authority of the same, as follows:

1. If, with intent to help the enemy, any person does, or attempts or conspires with any other person to do, any act which is designed or likely to give assistance to the naval, military or air operations of the enemy, to impede such operations of His Majesty's forces, or to endanger life, he shall be guilty of felony and shall on conviction suffer death.

Chapter Six

PRINGLE has told me that he wasn't at all happy when the court on the second day was adjourned for lunch. He had not shared my view of Teresa Larnigan's effect on the jury. On his Lordship perhaps; but Mr. Justice Collit was an exceptional being. No average man — and the jury was made up of average men — would believe that her relations with the prisoner had been innocent. It was asking too much imagination, too much sympathy, too much faith. Faith of course in the prisoner was the crux of the whole case; sympathy for him was just what was most signally lacking; and to hope for the exercise of a lively imagination among the respectable tradesmen of Greymouth was folly. The evidence that the defence had managed to bring forward might have persuaded them to believe that he was a strange character, it had certainly not proved him to be an ardent patriot, a war hero, or indeed in any respect the type of man they liked to consider pre-eminently British. No; the qualities they admired and for which they flattered themselves that their race was famous, those qualities in fact which had won the war, British phlegm, British endurance, British faith in British genius, were all conspicuous, in Martin Merriedew's case, by their absence. He was an odd fish and his peculiarities made them uneasy.

As for his remarkable influence on the woman Teresa Larnigan, why should they believe in its virtue unless they had known her before and could compare the woman she now was with the creature she had been? Even then, supposing there was someone among them who had seen her in the old days, hanging about at street corners, her face plastered with make-up, would he be convinced by her appearance and manner in court that she was now a virtuous and noble character? Her manner, Pringle feared, had left much to be desired as far as the jury was concerned, and her appearance counted for nothing in favour of her friend in the dock. Everyone knew that the most dissolute women and the most hardened criminals could present a good appearance in court. And had it been as good as all that, from his point of view? Poor Pringle had positively glared as he put me the question. Hadn't there been something animal, something irrepressibly vital in the woman that suggested a life of incorrigible high spirits and enjoyable sensuality? Yes, and it was just here that he had made his great mistake. He had been so impressed by Teresa Larnigan's honesty and good sense in helping him to prepare his case that he had believed everything that she said. He did so still. His mistake had been in thinking that she could carry conviction in the witness box. And she had done nothing of the sort, Kennington had seen to that. But even if Kennington had let her off, she would still have conveyed to the jury, because of her deep-rich, ample personality, an impression of carnal seductiveness.

He had seen his error the moment he sat down and Kennington got to work on her. He had known that he could afford no second mistake. There was only one blunder left now that he could make. All the rest was over and done with for better or for worse. He could call no new witnesses to undo the damage Teresa had done. There was only the prisoner himself. When Martin Merriedew had taken the stand, Mr. Pringle must rest his case. But should he allow this? Wasn't it much too dangerous?

The answer to that had depended, Pringle told me, on the answer to another question, namely, what was his case? Wasn't it that this man, Martin Merriedew, could not be judged as other men because he was mad? He had been driven slowly to this conviction himself during the weeks preceding the trial.

What else, or what more, could he do for his client than insert a doubt, just one little doubt, into the minds of his Lordship and the jury, of the man's sanity? He could not plead, of course, in this sense. Merriedew had pleaded Not Guilty, maintaining — and in this he was not unlike some other lunatics — that he was the only sane man in an insane world. And as if to prove it, when he had been examined a year ago at the request of his family by a couple of alienists, he had roused himself from his lethargy and given a display of pyrotechnics that had astonished the mental experts. Their report stated that the prisoner was capable not only of following the legal proceedings, instructing counsel, and giving evidence in his own defence, he had shown himself possessed of a penetrating intelligence and an exceptional talent for dialectics.

All the same, Pringle said to me, what other explanation was there, save mental derangement of a high order, for the utter failure of such a life, and for the colossal boast that went with the failure, of being instructed by the spirit of God in his every act? He might have been, with his gifts, almost anything, a great physician, the powerful head of a political movement, a beloved religious leader come to breathe new life into the Church. And what was he? Nothing. The solitary survivor of a scattered insignificant group of nonentities. Why? What had brought it about? What indeed but his own illogical, intolerant, irrational will? He had despised his gifts and thrown them away. He had doubted himself from the beginning, yet demanded all the while absolute faith in himself on the part of his friends.

"You know that, Lady Barbara. Your brother has told me his own story. Was it sane, such conduct? Put alongside it," Pringle squeaked at me, "the incident at Scotland Yard in '39. He turned up there on the outbreak of war, demanding to be interned. On what ground? On the ground that though he loved England he was a stranger in it, an alien, a refugee from no country and with no home anywhere to be sent back to. They laughed at him, naturally enough, as a harmless lunatic, and handed him over to his friend Gideon Fish, who came to fetch him. And that is what he is, in my belief: dreamer and lunatic, who never meant to do any harm to his people or offend against the law but was compelled by his inner obsession to do both. So what can I hope to do for him other than bring out by question and innuendo the crazy innocence of the deluded man?"

Pringle got quite worked up telling his story. He couldn't sit still, but prowled round my drawing room biting his nails; and every now and then he would stop, give a jerk to first one leg, then the other, and peer at me, blinking in a distressing manner.

He had been, he said, in two minds during the trial about putting Merriedew into the witness box. A deplorable state of affairs, he was the first to admit it. But it was impossible to know what his client would say in his own defence or how he would behave under cross-examination. If he were in one of his fits of depression, that might do no great damage. But if he gave a pyrotechnical display, as he had done to the medical men, the result would be fatal. And the prisoner himself had done nothing to help him to a conclusion. He had appeared, each time he saw him, to be completely indifferent to the proceedings.

He had been the same from the beginning with the solicitors, had offered no information that could help them, suggested the names of no witnesses, and made no comment, save one, as to the way he wished the case to be handled. Without Lord Greymouth and Miss Larnigan they wouldn't have known where to turn. Even so, he would have refused the brief, Pringle said, with a loud sniff and blinking miserably, if he hadn't in some curious way been attracted to the accused. Yes, he would go so far as to say that he had been fascinated. But exasperated at the same time, I was to understand: oh, but exceedingly so. His kaleidoscopic changes of mood, his alternating periods of penetrating, shrewd observation and extreme childlike simplic-

313

ity, had been intolerably bewildering. One might have thought from his appearance of deep abstraction in court that he hadn't listened to a word of the evidence against him. Nothing could have been more mistaken. He said that he had paid only a casual attention to what was said in the witness box because he knew beforehand what the witnesses were going to say, and had had other things of greater interest to think about; but he had grasped perfectly the points made against him, and in particular the damage done to his case by the failure of his former comrades to come forward to his defence. That seemed to hurt him more than the vicious attacks of Gideon Fish.

"Gideon knows," he said, "who I am. He has always loved and feared me and my power over him. There was a struggle of wills, his against mine, and he thought he would win by witnessing against me. But he is still afraid of me. The other are only afraid of the world. They loved me a little but they didn't know or believe in me and they have run away because they think that I have brought their faith into disrepute, and they despise me for it. Gideon doesn't believe in me but he loves and hates me and is still afraid of what I may do."

"But Merriedew made one contribution that last day," Pringle went on, "and could anything more fantastic be imagined? 'All these proceedings are of little importance,' he said. 'I've only one thing to ask of you, that you bring out the truth.' 'What truth,' I said, 'are you talking about?' 'The eternal truth,' he said, 'behind the confusion of passing appearances. You have been dealing with phantoms. All the court is peopled with phantoms, ghosts of the dead, ghosts of the past, phantoms risen up out of history. Make a clean sweep, Pringle. Take a broom to them, and clear the court so that the naked truth will be plain. That is what you and I must do when I give my evidence.' As if ever," Pringle said, "in any court of law, or any small matter of dispute in private life, the naked truth was ever made plain about anything!"

314

Pringle ran his long fingers through his lank grey hair, flung off, took a turn round the room, and stood for a moment with his back to me, rapping on a windowpane. Then he took up his place again in front of the grate and got on with what he was saying. He had at last decided, after hearing Teresa Larnigan, to stick to his original decision that Merriedew must go into the witness box. It was risky, Martin might well cook his own goose and ruin Pringle's last hopes by giving a devastatingly sane and lucid account of his conduct and his motives, he might even startle the court by suddenly pleading guilty, but he had a right to speak in his own defence if he wanted to and it was a right that no counsel, however fearful of the result, could deny him. Pringle, filled with foreboding, had gone down to see him in his cell at the lunch hour to put these considerations before him but had found that Martin Merriedew had quite made up his mind as to the result of the trial. It had been a particularly painful interview.

"Was he very unhappy?"

"Yes," Pringle said. "He was very unhappy. The word, indeed, is quite inadequate. Agony is perhaps better. But I do not know that I can find words to convey the relentless impression. He was sweating, but not exhausted; that was the cruelty. One felt that he was mercilessly strong, capable, that is to say, of an almost endless endurance of intolerable pain. It had been going on all night, I knew that. During the morning, in court, he had hidden the suffering under the iron inscrutability you noticed; but the police officer in charge of him had reported to me before the court met that he had been up all night. He had walked interminably up and down his cell and had seemed to be talking to himself. The man on night duty in the cells had heard his voice, going on and on, not loud, it was only a murmur, but urgent and hurried. It would go on for a time, then there would be a long silence; towards morning he had dropped to the floor and the officer on guard had gone in to him twice, thinking that perhaps he had fallen asleep or fainted with his head on his arms on the blanket; but the prisoner had lifted his head the first time and waved him away without speaking, and the second time he had said: 'Please leave me in peace. I haven't much time.' So the officer had gone away and left him alone. But he had kept an eye on him; and at about five o'clock was going in to him with a cup of tea when he heard him say a very queer thing, if, that is, he heard rightly. The words were not addressed to him of course but, as it seemed, to God. And what the guard thought he heard him say was: 'How often must I die?' And when he heard that, the man tiptoed away."

As he told me this Mr. Pringle faced me strangely from across the familiar room with its nice intimate furnishings and the photographs of Jane and James smiling from their frames on my desk.

"And was he praying," I asked, after a silence, "when you saw him at the lunch hour?"

"No, he was just quietly sitting on his bed, sweating. And he was most courteous. He wished to thank me, he said, for my efforts on his behalf. Then with a smile: 'They won't save me from the gallows, you know that as well as I; but we needn't trouble ourselves as to that, since neither of us will be to blame. I am willing to be hanged, if that is the law. But I must give my evidence first, I know that. You thought at first that I was guilty, now you tell yourself that I am mad; but you are beginning to suspect the truth, and it may be that you will believe completely in time. Don't let failure to win worry you with vain regrets. You have fought well for me. You could have done no more had you believed in me from the beginning with all your might. Remember what I say when it is finished.' "

II

Martin Merriedew wasn't long in the witness box. It was two-thirty when he took the stand, and it was just after three

316

when he was led back to the dock and Pringle began his concluding speech for the defence.

Although I did not know at the time what I have just written down, I could see that counsel was intensely nervous; but the emaciated, towering figure in the witness box was quiet. He was very close to me now, not more than seven or eight feet away. I could see the shape of the bones of his wasted face, the knife edge of the jaw, the red rims round his eyes that were sunk deep in his skull, and the sweat trickling down his livid forehead. At the same time I felt sure that I wasn't seeing him clearly. It was as if I were looking at him through a mist, and it seemed to me at moments that he loomed unnaturally large, as figures do sometimes in a fog. But his voice was strong and familiar, unmistakably, as I have said, the voice of a man I had known years ago.

And they were all there, those little phantoms out of the past of his happy youth. Miss Molly Tripp and Martha Blundle and Mary Holt were in the gallery, they had come back again by bus from Crabbe. Fothergill and Jeremy Green were behind the press. Teresa was alone, but Francis sat with Edward and Michael and the other witnesses. Was Francis, too, a phantom to the prisoner? Were his brothers, and his mother and sister who were waiting somewhere for news, nothing more than ghosts? Impossible to say what was passing in that mind; but it seemed as if the stuffy, crowded court had no reality to the man. When they sniggered in the gallery, as they did more than once, when Martha Blundle suddenly went off into hysterics and had to be hustled out, he appeared not to notice. But his face was not inscrutable now. It was naked and exposed and sweating.

"Martin Merriedew, you are accused of adhering to the King's enemies during the recent war, and are indicted on three counts. Have you anything to say in your defence?"

"Yes."

"Are you guilty on any or all of the three counts?"

"Not guilty on all and every count."

"What is your address?"

"His Majesty's prison in this city."

"You mistake the meaning of my question. I am asking for your private address, the place where you live?"

"I have no other place."

"You have no home in this country?"

"No."

"But you were born in England, weren't you?"

"Yes."

"And grew up in a village called Crabbe Minor?"

"Yes."

"Your parents were British-born, weren't they?"

"Yes."

"That makes you a British subject, doesn't it?"

"You may say so."

"It is not for me to say, it is the law of the land. You know that, don't you?"

"I know the law, yes."

"Then you know that a man born in England of British parents owes allegiance to his Majesty King George VI, don't you?"

The accused, staring at counsel as if with concentrated attention, was silent. Pringle waited a moment, then put his question in a different form.

"Do you or do you not recognize, Martin Merriedew, that you owe allegiance to his Majesty the King of England?"

"It is difficult to answer so that you will understand."

"Why is it difficult? It's a plain question, and a plain answer will do very well. An answer in one word is what I want, yes or no?"

Martin was silent again.

318

"Come, yes or no? Do you or do you not owe allegiance to his Majesty King George VI?"

"I owe him a secondary allegiance. My first allegiance is to God." A shrill laugh from somewhere in the gallery was quickly smothered.

"We are not enquiring just now into your religious beliefs, but into your conduct during the war."

"The two are inseparable."

"Your conduct during the war and your allegiance to God are inseparable, you say?"

"Yes."

"Well, what were you doing during the war?"

"I was nursing the wounded."

"You were exempted from military service because of your conscientious objections?"

"Yes."

"You consider it morally wrong to fight in defence of your country?"

"I do."

"Do you love your country?"

"I love England, yes."

"But your conscience would not allow you to fight to defend her?"

"With deadly weapons, no."

"With what weapons, then, would you defend your country?"

"With my life; I would give my life, and with love." A titter this time ran all round the gallery, so that the following words were all but lost. They were: "I gave my whole life, and all my heart."

"Very well. I understand you to say that you were ready to give your life in defence of your country, but you refused to fight. Is that correct?"

"Yes."

"That doesn't mean helping the enemy, or does it?"

Martin didn't answer. Pringle waited; then, as the witness was still silent: "Can't you answer the question?"

"How should I answer when your words have no meaning?"

"What words? What's wrong with them?"

"The word 'enemy'; it means nothing."

"On the contrary, it is the key word of the indictment against you. You are charged with adhering to the enemy during the war, and I am asking you now what you have to say about it?"

Again the witness was silent. Again Pringle waited. At last he broke out: "You have nothing to say to this charge?"

"I met with no enemy during the war."

"What's that?"

"What I just said."

"Well, what did you say?"

"It was you, not I, who said it."

"Don't bandy words with me, if you please; just answer my questions. Did you or did you not give aid and comfort to the enemy wounded you nursed in your hospital during the war? And did you on a certain night in 1942 in the month of March in North Africa help four of them to escape?"

"I nursed many German wounded but they were not my enemies, and it was not hard to love and comfort them."

"You say you loved these Germans?"

"Yes, they were wounded men."

"How do you suppose they got wounded?"

No answer.

"Didn't you know they had been fighting your own fellow countrymen and not only wounding but killing them by the thousand?"

"Yes. There were a great many dead on both sides and the wounded and dying would be brought in all together after a battle."

"Do I understand you to mean that to you they were all alike?"

"You could not have told them apart except by their clothes."

"And the Germans were the same to you as your own people?"

"It is natural to love one's own. I had thought when I was young that I would give my life for the people of this England, but the war made me understand that I couldn't do that."

"You want this court to understand that when Germany declared war on your country you felt bound to side with the enemy?"

Martin licked up the sweat that was trickling into his mouth before he answered. "No, you do not understand. The war made us all the same. There were no barriers left except one between life and death. I fought on the side of life."

"You refer to your hospital work?"

"Yes."

"And your wounded men were all alike to you, whether they were German or British."

"Some were braver than others under pain, but many were afraid to die, and then there was no difference between them."

"Now, please think for a moment of some who were not dying but were lightly wounded. Did you at any time help any of these lightly wounded Germans to escape?"

"There was no escape for anyone from that horror. No one could get away."

"That is not an answer to my question. You have heard a witness tell the court that you drove an ambulance of wounded Germans away from your hospital in North Africa, and allowed them to escape. Do you recall the occurrence?"

"I remember something of the kind."

"You have been accused of doing this intentionally. Is this true?"

"No, I don't think so."

"You are not certain one way or the other?"

"No. But it cannot be true."

"Why not?"

"They were in my care, I had nursed them, I was responsible for them, they would have been lost."

"How lost?"

"Lost in the desert."

Mr. Pringle seemed not to know how to proceed. He waited, eying the man in the witness box with an expression of acute discomfort. At last he said: "Well, if that is all you have to say to this charge, we will turn to something else. Do you remember a man who called himself Captain Banks?"

"Yes, he was a friend."

"Did you give him a book?"

"Yes."

"The book that has been put in evidence?"

"Yes, Milton's *Areopagitica*."

"Were you on intimate terms with this man Banks?"

"Not intimate, but he was a lonely man."

"Do you know what became of him?"

Martin didn't answer. Pringle waited again, then with growing exasperation: "Don't you know that this man who called himself Banks was shot as a spy?"

"They told me, yes; but they had told me before that he was missing."

"You mean that you didn't believe them?"

"Why should I believe them when they had lied?"

"But you know now, don't you, that he was a German, a secret agent, and was shot?"

"No, I never saw him again."

"Didn't you hear a witness state on oath that he had been shot as a spy?"

"It was the same man who brought the book and told me that my friend was missing."

"You are accusing the witness of perjury?"

"No. What has all this to do with me? I only know that the

322

man Banks was without other friends, so I befriended him. If he is dead, what matter? I can do no more for him."

"The matter is that you are accused of giving this German spy secret information of military importance to hand on to the enemy. Did you do anything of the kind?"

"That is a foolish question."

"Foolish or not, did you do such a thing?"

"No. Why do you plague me with such rubbish?"

"Never mind the rubbish, as you call it, just answer my questions. Did you ever send any military information of any kind to the Germans through this man Banks or any other secret agent?"

"You know as well as I, that I did not."

"You have seen the torn letter marked Exhibit 2?"

"I have."

"Did you write it?"

"It is in my hand."

"Do you remember writing it?"

"No."

"So you don't remember to whom you had written it?"

"No."

"Or what you meant by this reference to a unit of some sort?"

"No."

"You remember nothing about this letter?"

"I remember that Teresa had asked some questions."

"Teresa Larnigan?"

"Yes."

"You heard her say in the witness box that she thought the letter had been meant for her?"

"Yes."

"But you cannot corroborate her statement?"

"No."

"So for all you know you may have intended the letter for the enemy?"

Silence.

"Did you hear me?"

Silence.

"I will repeat my question. Could you have written this letter intending to send it on to the Germans?"

"I don't think so. I wrote some letters for the dying to their families in Germany, but this letter you are speaking of cannot have been one of them."

"Didn't you hear the witness Gideon Fish swear on oath that he found it in the pages of a book you had left behind?"

"Yes, that must be true."

"And didn't you hear my learned friend say that he believed it was intended to give military information to the enemy?"

"Yes, I heard him say this."

"Well, what have you to say to it?"

Silence.

"Answer me. Have you nothing to say in your own defence?"

"Are you asking me if I betrayed my own people?"

"Yes, that is what I am asking you. Did you or didn't you?"

The silence this time was so prolonged that Charles was about to intervene when Pringle threw up his hands and squealed: "Why don't you answer me? Don't you know that you are on trial for your life? Are you a fool that you want to be hanged or are you play-acting?" And then, when Martin Merriedew answered at last by saying, "I am trying to tell you the truth, but I can only be certain of this: I wished to betray no one," Pringle turned to the Judge:

"My lord, I am at a loss. I can get no sense from my client."

"Perhaps," Charles said, "I can help you."

III

Thinking back on that scene, I have sometimes wondered if Pringle was really driven distracted or if the play-acting he mentioned wasn't his own? I have never asked him and he hasn't told me. But if his purpose was to show Martin up in court as a lunatic, then it was a mistake to have suggested the idea of play-acting. For the jury got it, the press pounced on it, and the grey-wigs seated round him smiled. They had not, strangely enough, been amused up to then. The impact of the enigmatic personality in the witness box had been powerful enough to keep their attention riveted. Kennington himself had been puzzled but now he smiled and looked down his nose. Charles did not; Charles was grim; he spoke slowly, measuring his words.

"Martin Merriedew, you stand at the bar of the court accused of treason; and you have made things very difficult for your counsel, who is here to defend you. Indeed, you have treated this court with something very like contempt. But you are on trial for your life; you are not a fool, and you know very well that what you say under oath will influence the verdict the jury will give. I want you to answer the questions I shall put to you, in the same way that I shall put them, and I trust with the same purpose, to arrive at the truth of the charges against you. Do you understand me?"

"I do."

"It is customary — I will put it no more strongly than that — to address the Judge on the bench in his Majesty's Courts of Justice as 'my lord.' Is it a matter of conscience with you to omit this title?"

"It is."

"So be it. I can do without it. But the reason for the ceremonious approach which you disapprove of is this: while I sit on this bench I am the King. Do you understand this?"

"I understand what you are saying."

"But do not accept the truth of it?"

Martin was slow in answering, but at last he said: "To me you are a man as I am."

Charles thought a moment. "Well, let me put something

325

else to you. Do you recognize my authority over you under the law?"

"Such authority as the law can give is yours."

"But you, if I understand you, are a man who places his conscience above the law. Is that correct?"

"If I tell you the truth, you will not believe me."

"Whether I believe you or not, the verdict will not rest with me. You are being tried by a jury of your fellow citizens, loyal subjects of his Majesty the King. It will be for them to decide if you are telling the truth and are to be set free, or hanged for treason."

"I have always told the truth. What I have said I have said in public to the people. Why do you ask me now what I have said? Ask them. Ask the men and women of this city, or the people of my own village, or the wounded we nursed during the war."

"We have been doing that very thing, Martin Merriedew, to the best of our ability in this court. You have heard the evidence of the witnesses for and against you. I now am asking you to tell me if you place your conscience above the law?"

Martin was silent a moment, then with his eyes fixed on Charles he said: "You are not my king, nor the judge of my conscience and you cannot judge me; but you are the law, and I accept the law. I shall be hanged if you say it. But you would have no authority over me unless God allowed it."

Charles's face was a study. It was he now who kept the court waiting, and the silence was breathless. Then he sighed, and said as if disappointed in some way: "Very well, I will accept that as your reasoned statement. And now I want you to cast your mind back to Christmas Eve of 1944, that is, just over a year ago. I want you to tell me what happened in the canteen to which you went that night. Do you remember the occasion?"

"Yes."

"Well, what happened in that canteen?"

326

"The men were singing. The horror became unbearable as I listened. Then I had a vision — "

"What do you say?"

"I had a vision of the future."

It was at this point that Martha Blundle had her fit of hysterics. When order had been restored, Charles's sceptical, irritated, weary gaze came back to the prisoner, and for a moment searched the livid, sweating face. If he was wondering if the man in the dock was play-acting, he seemed to be satisfied that he was not, for his tone was matter-of-fact when he spoke.

"Well, what did you see in your vision of the future?"

"I saw new wars and the enemy of my people was a new enemy. The enemies of today had become our friends and were fighting shoulder to shoulder with our men, the men who were in the canteen that night, and their sons, who are only children now."

"And who was this new enemy?"

"I do not know; I could not tell, but the murder was the same, and the blood and the pain, so I called on them to stop."

"To stop?"

"Yes, to stop their singing, and come with me through the snow to the German lines. If they were to be friends so soon, I asked, why not make friends now?"

"Is that what you said to the men in the canteen?"

"I don't know what other words I used. But what I said made them angry."

"Did you tell them to throw down their arms and refuse to fight?"

"I may have done."

"Don't you know, Martin Merriedew, that to do that was to incite them to mutiny and that inciting to mutiny in wartime is treachery?"

"I wanted to save them."

"By inducing them to lay down their arms?"

327

"Yes."

"You believed the Germans would listen to you and do the same?"

"Yes. I believed that if our men would listen so would those on the other side!"

"But you knew all the time that what you were attempting to do was treason?"

"No. I believed that I was commanded to do it by the spirit of God."

"You would make God responsible for your treachery?"

"I am not guilty of treachery. I am who I am."

"Well, who are you?"

"If I told you, you would not believe me."

"Martin Merriedew, I have been patient with you up to now, because I think that you are speaking what you believe to be the truth; but I cannot allow you to pretend to some God-given authority that sets you apart from other men. I have allowed you to say that I am a man like yourself. Now you have the audacity to suggest that in some mysterious way you are different from all your fellow men. It is as if you claimed to be Christ Himself."

"And if I were?" The prisoner's voice was quiet, but it carried through the court. "Wouldn't you crucify me?"

"Tut, tut, man!" Charles's peevish tone was just the thing to keep the court silent. "We don't crucify people nowadays, however exalted their pretensions or however vile their conduct."

"No; you would be less merciful and declare me insane. Nevertheless — and this is the truth — today a thousand Christs would not be enough."

"Be quiet! Hold your tongue and listen. I am going to read you the words of the law under which you are being tried. They are embodied in the Treachery Act that was passed by the King with the advice and consent of the Lords Spiritual and Temporal and Commons, on the 23rd of May, 1940. You are being tried for your life under this Act, and the words are these:

" 'If with intent to help the enemy any person does or attempts or conspires with any other person to do any act which is designed or likely to give assistance to the naval, military or air operations of the enemy, to impede such operations of his Majesty's forces, or to endanger life, he shall be guilty of felony and shall on conviction suffer death.' Do you understand the meaning of these words?"

"I do."

"And you declare that you did not attempt in this canteen on Christmas Eve to impede the members of his Majesty's forces gathered there in the performance of their duty?"

"I tried to save them, and failed."

"I will ask you once more. Do you declare, having heard the words of the law, that you are not guilty of a treasonable act?"

"I am not guilty."

IV

Kennington had no questions and, taking his tone from Charles, was constrained, he said so, to stick to the bare facts of the case in his closing speech for the Crown, and leave the prisoner's delusions about God out of it. The case, indeed, was so singular that if one allowed one's attention to be distracted from the facts one might find oneself lost in the realms of metaphysics or, in plain man's language, the world of dreams.

The defence seemed to have based its plea on the character of the accused. His learned friend as good as asked the jury to believe that the man had not done the things he had done because he was incapable of doing them. He himself was well aware that the burden of proof lay with him. The jury must be convinced beyond reasonable doubt, on the evidence, that the prisoner at the bar had acted treacherously, and it mattered not a jot, if he did so act, whether the act in question was consistent with his character as revealed to them or not. He therefore did not propose to delve into the secret places of the man's peculiar mind as he had been invited to do by his learned friend. He would resist that temptation and stick to the facts. What were they?

The first fact — and it must have come to the jury with the force of a blow between the eyes — was that the prisoner, surrounded in his hospital by the most convincing signs of suffering inflicted on his fellow countrymen, had made friends with the enemy. No witness, not even the accused man himself, had disputed this fact. The accused had even gone so far as to say that it was not hard to love them. Admittedly the enemies to whom he referred were not attacking him or his fellow workers at the moment when he met with them; they were with one exception flat on their backs or at best limping about on crutches, and they were prisoners; but, to use another of the accused man's own words, they had been murdering our own men, or doing their best to, only a few hours before. Nevertheless, the prisoner made friends with them. He not only treated them correctly according to the rules of civilized behaviour, he went much further than that, he went out of his way to be so exceedingly friendly with these Germans that he had shocked the members of his own group, pacifists and conscientious objectors like himself, shocked them so deeply that not one of them had come forward in his defence.

"That, then," Kennington said, "is one incontrovertible fact. The exception among those with whom we know he had to do was, of course, the German spy who passed by the name of Banks. He too became the accused man's friend, and a very special friend. He wasn't helpless or wounded, he was actively engaged in running round the war zone on his secret deadly business. You may believe that the man in the dock didn't know it. You may believe that this spy fooled him up to the

330

end. I don't. But let us go back to the facts that admit of no two opinions.

"The second is of no great importance." Kennington's manner was easy as he went on. "I don't wish to make much out of it, but it is a fact nevertheless. The prisoner volunteered to deliver an ambulance-load of wounded to the railhead, where they were to be put on a hospital train and sent to the base. He drove them out of his camp, and that's the last that was ever heard of them. The prisoner walked back to his unit next morning, said he didn't know what had happened, and in fairness to him I would remind you that his commanding officer accepted his story. But this incident occurred in the early days of his service as a hospital orderly; his commanding officer did not have in front of him the long story of his suspicious behaviour that you have been furnished with in this court. I leave it to you to decide if the fact that these Germans escaped stands in his favour or not.

"The document, Exhibit 2, is another fact. My learned friend would have me read it together with the prisoner's letter to the witness Teresa Larnigan, but I don't see why I should. I prefer to take the thing as it stands by itself, and as it was found by the witness Gideon Fish in the pages of a book. And all I will draw your attention to now in regard to this paper is that the prisoner himself could not swear to its innocence. He was on oath and I believe that we were all struck by his determination at certain moments to tell the truth, even when he wasn't asked for it. But he could say nothing about this letter. It is unfinished and he couldn't finish it. I ask why, gentlemen of the jury, and leave you to answer the question for yourselves."

Kennington at this point did allow himself to stray from the facts. He did at some length what he had denied that he would do, and analysed Martin Merriedew's character with damaging effect, dwelling on his courage and his exceptional intelligence, recalling a former witness's statement that he had a cool head, and so on. I shan't follow him. He had said it all before. I had heard Martin's qualities twisted into defects ad nauseam. But counsel came at last to what he called the key, the damning, the fatal fact of the case: the prisoner's outburst in the canteen, and his incitement to mutiny. The accused had made no attempt to deny this charge. Instead he had excused the action. He had said that he had been in the right, and by way of excuse had made claims so extravagant, so foolish, and so shocking, that they were not only an insult to the intelligence of the jury, but were offensive to every Christian in the court.

He, counsel, would not dwell on the blasphemous claims of the prisoner. His Lordship had dealt with them and would no doubt do so again. The charge before them was not blasphemy, but incitement to mutiny, and the least offensive of the prisoner's excuses for his conduct had been that he had had a dream, a dream of the future. But the men in that canteen on that Christmas Eve had not been engaged in a war of the future, they were involved in an immediate struggle for the life of their nation, the safety of their king and their own homes, and the continued existence of everything they held dear. To weaken or attempt to weaken the will of our men to fight and, if need be, give their lives in defence of their country, at a moment of national peril, with the enemy guns shaking the walls of that flimsy shelter, was the prisoner's crime, and it was more deadly than murder.

v

Pringle had done his best to forestall counsel's closing speech by declaring that none of the so-called facts of this case spelt treachery; and until he came to the affair of the canteen it had seemed to me that he was on fairly strong ground. But on that piece of granite fact his argument splintered to fragments, and he was obliged to fall back on the extravagant, the irrational, the unbelievable innocence of Martin Merriedew's character.

He went back into the past. He held the prisoner up before the stolid eyes of the jury as a man obsessed by dreams of another, a better, a happier world, and consumed by the longing to make that world a reality. The dream was for him the reality. This world was of no importance to him, and he wanted nothing from it; money, success, power, he had refused them all, and given himself to the humblest service of his fellow men. He was a selfless man, so single-minded, so concentrated, so entirely devoted to realizing his ideal that he was incapable of thinking as other men thought, or of accepting the conventions of the society in which he lived. He had not been a passive objector to the conventions of the visible world. He had attacked the Church, the Medical Association, the Government. He had been a troublemaker always, but until war came he had been tolerated. A few had loved him, many had hated him, but he had been left free to follow his dream. The war had crashed into it.

"You may say," Pringle cried, "that he wasn't the only one whose world was destroyed, nor the only one who hated it. Out of the many millions of our men, and women too, who went overseas or stayed at home to be blitzed, if there were a handful who welcomed the war I don't know them. But his case was different from most. I was about to say from every other, and I shall say it. His case was unique in this — that every man and woman who took part in the war, hating it, had something tangible left to cling to, to fight for, to protect, a family, a home, a little house until it was destroyed, a plot of land, a cow grazing in the fields or a pig snuffling in a pigsty. But this man had nothing. He had left his family, use the word 'abandon' if you like, in pursuit of his dream. He had no home, no bit of land, he had nothing of his own save his dream; and so

333

when that was shattered, in one of his recurrent moods of great depression, he went to Scotland Yard and asked to be interned.

"You may think that the act of an idiot, members of the jury. It was simply his logical reaction to the terror that had been let loose on the earth. You glimpsed it in the letter that he wrote to his friend Teresa Larnigan. I do not ask you to applaud his conduct. I do not ask you to admire this man, or his work during the war, for he did pull himself together, and he did do his obscure and humble bit during the conflict. All I ask of you is this: I ask you to agree that he cannot be judged as other men are judged; and I mean by that that his actions are not to be assessed as one would be bound to access them were they the actions of an ordinary and average man.

"He has made extraordinary claims. I do not expect you to take them seriously. You may well have found them shocking. I was shocked myself. But the very fact that he did lay claim to divine authority as against the law, in the very presence of the law, is to my mind a proof of his innocence; and I ask you to consider this when you review the evidence."

Poor Pringle, he knew that he was talking to twelve average men, and he knew that Martin Merriedew had lost any sympathy his counsel might have gained for him by his own showing in the witness box. The jury, the members of the bar, the officers of the court, like the spectators, all detested and despised him now. I say "poor Pringle" because that is the way he appeared to me at the time. His case was lost. His client had lost it for him. He would be acquitted perhaps on counts one and two; but he would be found guilty on count three and sentenced to death.

That, it seemed to my numbed brain, was what it all came to. Martin Merriedew would be hanged and Pringle knew it. But I know now that he was, even when he sat down, counting on Charles for another and a different end.

334

Chapter Seven

CHARLES summed up next morning. We didn't meet before he left for the court, and we had exchanged no private word the night before. He had remained closeted with Tim until six, then had gone to change without coming to join me for his customary glass of sherry. Bill Cummins stayed with me. He and I played piquet, then we all dined with the Sheriff. His return dinner to Charles was an official courtesy and an obligation from which I could not ask to be excused without confessing to a state of mind that I was determined to conceal. Not from Charles; I couldn't hope to conceal from Charles my sense of intolerable strain; but from the others, and most particularly from Fairchild. I hoped that Charles would pretend to be deceived, and he did. Even Tim couldn't have guessed from our manner to each other, at the great distance between us, a distance that nothing less than the complete collapse of all my defences could have bridged. Had I broken down and indulged in a wild burst of hysterical weeping, had I flung myself on Charles and howled, it might just possibly have been better for us both. But I didn't do that. I felt that I had no right to make a scene, no right to obtrude in any way, no right, in fact, to be there. And then, of course, I hadn't been bred to collapse before the end of a race. So we separated immediately on returning at 10:15, the official hour, from dinner; and even that night faded at last into a grey morning.

I have no fault to find with Judge Collit's summing up in the case of *Rex* v. *Merriedew*, nor do I criticize, as was done in

335

certain quarters, his unconventional way of handling the witnesses. On the contrary, I am grateful to him. Knowing him as I do, I understand the effort it cost him to listen carefully to Martin Merriedew and endeavour to understand him. Of the witnesses for the defence, Teresa Larnigan was the only one he found tolerable. He told me, on the single occasion when we discussed the case, that he had liked the woman, adding that she reminded him of Charlotte and me. She had, he said, two qualities common to us both: vitality and great loyalty. But the others, the Reverend Nathaniel Smith-Carey notably, and above all Martin Merriedew himself, were of a type that set his teeth on edge; and I knew it. But I had become increasingly aware, as the proceedings drew to a close, that he had allowed his personal distaste for saints and what he considered sanctimonious rubbish to weigh not so much as a grain in his balancing of the evidence, and indeed had gone to the limit of what was compatible with British justice in the leniency he accorded the defence. And he told me another thing on the unique occasion when we discussed the trial: namely, that my presence in court had had its effect. It had made him, he said, more patient than he would otherwise have been; so I have that grain of comfort securely lodged in the shifting confusion of my uncertain, unhappy mind, and one much more weighty consideration, the knowledge — and Francis agrees with me on this if on nothing else — that we were right in not asking Charles to refuse the case.

II

His summing up was not long but I won't give the whole, only the gist of it.

He reminded the jury that the prisoner at the bar was being tried under the Treachery Act. The Act had been necessitated, he explained, by the emergency of war, and was designed to protect the nation during a period of peril, peril not only in battle and from weapons of war, but from an invasion of invisible enemies who found their way into the ranks of our own army and into our very homes. It was the business of this army of spies not only to collect information that might be of help to the enemy, but to undermine the morale of our fighting men and civilian population. And the Treachery Act had been passed to make such work as difficult, as dangerous, as costly, as possible. It was a war measure to protect our people from any and every kind of treachery, and was rightly of a great simplicity. The only penalty allowed under it was the death penalty, and to suffer the death penalty a conviction on only one count of the indictment was necessary.

The accused, Martin Merriedew, had been indicted on three counts. To help prisoners to escape was undoubtedly an act of treachery, but the jury might perhaps find that the Crown had not proved its case on this count. The evidence was by inference, and he doubted if there was such a thing. He himself could not see how the guilt or the innocence of the accused could be proved, short of searching out the four wounded Germans who had been in the ambulance, and who, according to the defence, must have hit the prisoner over the head, wrecked the ambulance, and made off across the desert. The Crown had failed to find these Germans, if they had looked for them; and he didn't blame them if they hadn't. This incident had occurred in '42, and there had been a great deal of fighting since. The wounded Germans in question might well have found their way back to their own lines to be patched up and fall in a subsequent battle. Moreover, though the fighting had stopped in Europe on the 10th of May of last year, we were not yet at peace with Germany, and one really could not expect the military authorities in that country, many of whom were themselves prisoners on trial for their lives at Nuremberg, to assist us in seeking out four of their nationals who might well be dead.

He had dwelt at some length on this first count with one idea only: that of warning the jury in a case carrying the death penalty against trusting to inconclusive circumstantial evidence. But he would add here one other word of caution. He would ask the members of the jury to make a supreme effort to put out of their minds the very natural prejudice produced by the war itself. There was probably not a member of the jury nor a man or woman in the court who had not suffered some grievous loss through the conflict; a son, a brother, a friend, or it might be merely a loss of property. None had escaped the consequences of the conflict. All had paid and would go on paying the immense account of destruction. But, and he said it solemnly, no personal grief or anger with the enemy should be allowed to cloud a just man's mind or influence his judgment when he came to review the evidence for or against the prisoner.

He would pass to the second count. The man at the bar was accused of being in secret communication with the enemy and of furnishing them with information in regard to our military forces. If this was true, or if it were true that he had merely attempted but failed to do something of the kind, then he was a traitor.

There had been a lot of wrangling about a letter, about two letters, both written undoubtedly by the prisoner. The defence argued that both had been addressed to the witness Teresa Larnigan, and that both were foolish letters, but not criminal and not treacherous. He agreed with the opinion of the defence as to the letter to Miss Larnigan. It was a foolish letter, and he would have something in particular to say about that presently, because it was the letter of a man who had been exempted from military service on the ground that his conscience would not allow him to fight and attempt to kill the enemy.

Then there had been a book, and counsel for the defence had quoted from it with some dramatic effect. "Give me the liberty to know, to utter and to argue freely according to conscience above all liberties." The words were John Milton's, and had a fine ringing sound; but he couldn't see that counsel had any business to drag them into the case. It was all very well to talk about liberty of conscience in peacetime, but liberty was the first thing every man and woman in the land was asked to give up during a war. Liberty of action, of movement, of choosing one's occupation, all were taken from us as well as freedom of speech. What, then, of freedom of thought? Well, a man's thoughts were his own, even in battle, so long as he kept them to himself, and they didn't interfere with his doing his duty. But that was just what the prisoner at the bar had not done. He had claimed as a right the liberty to utter, according to his conscience, sentiments incompatible with his duty as a loyal subject of the King, when a deadly war was going on. This was the substance of the third count against him, and he would come to it in a moment. Just now he was considering these letters and the book the prisoner had given to a German spy who had made friends with him. The letter, Exhibit 3, addressed to Miss Larnigan and offered by her to the police, was not in his opinion a treacherous document; but it was a bad letter. Indeed the prisoner seemed to have laid claim throughout the war to a degree of freedom on the score of conscience that was disquieting. If being allowed by the law to refuse to fight for your country in wartime carried with it the right to rail against the conduct of the war and the very fact that we were at war, then he felt that there was something wrong with the law and that it might well be changed. The law in England was not a static or a dead thing. It was a living body like an oak tree or the British Constitution. This law, the Treachery Act, which he was administering today, was a sporadic growth, vital and necessary for the time of emergency, but it would be lopped off when the emergency was over. In the same way or, more correctly, in the opposite sense, the law regulating the rights of pacifists and conscientious objectors might well be modified in the sense of a greater severity if it was abused; and the fear of that, no doubt, explained the absence in court of the prisoner's co-objectors, if he might coin the phrase. The jury must have noticed the absence of these young men, who had been of one mind with the prisoner on the outbreak of war. They would not attach too much importance to it. The Author of the Christian faith was reported in the Scriptures as saying that hot and cold were preferable to lukewarm; and his impression was that, while the prisoner had been prepared to go to all lengths in obeying the command to love his enemies, his friends and co-workers had been lukewarm about it. Indeed it was this impression of fierce sincerity that had induced him to listen with attention to the accused's own fantastic statements and outrageous claims. He had found them offensive, but he believed the deluded man was sincere according to his lights in making them. So much for his all but blasphemous utterances. They had little or no bearing on the question at issue, a question of treachery.

He had digressed. He had been speaking of the rights of pacifists in wartime, and in particular of those Christians who took literally Christ's commands. If loving one's enemies meant aiding and abetting those enemies in their deadly determination to defeat one's own people in war, then that was a serious matter indeed. It was not a rule of Christian conduct, but an incentive to a crime punishable by death.

To return to the indictment. The jury might be in doubt as to the relations of the prisoner with the German spy called Captain Banks; and they might be in doubt as to the purport of the fragmentary letter, Exhibit 2. He was in doubt himself, and he would remind them that the benefit of any doubt was with the prisoner. If they had any doubt whatever as to his guilt in these matters, then they must acquit him. It was not necessary for the defence to prove him innocent, it was obligatory on the prosecution to prove him guilty.

He came to the third count of the indictment, and the words of the Treachery Act were unmistakable in their clarity. "Anyone who attempts to do any act which is likely to impede the naval, military or air operations of his Majesty's forces shall be guilty of felony and shall on conviction suffer death." Charles read the words once more, then said: "You have heard the evidence of two witnesses who have declared under oath that they heard the prisoner call on the troops assembled in a N.A.A.F.I. canteen on Christmas Eve of 1944 to stop fighting. You may doubt the accuracy of their memory as to the exact words he used. It is of no consequence, for you have heard the evidence of the prisoner himself, and that evidence can leave no doubt in your mind that the prisoner did attempt to impede the military operations of his Majesty's forces. It was a feeble attempt," Charles said, "and it failed. The troops whom he addressed reacted with what I may call a proper display of rage, and went for him. They knocked him about and threw him out of the canteen. But the fact that he failed in his purpose makes his crime no less. The intention was there and he has confessed to it. It was a strange thing. In all my years at the bar I have never heard anything like it. In almost the same breath the man on trial for his life confessed his guilt and declared he was not guilty.

"I will not keep you. I will not go into his talk of a vision. He may have had one. He may suffer, as his counsel made out, from periodic delusions. You may feel that the story of his life, as well as his strange words in the witness box, proves him to be an irrational man, obsessed by the conviction of a divine mission. Adolf Hitler cherished just such a conviction and made just such pretensions; and his nation shared his convictions with him and worshipped him as a saviour. Mussolini too, in lesser degree, was hailed by his people as a deliverer, and

I daresay there are a handful of people in this English county who once believed, and may still believe, that Martin Merriedew is a prophet of some sort, and should have become a dictator. There are unmistakable signs of megalomania in the prisoner, of an overweening pride when he made his assumption of God-given authority; signs in fact of a mind so deluded as to be hardly sane. But he did not come before you as a madman, members of the jury. He was fit to plead, and he pleaded Not Guilty. You will retire, if you please, and consider your verdict."

III

I didn't wait. I got up, got as far as the stuffy little corridor behind the bench, then must have fainted. Tim took me back to our lodgings; Fairchild helped me to my room; someone put me to bed, got hot-water bottles (I was cold, cold, oh, how cold!), then left me mercifully alone.

The jury was out only a matter of minutes, but it was lunchtime when Charles came to find me. He stood at the foot of the bed.

"You've been told?"

"Yes, Tim telephoned. Not guilty on the first two counts, guilty on the third count. Is that correct?"

"Quite correct."

We looked at each other closely, carefully, as if we were two strangers meeting for the first time, but who anticipated a long antagonism, or at best an uncertain partnership, in the future. At last he said: "They tell me lunch is served."

"May I be excused?"

"Certainly. Fairchild will bring you something. What would you like?"

"Nothing, thank you."

"You won't reconsider and come down?"

"Not unless it is necessary."

"Nothing less so. There's only Tim and I've only an hour."

342

"Another case?"

"Yes; bigamy this time."

"Poor Charles. It does go on, doesn't it?" I managed a smile. "Life, I mean, and crime."

"Yes."

I closed my eyes; he got as far as the door. With his hand on the doorknob he said: "I wanted to tell you, I've been with counsel. We are approaching the Home Secretary, and I think I can promise you that he won't hang."

IV

That was four years ago, and Teresa thinks Martin Merriedew is still in Broadmoor. She hasn't seen him, but she is expecting him back. Some of his group have come together again and set up a centre of some sort to keep his memory green while they wait for him. But I am informed on reliable authority that he is dead, and I am glad. It would be unbearable to think of him as still there in that place, among the guilty but insane.

Sometimes I feel a great longing to join Teresa in Warrington and do something useful with what is left of my life. I saw the idiot children in the almshouse infirmary, and remembered the pact Francis and Martin signed in their school days; but when I went to call on Teresa I wasn't well received. She said, "Yes, I know who you are, you were in court, you are the wife of the judge," and her blue eyes were icy. She softened a little after I told her why I had come. "For charity, talk to me," I said, "tell me something. I haven't come to sympathize or to offer to help you, I can't help, I can do nothing. I have come only for my own sake." And that seemed to pacify her, because she took me to her room in the lodge, and did talk for a little about Martin Merriedew. "He will come back," she said. "I know he'll come back. He'll turn up someday, just the way he did on the station platform, you remember?"

I hadn't the heart to tell her that I was certain he was dead,

343

and I didn't feel that I could intrude on her again unless I could share her belief in his return, so I haven't been back. Then again, I'm afraid that I wouldn't find the group of his followers much to my liking. They are trying to carry out his original idea, apparently, but with, I gather, some modifications. Not absolute poverty; austerity is the rule now, and work of the humblest kind; but they pray a lot, all together, and call on Martin as they pray, to come back to them. I couldn't bear that. Even Teresa seemed to me a bit touched when she talked of it. But the strangest thing of all is that Edward has joined them. That I cannot understand. I could never abide Edward. I certainly couldn't join him in a life of prayer and good works.

I am too old to begin the good life, and too lazy, too fond of my small comforts and pleasures. Then there is Charles.

We don't go on circuit any more. He is at the Court of Appeal now. I read about his cases in the morning paper. It arrives with my breakfast tray. I breakfast in bed these days, and look forward eagerly to my letters, hoping there will be one from James, or an invitation to a pleasant evening. There often is neither; but I can count on my morning paper and I read it avidly. I read every word, then I get up, usually about ten, inspect the lines round my eyes and mouth, put cream on my face, lie in my bath, and presently go out to meet Jane or Camilla, and do a bit of shopping. Jane is very sweet, but usually in a hurry to get back to her babies, and I'm not good at babies, so I don't go with her as a rule. Camilla and I lunch on a Tuesday in one of our pubs. We are still close friends, but we don't talk about Martin Merriedew or Gideon Fish, who threw himself under a train the day Martin went to Broadmoor. We, Camilla and I, talk about little humdrum, unfrightening things and normal people, or her latest lame duck, an unknown, unrecognized poet, painter, pianist, who has failed and will always just fail to catch the public fancy; shadowy people, who emerge out of the anonymous crowd, are lighted up for a moment by her well-meaning false enthusiasm, then go limping past in a long procession to be swallowed up again in the mass of those who don't count.

I have lost Francis. I still see him sometimes. The last time I went down I found him mending one of the crimson curtains in the Spanish drawing room; but I've already told about that, and about the way he goes limping up and down hunting for vermin and swatting flies, while Daphne shows people round. There is nothing new. One day for Francis and Daphne is like another. The crumbling process is not a thing you notice from day to day. It goes on relentlessly in a rhythm we are not attuned to, just as the grass grows and the petals of a flower unfold. Watch as close, as close, you still can't see it. There was a bud this morning, now there is a rose in full bloom. That's a miracle.

Charlotte writes now and then from the South of France. She divides her time between her jasmine farm and the casinos of Cannes and Monte Carlo. She doesn't wonder about Martin Merriedew. Why should she, seeing that he is dead, or as good as? Katharine and Jasper Merriedew are quiet in the graveyard of our lovely old church. Mr. Nightingale too has passed on, as he would say, but there is a new vicar. Michael commands a brigade in Malaya, and Kitty is nursing at St. Giles, I believe, in London. Miss Molly? Miss Sally? Martha Blundle, and the rest? I don't know. Crabbe village itself will have disappeared soon. The steam drills of the Town Planners are seeing to that. All that is left for me down there in the West Country is a phantom brother in a great empty house.

But I still have Charles. He comes in most days at six for his glass of sherry. We give little dinners, or if we are alone we sit at either side of the fire. Sometimes when I notice how thin his hair is on top I am frightened; but I shut down on the panic, I stifle the cry of my heart, curb the impulse to rush into his arms and say again, as I said to him years ago, "If one could be certain about God, Charles, one would be safe."

It is too late to do that. His arms are too old, they have forgotten how to reach out to me, and I am too stiff. I go back to my thriller, or take up my pen to write to James. It is too late to do more than keep quiet. Nevertheless, it is a comfort to know that he is there, and that he will come home to me again tomorrow, that there are still many tomorrows that I can count on.

When we talked that once of Martin Merriedew's trial — it was long ago — I asked him: "Are you quite certain yourself that he was mad?"

"Crazy as a coot" was what he said.

I don't agree. I feel that I have missed something. The chance, perhaps, to be safe? Could it be that? I don't know. I have written this book because of a great uncertainty. It is finished and I am still uncertain; but I have Charles; I stick to Charles.